Quantum Physics of Consciousness

2nd Edition

Edited By
Subhash Kak, Ph.D.
Oklahoma State University, Oklahoma

Sir Roger Penrose
University of Oxford, Oxford, United Kingdom

Stuart Hameroff, M.D.
University of Arizona, Arizona

Quantum Physics of Consciousness
2nd Edition

Quantum Physics of Consciousness

ISBN: 978-1-938024-46-7

1. Consciousness, 2. Cosmology 3. Quantum Physics, 4. Evolution,
5. Neuroscience, 6. Universe, 7. Brain, 8. Mind

Contents

The Universe, Quantum Physics, and Consciousness 4
    Subhash Kak, Ph.D.

Quantum Reality and Mind 20
    Henry P. Stapp, Ph.D.

Cosmos and Quantum: Frontiers for the Future 30
    Menas Kafatos, Ph.D.

Neoclassical Cosmology and
    Menas Kafatos's "Cosmos and Quantum: Frontiers for the Future" 54
    Theodore Walker Jr., Ph.D.

Can Discoverability Help Us Understand Cosmology? 59
    Nicholas Beale, MA FRSA

On Meaning, Consciousness and Quantum Physics...72
    Yair Neuman, Ph.D. and Boaz Tamir, Ph.D.

Quantum Reality and Evolution Theory 81
    Lothar Schäfer, Ph.D.

Four Perspectives on Consciousness 93
    Varadaraja V. Raman, Ph.D.

Synchronicity, Quantum Information and the Psyche...104
    Francois Martin, Ph.D., Federico Carminati, Ph.D.,
    Giuliana Galli Carminati, Ph.D.

Speculations about the Direct Effects of Intention on
    Physical Manifestation...114
    Imants Barušs, Ph.D.

Consciousness and Quantum Measurement: New Empirical Data................124
    York H. Dobyns, Ph.D.

Consciousness and Quantum Physics: A Deconstruction of the Topic...........131
    Gordon Globus, M.D.

Logic of Quantum Mechanics and Phenomenon of Consciousness...............138
    Michael B. Mensky

A Quantum Physical Effect of Consciousness 151
    Shan Gao

The Conscious Observer in the Quantum Experiment 160
    Fred Kuttner and Bruce Rosenblum

Does Quantum Mechanics Require A Conscious Observer? 168
    Michael Nauenberg

Consciousness Vectors 174
    Steven Bodovitz

Quantum Physics, Advanced Waves and Consciousness 182
    Antonella Vannini Ph.D, and Ulisse Di Corpo

The Quantum Hologram And the Nature of Consciousness 195
    Edgar D. Mitchell, Sc.D., and Robert Staretz, M.S.

Consciousness in the Universe: Neuroscience, Quantum Space-Time
    Geometry and Orch OR Theory 229
    Roger Penrose, PhD, OM, FRS, and Stuart Hameroff, MD

Quantum Physics and the Multiplicity of Mind: Split-Brains,
    Fragmented Minds, Dissociation, Quantum Consciousness 270
    R. Joseph, Ph.D.

Many Mansions: Special Relativity, Higher-Dimensional Space, Neuroscience
    Consciousness and Time 305
    John Smythies, Ph.D.

The Universe, Quantum Physics, and Consciousness
Subhash Kak, Ph.D.

Head, Department of Computer Science, Oklahoma State University, Stillwater

Abstract

This article presents the case for the existence of a separate principle of consciousness to complement physical law. Since this principle cannot be dynamical, it is suggested that it manifests itself by enhancing probabilities associated with natural processes in a manner that favors life. Improbable coincidences attested in the literature are presented as evidence of this probability enhancement.

1. Introduction

There are two essential parts to understanding the universe: its representation in terms of material objects, and the manner in which this representation changes with time. In philosophy, these are the positions of two different schools, one believing that reality is being, and the other that it is becoming.

The conception of the cosmos, consisting of the material universe and observers, has been shaped by ideas that belong to these two opposite schools. The conception of the world as being is associated with materialism, while that of becoming is associated with idealism. In the materialist view, mental experience is emergent on the material ground and contents of the mind are secondary to the physical world. Conversely, in the idealist position consciousness has primacy.

The question of consciousness is connected to the relationship between brain and mind. Reductionism considers them to be identical -- with mind representing the sum total of the activity in the brain -- at a suitable higher level of representation. Opposed to this is the viewpoint that although mind requires a physical structure, it ends up transcending that structure. There exist a host of other views of mind, shaped by culture and life-experience, which are characterized by a tension between opposite beliefs systems applied to different aspects of life. Quantum mechanics is relevant to a discussion of the cosmos, since it is the deepest theory of physics and it is a theory of observables in which information is the fundamental quantity. John Archibald Wheeler used the slogan "It from bit" to stress that our constructions of reality are based on responses on our instruments to yes-no questions. He declared "that all things physical are information-theoretic in origin and this is a participatory universe" (Wheeler, 1990), where the term "participatory" implies that observations effect the evolution of the universe. Whereas observables are central to quantum mechanics, there is nothing in it on who makes the observations or if observers fit into its framework.

Just as there exists the outer cosmos – the physical universe –, there also exists the corresponding inner cosmos of the mind. The mind processes signals coming into the brain to obtain its understandings in the domains of seeing, hearing, touching, and tasting using its store of memories. The cognitive act is an active process where the selectivity of the sensors and the accompanying processing in the brain is organized based on the expectation of the cognitive task and on effort, will and intention.

The structure of the inner cosmos belongs to the domain of psychology, but it is fair to assume that at some level it mirrors the outer cosmos. In the schematic of Figure 1 it is indicated that if quantum theory describes processes for the outer cosmos, consciousness does so for the inner cosmos. Since quantum theory must ultimately underlie the processes in the inner cosmos, it appears that for the sake of symmetry it should be possible for consciousness to influence the outer cosmos.

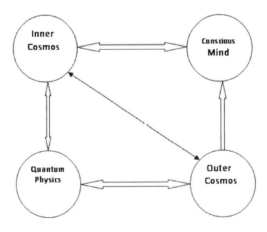

Figure 1. Inner and outer cosmoses, the law, and consciousness.

In the view that consciousness is complementary to space, time and matter, it needs material support to be embodied as "awareness". Conversely, it is meaningless to speak of a universe without observers. If we accept that we have discovered the basic laws of nature and also that classical machines cannot be conscious, one may like to assume that quantum processing in the brain, given appropriate brain structures, leads to awareness. Different states of consciousness such as wakefulness, sleep, dream-sleep, coma have distinct neurochemical signatures, and these different states may be taken to be modifications caused by the neural circuitry on a basic state of consciousness. But quantum machines cannot be assumed to have the capacity to be conscious because of the observer paradox outlined in the next section.

Although consciousness cannot be studied directly, it is accessible to further understanding indirectly. In this article, we show why observers are essential in the universe. We do this not by resorting to anthropic arguments, but rather to quantum theory itself. We suggest that improbable coincidences corroborated in literature support the existence of a universal consciousness principle, but, of course, they cannot be taken to be proof for it.

2. The Observer Paradox

Although the inner cosmos is physically located in the brain, we cannot speak of where in the brain the perceiving self resides because that would amount to a homunculus argument. The perceiving self cannot be in a unique neuron in the brain, because that would require such a neuron to have the capacity to process all the information that the individual possesses, which is clearly impossible for a cellular structure that can only do simple processing. Conversely, if the perceiving self was distributed over an area, then we need to postulate another homunculus within this area to process the information reaching the self.

Thus the conscious self can neither be localized to a single cell, nor assumed to be distributed over the entire brain or a part of it. We cannot speak of where the self is, but only of how the self obtains knowledge. Since the self is associated with the brain it uses it as the lens through which to perceive the world. Our knowledge of the word is, therefore, contingent on the neurophysiologic nature of the brain. If we are able to make sense of the world it is because we are biologically programmed to do so and we have innate capacity for it. Our conception of the cosmos is based on the relationship between our brain and mind. This idea is expressed in the slogan that the outer is mirrored in the inner. In an elaboration of this idea it is assumed that patterns seen in the outer world characterize the inner world as well.

Sacred architecture in many cultures replicated conceptions of the universe. The cathedral is a representation of the heavens of the Christian cosmos. In ancient India, it was concluded, using elementary measurements, that the relative distance to the sun and the moon from the earth is approximately 108 times their respective diameters. The diameter of the sun is likewise approximately 108 times the diameter of the earth, and this fact could have been established from the relative durations of the solar and lunar eclipses.

The number 108, taken as a fundamental measure of the universe, was used in ritual and sacred geometry. Each god and goddess was given 108 names; the number of dance poses in the Natya Shastra, an ancient text on theater, dance, and music, was taken to be 108, as was the number of beads in the rosary (Kak, 2008). The Hindu temple had the circumference to the measure of 180 (half of the number of days in the year) and its axis had the measure of 54 (half the number 108) (Kak, 2009a), and we find these dimensions in sacred ground for fire altars of the second millennium B.C.E to the second millennium C.E. Vishnu temple at Angkor Wat. The body, breath, and consciousness were taken to be equivalent to the earth, the space, and the sun, respectively. The telling of the beads was to make a symbolic journey from the earth to the sun, from the body to the inner light of consciousness.

One kind of connection between the outer and the inner is provided by biological clocks in the cells which work according to the rhythms of the sun, the moon, the tides, and other astronomical phenomena (Winfree, 1987). Other biological processes are adjustments to sensory inputs and the observer may also be viewed as an ecological system seeking its balance in a complex environment. From a systems point of view the organism may be viewed as evolving to attractor states. In a dynamical system the observer has no direct role, excepting to alter probabilities associated with the evolution.

3. Quantum Physics, Observers, and the Cosmos

The astonishing success of modern science rests on the discovery that the representation and its rate of change are proportionate. For example, in quantum physics, the evolution of a system or an object, represented by $|\varphi\rangle$ is given by the Schrödinger equation:

$$i\hbar \frac{d|\varphi\rangle}{dt} - H|\varphi\rangle$$

Likewise, in classical systems the unknown function and its various derivatives are related making it possible to compute future values. In many discrete time systems found in plant and animal life that are characterized by Fibonacci series, the time difference of the generative function equals the function itself.

Quantum physics is different from classical physics in so much that the quantum system is a superposition of many possibilities and while the evolution of the quantum state is deterministic (given by the Schrödinger equation) its observation results in a collapse of the state to one of its components in a probabilistic manner.

Both classical physics and quantum physics present a machine-view of the universe. This machine, which may be deterministic or stochastic, has no place for observers. In social sciences and philosophy freedom and agency for the observer is postulated, but these disciplines do not derive from physics. Either freedom is illusory or the machine paradigm is incomplete in describing the world.

Since material science can only deal with objective associations, it can do no better than see each system as a mechanism of some kind, leading to several difficulties. The brain is viewed as a machine, yet the brain-machine has awareness whereas the computer does not. Quantum physics is associated with its own paradoxes related to observers such as those implying propagation of effects instantaneously across space (for entangled particles) and time (as in the Wheeler's delayed choice experiment) if one uses ordinary language to describe phenomena (Penrose, 1994; Kak, 2004). This indicates that reality has aspects that are not captured by consistent linguistic narratives.

Physics deals with space, time and matter. As observers we are more than matter at a specific location in space and time; we also have consciousness. Although it is logical to see consciousness as emergent on matter it is also tempting to see it having a more fundamental existence. To claim that consciousness is emergent and therefore inherent in the scientific law and yet deny it ontological reality is not reasonable.

If we view quantum theory as a theory of wholes, then it should apply to large aggregation of objects. More specifically, since biological organisms are entities, their behavior should be governed at some level by quantum laws.

The anthropic principle has been invoked to explain the nature of laws. In one formulation of the principle, the physical laws are restricted by the requirement that they should lead to intelligent life at some stage in the evolution of the universe. Since life on earth would cease when the sun exhausts its fuel, and as evolution of consciousness could not have been in vain, the proponents of the principle argue that man will create silicon-based "conscious machines" that will seed the universe and the entire universe will become a conscious machine (Barrow and Tipler, 1986). In the archaic view, the universe is conscious. In more sophisticated versions of this archaic view, consciousness itself is the ground stuff of reality and on this ground the complex of space, time and matter is seeded.

Evolution in quantum mechanics is deterministic as in classical mechanics except for the difference that as the system interacts with another system, its state function collapses. This dichotomy exists only for separated systems, in which one of them is being observed by the other. Given that the state of the entire universe is defined at the initial point, its evolution must be completely deterministic. Any seeming randomness now should merely be an amplification of the randomness in the initial state and the entropy at the origin should not change as the universe evolves. In other words, the physical universe governed by quantum laws has no place for the emergence of life.

Our currently accepted conceptions of the beginning of the universe postulate much more uniformity than exists now. One way entropy could increase in the universe is by the process of reduction of its state function by some other system. Since the universe, by definition, cannot have any other matter in it, it becomes essential to postulate a mechanism other than that of physical laws, which permits the state function to reduce. This other mechanism may be the working of the "consciousness principle" which can just by the process of "observation" increase entropy (Kak, 2007).

It should be stressed that the "consciousness principle" cannot be a new physical law, because if it were so that then it would only replace the currently accepted dynamics of the universe by a different one. Such a physical law would not alter the conception of the universe as a deterministic or stochastic machine without any possibility of life. Consciousness or awareness implies binding to events and entities, abstract or real, that are separated in time and space, and the perceptible influence of the "consciousness principle" may be seen in improbable correlations as a result of drift of probabilities in the equations of dynamics.

A "consciousness principle", rather than the improbable creation of complex molecules by chance that has been refuted (Hoyle and Wickramasinghe, 1984; Joseph 2009; Wickramasinghe, 2009), must be the explanation for the rise of life all over the universe. Consciousness interpenetrates the universe, but it needs appropriate physical structures to be embodied. Molecules of life at the general level, and the brains of animals under appropriate biochemical conditions at a higher level, represent such physical structures.

4. Information in the Cosmos

One cannot speak of information in a universe without observers. Information arises out of a communication game played between a sender of signals and their recipient. For physical systems, the game may be seen as being played between Nature and the scientist. The average information obtained from a quantum system is given by the von Neumann measure, which is a generalization of thermodynamic entropy and perfectly in accord with commonsense when we consider a mixed quantum state. But this entropy for an unknown pure state is zero even though testing many copies of such a state can reveal information about the choice that was made by the sender.

The idea of zero entropy for an unknown pure state is reasonable from the perspective that once the state has been identified; there is no further information to be gained from examining its copies. But it is not reasonable if the game being played between sentient beings. Assume the sender chooses one out of a certain number of polarization states (say, for a photon) and supplies several copies of it to the receiver. Measurements made by the receiver on the copies will reveal information regarding the choice made by the sender. If the set of choices is infinite, then the "information" generated by the source is unbounded. The information in the pure state is limited by the "relationship" between the source and the receiver, and by the precision of the receiver's measurement apparatus. If the sender chose a polarization state that the receiver's measurement apparatus was already synchronized with, the receiver could recognize the state quite readily. I recently investigated information obtainable from an unknown pure state within the framework of communication between source and receiver (Kak, 2007; Kak, 2009b). I proposed a measure of entropy that covers both pure and mixed states. In general, then, entropy has two components:

one informational (related to the pure components of the quantum state, which can vary from receiver to receiver), and the other that is thermodynamic (which is receiver independent). The increase of information with time is a consequence of the interplay between unitary (related to pure states) and non-unitary (related to mixed states) evolution, which makes it possible to transform one type of information into another. This complementarity indicates that a fundamental duality is essential for information.

For a two-component elementary mixed state, the most information in each measurement is one bit, and each further measurement of identically prepared states will also be one bit. For an unknown pure state, the information in it represents the choice the source has made out of the infinity of choices related to the values of the probability amplitudes with respect to the basis components of the receiver's measurement apparatus. Each measurement of a two-component pure state will provide at most one bit of information, and if the source has made available an unlimited number of identically prepared states the receiver can obtain additional information from each measurement until the probability amplitudes have been correctly estimated. Once that has occurred, unlike the case of a mixed state, no further information will be obtained from testing additional copies of this pure state.

The receiver can make his estimate by adjusting the basis vectors so that he gets closer to the unknown pure state. The information that can be obtained from such a state in repeated experiments is potentially infinite in the most general case. But if the observer is told what the pure state is, the information associated with the states vanishes, suggesting that a fundamental divide exists between objective and subjective information.

This approach is consistent with the positivist view that one cannot speak of information associated with a system excepting in relation to an experimental arrangement together with the protocol for measurement. The experimental arrangement is thus integral to the amount of information that can be obtained.

The informational measure outlined here resolves the puzzle of entropy increase. We can suppose that the universe had immensely large informational entropy associated with a pure state in the beginning, a portion of which has, during the physical evolution of the universe, transformed into thermodynamic entropy.

5. The Problem of Consciousness

The reason why consciousness is not accessible to science is that it is not objective. It is the light that the observer uses to throw on objects but this light cannot be turned upon itself. Rational science is related to associations and it must, therefore, be material and reductionist. Consciousness cannot be fitted in the framework of rational science.

There are indirect ways to study consciousness. Neurophysiological experiments have shown that the mind orders events in order to provide consistent picture and that there is a small time lag between initiation of neurological function and its conscious awareness. Mind is an active participant in the creation of models of the world, seen most clearly when subjects who have impairments resulting from strokes or trauma are studied (Joseph, 1986, 1988; Gazzaniga, 1995; Kak, 2004).

It is argued by some that once machines become sufficiently complex they would be conscious. But machines only follow instructions, and it is not credible that they should suddenly, just on account of the increase in the number of connections between computing units, become endowed with self-awareness. To speak of consciousness in the machine paradigm is a contradiction in terms. If a machine could make true choices (that is not governed by a random picking between different alternatives), then it has transcended the paradigm because its behavior cannot be described by any mathematical function.

Some ascribe awareness of the brain to the fact that the brain is a self-organizing system which responds to the nature and quality of its interaction with the environment, whereas computers can't do that. But other ecological systems, which are biological communities that have complex interrelationship amongst their parts, are self-organizing, without being self-aware. This suggests that while self-organization is a necessary pre-requisite for consciousness, it is not sufficient. Cognitive scientists and biologists have considered evolutionary aspects related to cognitive capacity, where consciousness is viewed as emerging out of language. Linguistic research on chimpanzees and bonobos has revealed that although they can be taught basic vocabulary of several hundred words, this linguistic ability does not extend to syntax. By contrast, small children acquire much larger vocabularies -- and use the words far more creatively -- with no overt training, indicating that language is an innate capacity.

It is theorized that human language capacities arose out of biological natural selection because they fulfill two clear criteria: an extremely complex and rich design and the absence of alternative processes capable of explaining such complexity. Other theories look at music and language arising out of sexual selection. But, howsoever imaginative and suggestive these models might be, they do not address the question of how the capacity to visualize models of world that are essential to language and consciousness first arise.

According to the nativist view, language ability is rooted in the biology of the brain, and our ability to use grammar and syntax is an instinct, dependent on specific modules of the brain. Therefore, we learn language as a consequence of a unique biological adaptation, and not because it is an emergent response to the problem of communication confronted by ourselves and our ancestors. This is seen most tellingly amongst deaf children who are not taught to sign a language. Such children spontaneously create their personal signs, slowly adding grammatical rules, complete with inflection, case marking, and other forms of syntax (Goldin-Meadow and Mylander, 1998).

6. Creativity and Discovery

Some individuals, who have serious developmental disability or major mental illness, perform spectacularly at certain tasks in the areas of mathematical and calendar calculations, music, art, memory, and unusual sensory discrimination and perception (Joseph, 2000 Sacks, 1985). Such cognitive ability cannot be viewed simply as a processing of sensory information by a central intelligence extraction system.

There also exist accounts in the literature speaking of spontaneous discovery in a variety of creative fields. But as unique events that happened in the past, they cannot be verified. In the scientific field, Jacques Hadamard surveyed 100 leading mathematicians of his time, concluding many of them appeared to have obtained entire solutions spontaneously. This list included the claim by the French mathematician Henri Poincaré that he arrived at the solution to a subtle mathematical problem as he was boarding a bus, and the discovery of the structure of benzene by Kekulé in a dream (Hadamard, 1954). More recently, the physicist Roger Penrose claims to have found the solution to a mathematical problem while crossing the street (Penrose, 1989). Intuitive discovery must be common, and the reason why we don't hear of more such stories is because some people are unprepared to appreciate their intuition or translate it into a meaningful narrative, others feel uncomfortable speaking of their personal experience. The preparation of the scientist comes in the amplification of his intuition. It is also true that the creative intuition is not always correct, and the scientist's judgment is essential in separating the false solution from the true one.

Anomalous abilities and first person accounts of discovery that appear to be spontaneous could either indicate that consciousness is more than a phenomenon based solely on matter or that these accounts are just a listing of co-incidences. Conversely, there is no way to prove the veracity of the scientist's account of discovery. It is possible that the account is one that the scientist has come to believe over time and it does not correspond to fact.

7. Coincidences

The standard scientific view on coincidences is that correlated spatially or temporally separated events must be entirely by chance. Scientific cosmology cannot suppose otherwise, because doing so would imply that it is not complete. Furthermore, many claims of coincidence cannot be accepted at face value. They may be a result of poor observation or recall, self-deception, or deception by others.

In some coincidence events a person may claim to obtain information from another person without the use of the currently known senses or inference, and in precognition one may claim to have knowledge of a future event. In parapsychology experiments, volunteers guess random choices that are made at a remote location to determine if these guesses deviate from chance. The sender attempts to mentally communicate a randomly chosen "target" to the receiver. The sender and receiver are in separate acoustically shielded rooms. A computer is used to choose a target from a large selection of possible targets that may be video clips, and plays that clip repeatedly to the sender. At the same time, the receiver reports out loud any thoughts or images that come to mind, and these verbal reports are recorded. Neither the experimenter nor the receiver has any idea of what target the sender is viewing. At the end of the sending period, the sender remains in his room while the computer plays four video clips to the receiver – the target plus three decoys. The receiver's task is to compare each clip to the mentation, and to select which of the clips most closely matches it.

If no information transfer is taking place, then we would expect the receiver to correctly identify the clip that was viewed by the sender 25 per cent of the time by chance alone. Extrasensory or telepathic perception is inferred to have taken place if the target is correctly identified more often than chance expectation.

The results of such experiments have not quite been supportive of the idea of extrasensory communication. According to researchers in the field, deviation from chance is limited to participants tested by believer experimenters; participants tested by skeptical experimenters obtain chance results!

If it is taken that the experiments are negative, they only rule out the idea of communication of images by some as-yet unknown process. There is also a basic weakness in the conception of the experiment. Unlike images stored in a computer, those presented to human subjects carry varying value and they are remembered in association with prior memories, which are unique for each individual.

Now we speak of two accounts of coincidence and critically examine them. The fictional account of cannibalism in the novel The Narrative of Arthur Gordon Pym of Nantucket by the American author Edgar Allan Poe (1809-1849) was published in 1838. In a complicated story of sailing adventure involving shipwreck, the cabin boy Richard Parker is chosen and killed for food. In 1884, in a real-life event that became a sensation in Britain, a 17 year old named Richard Parker, a runaway who becomes a cabin boy, is shipwrecked together with the crew. After several days of starvation, the crew kills Parker for food. The crew is eventually rescued, brought to London, and tried for murder. Although this coincidence is striking, it may be attributed to the popularity of the name Richard Parker in that period time.

Another coincidence is that of the novel, Futilty, about the unsinkable ship Titan that is shipwrecked with much loss of life when it strikes an iceberg on its maiden voyage. In 1912, the Titanic, struck an iceberg at midnight on her maiden voyage and sank on 15 April with great loss of life. There are several correspondences between the two boats but these may be due to the fact that both the novel and the design of the actual ship were based on proposals that were being written about in the 1890s. The coincidence may not be as remarkable as appears on first sight.

8. A Scientific Coincidence

A much more striking coincidence concerns an early value of the speed of light in the wellknown commentary on the Rigveda by the medieval scholar Sayana (1315-1387), prime minister in the court of the Vijayanagar Empire. It associates the speed of 2,202 yojanas in half a nimesha with the sun (or sunlight) (Kak, 1999). The distance and time measures of yojana and nimesha are well attested in Indian astronomical and encyclopedic texts and this number corresponds closely to the correct value of the speed.

The division of time according to the medieval Vishnu Purana 1.3.3 (Wilson, 1840) is:

1 day = 30 muhurtas

1 muhurta = 30 kalas

1 kala = 30 kashthas

1 kashtha = 15 nimesha

Thus 1 day = 86,400 seconds = 405,000 nimesha

Thus, 1 nimesha = 16/75 seconds. Half a nimesha would be 8/75 seconds. It is clear that half a nimesha was used in the text because that is the thirtieth part of a kala, in the regular sequence where the larger units are greater by a factor of 30.

1 yojana is defined in the Arthashastra (of Kautilya who was advisor to the Mauryan emperor Chandragupa who reigned 322 – 298 B.C.E.) as being equal to 8,000 dhanus or "bow" (Kangle, 1986). The Arthashastra further takes a dhanus to equal 108 angulams (finger widths). Independent confirmation of the dhanus unit is made possible by examining ancient monuments and seeing the largest unit that maps the main dimensions of the monument in meaningful integer multiples of the unit. This has been done both for the 3rd millennium BC city of Dholavira from West India as well as from monuments of medieval India (Danino, 2008; Balsubramaniam, 2009), and it is found that there exists continuity across ages in the use of this unit. The unit of dhanus in use in Dholavira and later India is 1.904 meters. The unit of angulams has been validated from scales obtained in Harappa and it 1.763 cm long. Therefore, the speed of 2,202 yojana in half a nimesha is:

$(2202 \times 8000 \times 1.904 \times 75)/8 = 314{,}445.6$ kilometers per second.

We find a good fit between the speed of light in this ancient account and the actual value. Since there was no way this speed could have been measured in medieval India, it is a very improbable coincidence. Note further that until just over 200 years ago it was not even known in the Western tradition that light had finite speed. In 1676, Rømer calculated this speed in terms of the speed of earth's rotation around the sun, and this value, we now know, was about 8% less than the modern value. Sayana could not have obtained this figure from the West or anywhere else.

Perhaps the value of the speed of light should not surprise us since there are other numbers the precision of whose value in the ancient texts cannot be explained. These include the size of the earth which is described to within one percent accuracy in the accounts of Eratosthenes, Aryabhata, and al-Biruni. The apocryphal account of Eratosthenes's measurement of the size indirectly by measuring the shift in the shadow of the sun at noon between Syene and Alexandria is not credible since the distance between the two cities was not known accurately and the shift in the angle of the shadow could not have been measured with the accuracy that the calculation of the earth's diameter demands.

The problem of scientific discovery was discussed from another perspective by the Scottish philosopher David Hume in his "An Enquiry Concerning Human Understanding". Hume argued that our scientific understanding is a consequence of inductive inference, which involves a leap of imagination from the world of the observed to that of the unobserved, which in his words was "beyond the present testimony of the senses, and the records of our memory." He argued that it was instinct, rather than reason, that explained our ability to make inductive inferences. In the traditional explanation of the workings of mind, habits picked up in childhood and in school are the impediments that prevent one from being connected to one's intuition (Hume's instinct). Real creativity requires challenging dogma as well as one's own certitudes. It is believed that one sees unexpected connections, which is an element of creativity, in extraordinary states of mind. Looking within can reveal unexpected knowledge about the universe for we are a part of the universe (Kak, 2004).

9. Concluding Remarks

We argued that improbable coincidences corroborated in literature support the view that nonmaterial entities have independent existence. The most compelling of these is the speed of light in medieval literature that could not have been obtained from measurement because the science and technology to do so did not exist at that time. It is also fascinating that this coincidence appears to have been justified by fitting it into the conception of the universe current in ancient India. Nevertheless, such evidence, just like first person accounts of spontaneous scientific discovery, cannot, in itself, be conclusive in establishing that the world of ideas has independent existence.

Evolution in quantum physics is deterministic, but when the system interacts with another system its state function collapses. Neither the framework of quantum physics nor that of classical physics has any place for observers. A quantum mechanical universe will evolve by a global unitary operator in a purely deterministic manner.

Quantum mechanics is not a local theory in the sense that parts far apart cease to be causally connected to each other; entanglement between particles persists no matter how apart they are. It cannot be assumed that as the universe evolved, interaction between different isolated parts of it came about in a non-unitary manner, leading to creation of information. The entropy at the origin should not change as the universe evolves.

Since information in the universe is increasing, it can only be come about by a principle that lies outside of quantum theory. Entropy increase in the universe requires reduction of its state function by some other physical system but the universe, by definition, does not have any other matter in it. We are compelled, therefore, to postulate a state function reducing mechanism other than that of physical laws. We have argued that this mechanism evolves out of the consciousness principle and it has, by means of probability enhancement of events (which is non-unitary), generated conditions all over the universe that favor life.

The working of the "consciousness principle" in the laboratory may be seen in the quantum Zeno effect in which the process of observation increases entropy. This principle, rather than the creation of complex molecules by chance, leads to the rise of life in the universe. Consciousness interpenetrates the universe, but it needs appropriate physical structures to be embodied.

References

Balasubramaniam, R. (2009). New insights on the modular planning of the Taj Mahal. Current Science, vol. 97, 42-49.

J.D. Barrow and F.J. Tipler (1986). The Anthropic Cosmological Principle. Oxford University Press.

Danino, M. (2008). New insights into Harappan town-planning, proportions, and units, with special reference to Dholavia, Man and Environment, 33, 66-79.

Gazzaniga, M.S. (1995). The Cognitive Neurosciences. The MIT Press, Cambridge.

Goldin-Meadow, S., Mylander, C. (1998). Spontaneous sign systems created by deaf children in two cultures. Nature, 391, 279-281.

Hadamard, J. (1954). The Psychology of Invention in the Mathematical Field. Dover, New York.

Hoyle, F., Wickramasinghe, C. (1984). Evolution from Space. Simon and Schuster, New York.

Joseph, R. (1986). Confabulation and delusional denial: Frontal lobe and lateralized influences. Journal of Clinical Psychology, 42, 845-860.

Joseph, R. (1988). Dual mental functioning in a split-brain patient. Journal of Clinical Psychology, 44, 770-779.

Joseph, R. (2009). Life on Earth Came From Other Planets. Journal of Cosmology, 1, 1-56.

Kak, S. (1999). The speed of light and Puranic cosmology. Annals Bhandarkar Oriental Research Institute, vol. 80, 113-123; arXiv:physics/9804020

Kak, S. (2004). The Architecture of Knowledge. Motilal Banarsidass, Delhi.

Kak, S. (2006). Encounters with the worlds of commonsense and science. In The Enworlded Subjectivity: Its Three Worlds and Beyond (ed. R. Balasubramanian), CSC, New Delhi, pp. 173- 201, 2006; http://www.cs.okstate.edu/~subhashk/Commonsense%20and%20science.pdf

Kak, S. (2007). Quantum information and entropy, International Journal of Theoretical Physics 46, 860-876.

Kak, S. (2008). The Wishing Tree. iUniverse, New York.

Kak, S. (2009a). Time, space and structure in ancient India. Presented at the Conference on Sindhu-Sarasvati Valley Civilization: A Reappraisal, Loyola Marymount University, Los Angeles, February 21 & 22; arXiv:0903.3252

Kak, S. (2009b). The transactional nature of quantum information. Presented at the 11th International Conference on Squeezed States and Uncertainty Relations and 4th Feynman Festival, Olomouc, Czech Republic, June 22-26, 2009; arXiv:0907.2465

Kangle, R.P. (1986). The Kautiliya Arthasastra. Motilal Banarsidass, Delhi.

Penrose, R. (1989). The Emperor's New Mind. Oxford University Press, Oxford.

Penrose, R. (1994). Shadows of the Mind. Oxford University Press.

Sacks, O. (1985). The Man Who Mistook His Wife for a Hat. HarperCollins, New York.

Wheeler, J.A. (1990). Information, physics,

quantum: the search for links. In Complexity, Entropy, and the Physics of Information, W.H. Zurek (Ed.). Addison-Wesley, pp. 3-28.

Wickaramasinghe, C. (2009). Astrobiology, Comets and the Origin of Life. World Scientific, Singapore.

Wilson, H.H. (tr.) (1840). The Vishnu Purana. John Murray, London.

Winfree, A.T. (1987). The Timing of Biological Clocks. Scientic American Books, New York.

Quantum Reality and Mind
Henry P. Stapp, Ph.D.

Lawrence Berkeley Laboratory, University of California, Berkeley, California

Abstract

Two fundamental questions are addressed within the framework of orthodox quantum mechanics. The first is the duality-nonduality conflict arising from the fact that our scientific description of nature has two disparate parts: an empirical component and a theoretical component. The second question is the possibility of meaningful free will in a quantum world concordant with the principle of sufficient reason, which asserts that nothing happens without a sufficient reason. The two issues are resolved by an examination of the conceptual and mathematical structure of orthodox quantum mechanics, without appealing to abstract philosophical analysis or intuitive sentiments.

Key Words: Quantum Reality, Mind, Mind-Matter, Free Will, Duality, Mental monism

1. Introduction

The first purpose of this article is to explain the nature of the connection between mind and matter and how orthodox quantum mechanics is both dualistic and nondualistic: it is dualistic on a pragmatic, operational level, but is nondualistic on a deeper ontological level.

The second purpose is to reconcile a meaningful concept of human freedom with the principle of sufficient reason; with the principle that nothing happens without a sufficient reason.

To lay a framework for discussing these two issues I shall begin by describing some contrasting ideas about the nature of reality advanced by three towering intellectual figures, Rene Descartes (1596-1650), Isaac Newton (1642-1727), and William James (1842-1910).

René Descartes conceived nature to be divided into two parts: a mental part and a physical part. The mental part, which he called "res cogitans", contains our thoughts, ideas, and feeling, whereas the physical part, called "res extensa", is defined here to be those aspects of nature that we can describe by assigning mathematical properties to space-time points. Examples of physical aspects of our understanding of nature are trajectories of physical particles, the electric field $E(x,t)$, and the quantum mechanical field (operator) $A(x,t)$. Descartes allowed the mental and physical aspects to interact with each other, but only for those physical parts that are located inside human brains. This is the classic Cartesian notion of duality.

Isaac Newton built the foundations of "modern physics" upon the ideas of Descartes, Galileo, and Kepler. The astronomical observations of Tycho Brahe led to Kepler's three laws of planetary motion. These laws, coupled to Galileo's association of gravity with acceleration, led directly to Newton's inverse square law of gravitational attraction, and his general laws of motion. Newton extended these dynamical ideas, with tremendous success, down to the scale of terrestrial motions, to the tides and falling apples etc.. He also conjectured an extension down to the level of the atoms. According to that hypothesis, the entire physically described universe, from the largest objects to the smallest ones, would be bound by the precept of physical determinism, which is the notion that a complete description of the values of all physically described variables at any one time determines with certainty the values of all physically described variables at any later time. This idea of universal physical determinism is a basic precept of the development of Newtonian dynamics into what is called "classical physics".

1a. The Omission of the Phenomenal Aspects of Nature

The dynamical laws of classical physics are formulated wholly in terms of physically described variables: in terms of the quantities that Descartes identified as elements of "res extensa". Descartes' complementary psychologically described things, the elements of his "res cogitans", were left completely out: there is, in the causal dynamics of classical physics, no hint of their existence. Thus there is not now, nor can there ever be, any rational way to explain, strictly on the basis of the dynamical precepts of classical physics, either the existence of, or any causal consequence of, the experientially described aspects of nature. Yet these experiential aspects of nature are all that we actually know.

This troublesome point was abundantly clear already at the outset:

Newton: "…to determine by what modes or actions light produceth in our minds the phantasm of colour is not so easie."

Leibniz: "Moreover, it must be confessed that perception and that which depends upon it are inexplicable on mechanical grounds, that is to say, by means of figures and motions."

Classical physics, by omitting all reference to the mental realities, produces a logical disconnect between the physically described properties represented in that theory and the mental realities by which we come to know them. The theory allows the mental realities to know about the physical aspects of nature, yet be unable to affect them in any way. Our mental aspects are thereby reduced to "Detached Observers", and Descartes' duality collapses, insofar as the causally closed physical universe is concerned, to a physics-based nonduality; to a physical monism, or physicalism. Each of us rejects in actual practice the classical-physics claim that our conscious thoughts and efforts can have no affects on our physical actions. We build our lives, and our political, judicial, economic, social, and religious institutions, upon the apparently incessantly reconfirmed belief that, under normal wakeful conditions, a person's intentional mental effort can influence his physical actions.

William James, writing in 1892, challenged, on rational grounds, this classical-physics-based claim of the impotence of our minds. At the end of his book Psychology: The Briefer Course he reminded his readers that "the natural science assumptions with which we started are provisional and revisable things". That was a prescient observation! Eight years later Max Planck discovered a new constant of nature that signaled a failure of the precepts of classical physics, and by 1926 the precepts of its successor, quantum mechanics, were firmly in place.

The most radical shift wrought by quantum mechanics was the explicit introduction of mind into the basic conceptual structure. Human experience was elevated from the role of 'a detached observer' to that of 'the fundamental element of interest':

Bohr: "In our description of nature the purpose is not to disclose the real essence of phenomena but only to track down as far as possible relations between the multifold aspects of our experience." (Bohr, 1934, p.18).

Bohr: "The sole aim [of quantum mechanics] is the comprehension of observations…(Bohr, 1958, p.90).

Bohr: The task of science is both to extend the range of our experience and reduce it to order (Bohr, 1934, p.1)

Heisenberg: "The conception of the objective reality of the elementary particles has evaporated not into the cloud of some new reality concept, but into the transparent clarity of a mathematics that represents no longer the behaviour of the particles but our knowledge of this behavior" (Heisenberg, 1958a, p. 95).

This general shift in perspective was associated with a recasting of physics from a set of mathematical connections between physically described aspects of nature, into set of practical rules that, eschewing ontological commitments, predicted correlations between various experiential realities on the basis of their postulated dynamical links to certain physically describable aspects of our theoretical understanding of nature.

In view of this fundamental re-entry of mind into basic physics, it is nigh on incomprehensible that so few philosophers and non-physicist scientists entertain today, more than eight decades after the downfall of classical physics, the idea that the physicalist conception of nature, based on the invalidated classical physical theory, might be profoundly wrong in ways highly relevant to the mind-matter problem.

Philosophers are often called upon to defend highly counter-intuitive and apparently absurd positions. But to brand as an illusion, and accordingly discount, the supremely successful conceptual foundation of our lives---the idea that our conscious efforts can influence our physical actions---on the basis of its conflict with a known-to-be-false theory of nature that leaves out all that we really know, is a travesty against reason, particularly in view of the fact that the empirically valid replacement of that empirically invalid classical theory is specifically about the details of the connection between our consciously chosen intentional actions and the experiential feedbacks that such actions engender.

1b. Von Neumann's Dualistic Quantum Mechanics.

The logician and mathematician John von Neumann (1955/1932) formalized quantum mechanics in a way that allowed it to be interpreted as a dualistic theory of reality in which mental realities interact in specified causal ways with physically described human brains. This orthodox quantum ontology is in essential accord with the dualistic ideas of Descartes.

An objection often raised against Cartesian dualism is couched as the query: How can ontologically distinct aspects of nature ever interact? Must not nature consist ultimately of one fundamental kind of stuff in order for its varied components to be able to cohere.

This objection leads to a key question: What is the ontological character of the physical aspect of quantum mechanics?

2. The Ontological Character of the Physical Aspect of the Orthodox (von Neumann-Heisenberg) Quantum Mechanics.

The physical aspect of the quantum mechanical conception of nature is represented by the quantum state. This state is physical, in the defined sense that we can describe it by assigning mathematical properties to space-time points. But this physical aspect is does not have the ontological character of a material substance, in the sense in which the physical world of Newtonian (or classical) physics is made of material substance: it does not always evolve in a continuous manner, but is subject to abrupt "quantum jumps", sometimes called "collapses of the wave function".

Heisenberg (1958b) couched his understanding of the ontological character of the reality lying behind the successful quantum rules in terms of the Aristotelian concepts of "potentia" and "actual". The quantum state does not have the ontological character of an "actual" thing. It has, rather, the ontological character of "potentia": of a set of "objective tendencies for actual events to happen". An actual event, in the von Neumann-Heisenberg orthodox ontology, is "The discontinuous change in the probability function [that] takes place with the act of registration…in the mind of the observer". (Heisenberg, 1958b, p. 55)

The point here is that in orthodox (von Neumann-Heisenberg) quantum mechanics the physical aspect is represented by the quantum state, and this state has the ontological character of potentia---of objective tendencies for actual events to happen. As such, it is more mind-like than matter-like in character. It involves not only stored information about the past, but also objective tendencies pertaining to events that have not yet happened. It involves projections into the future, elements akin to imagined ideas of what might come to pass. The physical aspects of quantum mechanics are, in these ways, more like mental things than like material things.

Furthermore, a quantum state represents probabilities. Probabilities are not matter-like. They are mathematical connections that exist outside the actual realities to which they pertain. They involve mind-like computations and evaluations: weights assigned by a mental or mind-like process.

Quantum mechanics is therefore dualistic in one sense, namely the pragmatic sense. It involves, operationally, on the one hand, aspects of nature that are described in physical terms, and, on the other hand, also aspects of nature that are described in psychological terms. And these two parts interact in human brains in accordance with laws specified by the theory. In these ways orthodox quantum mechanics is completely concordant with the defining characteristics of Cartesian dualism.

Yet, in stark contrast to classical mechanics, in which the physically described aspect is matter-like, the physically described aspect of quantum mechanics is mind-like! Thus both parts of the quantum Cartesian duality are ontologically mind-like.

In short, orthodox quantum mechanics is Cartesian dualistic at the pragmatic/operational level, but mentalistic on the ontological level.

This conclusion that nature is fundamentally mind-like is hardly new. But it arises here not from some deep philosophical analysis, or religious insight, but directly from an examination of the causal structure of our basic scientific theory.

3. Natural Process, Sufficient Reason, and Human Freedom.

There are two fundamentally different ways to cope with the demands of the theory of relativity.

The first is the classical-physics-based Einsteinian idea of a Block Universe: a universe in which the entire future is laid out beforehand, with our experiences being mere perspectives on this preordained reality, viewed from particular vantage points in spacetime.

A second way to accommodate, rationally, the demands of special relativity is the quantum-physics-based Unfolding Universe, in which facts and truths become fixed and definite in the orderly way allowed by relativistic quantum field theory (Tomonaga, 1946; Schwinger 1951; Stapp, 2007, p. 92) with our experiences occurring in step with the coming into being of definite facts and truths.

I subscribe to the latter idea: to the idea of an unfolding reality in which each experienced increment of knowledge is associated with an actual event in which certain facts or truths become fixed and definite.

I also subscribe to the idea that this unfolding conforms to the principle of sufficient reason, which asserts that no fact or truth can simply "pop out of the blue", with no sufficient reason to be what it turns out to be.

An important question, then, is whether such a concordance with the principle of sufficient reason precludes the possibility of meaningful human freedom. Is human freedom an illusion, in the sense that every action that a person makes was fixed with certainty already at the birth of the universe?

Laplace's classical argument for the "certainty of the future" states (in condensed form):

"For a sufficiently powerful computing intellect that at a certain moment knew all the laws and all the positions, nothing would be uncertain, and the future, just like the past, would be present before its eyes."

This view argues for "certainty about the future"; for a certainty existing at an earlier moment on the basis of information existing at that earlier moment. It contemplates:

1. A computing intellect existing outside or beyond nature itself, able to "go" in thought where the actual evolving universe has not yet gone.

2. Invariant causal laws.

But nothing really exists outside the whole of nature itself! Thus nature itself must make its own laws/habits. And these habits could themselves evolve. Even if there is a sufficient reason, within the evolving reality, for every change in the laws, and every generation of a fact, it is not evident that any intellect standing outside the evolving reality itself could compute, on the basis of what exists at a certain moment, all that is yet to come. For the evolution of reason-based reasons may be intrinsically less computable than the evolution of the mathematically formulated physically described properties of the classical-physics approximation to the actual laws of nature. Reason encompasses computable mathematics, but computable mathematics may not encompass reason. Reason is a category of explanation more encompassing than mathematical computation.

The laws of classical mechanics are cast in a particular kind of mathematical form that allows, in principle, a "mathematical computation" performed at an early time to predict with certainty the state of the universe at any later time. But this is very special feature of classical mechanics. It is far from obvious that the---definitely nonclassical---real world must exhibit this peculiar 'computability" feature.

The notion that a reason-based unfolding of the actual world is computable is an extrapolation from the classical-physics approximation that is far too dubious to provide the basis of a compelling argument that, in a mind-based quantum universe evolving in accordance with the principles of both quantum mechanics and sufficient reason, the outcomes of human choices are certain prior to their actual occurrence. It is far from being proved that, in a universe of that kind, the exact movement of the computer key that I am now pressing was certain already at the birth of the universe. "Reasons" could lack the fantastic computability properties that the physically described features of classical physics enjoy. But in that case our present reason-based human choices need not have been fixed with certainty at the birth of the universe. Within orthodox quantum mechanics meaningful human freedom need not be an illusion.

4. Reason-Based Dynamics Versus Physical-Description-Based Dynamics.

The arguments given above rest heavily upon the contrast between the reason-based dynamics of the unfolding universe described by quantum mechanics and the physical-description-based dynamics of the block universe described by classical mechanics. In this final section I shall pinpoint the technical features of orthodox quantum mechanics that underlie this fundamental difference between these two theories.

Von Neumann created a formulation of quantum mechanics in which all the physical aspects of nature are represented by the evolving quantum mechanical state (density matrix) of the universe. Each subsystem of this physically described universe is represented by a quantum state obtained by performing a certain averaging procedure on the state of the whole universe. Each experience of a person is associated with an "actual event". This event reduces, in a mathematically specified way, the prior quantum state of this person's brain---and consequently the quantum state of the entire universe---to a new "reduced" state. The reduction is achieved by the removal of all components of the state of this person's brain that are incompatible with the increment of knowledge associated with the experience. The needed mapping between "experiential increments in a person's knowledge" and "reductions of the quantum mechanical state of that person's brain" can be understood as being naturally created by trial and error learning of the experienced correlations between intentional efforts and the experiential feedbacks that these efforts tend to produce.

A key feature of von Neumann's dynamics is that it has two distinct kinds of mind-brain interaction. Von Neumann calls the first of these two processes "process 1". It corresponds to a choice of a probing action by the person, regarded as an agent or experimenter. The second kind of mind-brain interaction was called by Dirac "a choice on the part of nature". It specifies nature's response to the probing action selected by a logically preceding process 1 action. Von Neumann uses the name "process 2" to denote the physical evolution that occurs between the mind-brain (collapse) interactions. I therefore use the name "process 3" to denote the reduction/collapse process associated with nature's response to the process 1 probing action.

The mathematical form of process 1 differs from that of process 3. This mathematical difference causes these two processes to have different properties. In particular, process-1 actions have only local effects, in the sense that the dependence of the predictions of quantum mechanics upon a process-1 action itself, without a specification of the response, is confined (in the relativistic version) to the forward light-cone of the region in which the process-1 physical action occurs: the empirically observable effects of a process-1 action never propagate faster than the speed of light. On the other hand, nature's response (process 3) to a localized process-1 action can have observable statistical effects in a faraway contemporaneous region. The no-faster-than-light property of the empirically observable effects of any process-1 action is what justifies the word "relativistic" in relativistic quantum theory, even though the underlying mathematical description involves abrupt process-1-dependent faster-than-light transfers of information in connection with nature's response to the process-1 action.

Process 2 is a generalization of the causal process in classical mechanics, and, like it, is deterministic: the state of the universe at any earlier time completely determines what it will evolve into at any later time, insofar as no process 1 or process 3 event intervenes. But if no process 1 or process 3 event intervenes then the process 2 evolution would take the initial "big bang" state of the universe into a gigantic smear in which, for example, the moon would be smeared out over the night sky, and the mountains, and the cities, and we ourselves, would all be continuously spread out in space.

It is the process 1 and process 3 actions that, in the orthodox ontology, keep the universe in line with human experiences. On the other hand, the von Neumann ontology certainly does not exclude the possibility that non-human-based analogs of the human-based process 1 and follow-up process 3 actions also exist. Rather, it explains why the existence of reduction processes associated with other macroscopic agents would be almost impossible to detect empirically. These features of the von Neumann ontology justify focusing our attention here on the human involvement with nature.

Process 1, unlike process 2, is not constrained by any known law. In actual practice our choices of our probing actions appear to us to be based on reasons. We open the drawer in order to find the knife, in order to cut the steak, in order to eat the steak, in order to satisfy our hunger. Whilst all of this chain of reasons would, within the deterministic framework of classical physics, need to be, in principle, explainable in mathematical ways based upon the physical description of the universe, there is no such requirement in orthodox quantum mechanics: the sufficient reasons could be "reasons"; reasons involving the experiential dimension of reality, rather than being fully determined within the physical dimension. And these reasons could be, at each individual moment of experience, sufficient to determine the associated process 1 choice, without those choices having been mathematically computable from the state of the universe at earlier times.

The process 3 selection on the part of nature, unlike the process 1 choice, is not completely unconstrained: it is constrained by a statistical condition. According to the principle of sufficient reason, the process 3 choice must also be, in principle, determined by a sufficient reason. But, as emphasized above, nature's choice is nonlocal in character. Thus the reason for a process 3 choice need not be located at or near the place where the associated process 1 action occurs. Yet, as was clear already in classical statistical mechanics, there is an á priori statistical rule: equal volumes of phase space are equally likely. The (trace-based) statistical rule of quantum mechanics is essentially the quantum mechanical analog of this á priori statistical rule. The quantum statistical rule is therefore the natural statistical representation of the effect of a reason-based choice that is physically far removed from its empirical process 3 manifestation.

In closing, it is worth considering the argument of some physicalist philosophers that the replacement of classical mechanics---upon which physicalism is based---by quantum mechanics is not relevant to the resolution of the mind-matter problem for the following reason: that replacement has no bearing on the underlying problem of human freedom. The argument is that the essential difference between the two theories is (merely) that the determinism of classical mechanics is disrupted by the randomness of quantum mechanics, but that an introduction of randomness into the dynamics in no way rescues the notion of meaningful human freedom: a random choice is no better than a deterministic choice as an expression of meaningful human freedom.

This physicalist argument flounders on the fact that the element of quantum randomness enters quantum mechanics only via process 3, which delivers nature's choice. Man's choice enters via process 1, which is the logical predecessor to nature's process 3 "random" choice. In orthodox quantum mechanics, no elements of quantum randomness enter into man's choice. Nor is man's choice fixed by the deterministic aspect of quantum mechanics: that aspect enters only via process 2. Von Neumann's process 1 human choice is, in this very specific sense, "free": it is von Neumann's representation of Bohr's "free choice of experimental arrangement for which the quantum mechanical formalism offers the appropriate latitude" (Bohr 1958. p.51). Human choices enter orthodox quantum mechanics in a way not determined by a combination of the deterministic and random elements represented in the theory.

References

Bohr, N. (1934). Atomic Physics and the Description of Nature. Cambridge University Press, Cambridge, UK.

Bohr, N. (1958). Atomic Physics and Human Knowledge. Wiley, New York, US.

Heisenberg, W. (1958a). The representation of ature in contemporary physics. Daedalus, 87 (summer), 95-108.

Heisenberg, W. (1958b). Physics and Philosophy. Harper, New York, US.

James. W. (1892). Psychology: The Briefer Course. In: William James: Writings 1879-1899. Library of America (1992), New York, US.

Schwinger, J. (1951). Theory of Quantized Fields 1. Physical Review, 82, 914-927.

Stapp, H.P. (2007). Mindful Universe: Quantum Mechanics and the Participating Observer. Springer, Berlin.

Tomonaga, S. (1946). On a relativistically invariant formulation of the quantum theory of wave fields. Progress of Theoretical Physics, 1, 27-42.

Von Neumann, J. (1955/1932). Mathematical Foundations of Quantum Mechanics. Princeton University Press, Princeton New Jersey, US. (Translation of the German original: Mathematische Grundlagen der Quantenmechanik, Springer, Berlin, 1932.)

Cosmos and Quantum: Frontiers for the Future

Menas Kafatos, Ph.D.

Schmid College of Science, Chapman University,
Orange, California.

Abstract

Modern quantum theory has opened the door to a profoundly new vision of the cosmos, where the observer, the observed and the act of observation are fundamental and interlocked. No more is the universe to be studied as a mechanical conglomerate of parts. The interconnectedness of everything is particularly evident in the non-local interactions of the quantum universe. As such, the very large and the very small are also interconnected. In the present work, we look at several levels in the universe, where quantum theory may play an important role. We also look at the implications for a new, radically different view of the cosmos.

Key Words: Quantum Universe, perennial philosophy, consciousness, wholeness, future science.

1. "Introduction

The quantum view of the cosmos, where process is much more important than "building blocks", is not too foreign to the ancient perennial views of human beings, their role and relationship to the universe. However, the methodologies and approaches of science (or natural philosophy) and of perennial philosophy are fundamentally different: One deals with the study and understanding of the objective world, the other with the study and understanding of the subjective experience. The fact that diametrically opposite approaches point to the way of what we term the underlying undivided wholeness, indicates that it is perhaps this undivided wholeness that is most fundamental for both the external world and the internal world. It is not surprising then that as we attempt to search for the holy grail of science, the unification of diverse fields, we are led back to the dawn of civilization and to the holy grail of understanding the deepest parts of ourselves. Quantum theory has opened the door to the central role of consciousness but has not solved the problem of what consciousness is. The successes of science are indeed impressive given its continuous development over the past centuries. Nevertheless, we believe that present-day science needs to be extended beyond its present limits and it needs a new ontological model of reality, a new philosophy of science as well as a revised methodology of which derives from the above. Although we are not neglecting the impressive accomplishments of science as it has been developed over the last few centuries, our emphasis is towards the future (cf. Kafatos and Drăgănescu, 2001).

As we ponder the next steps of development of science, we should keep in mind that the quantum view is counterintuitive with everyday views of the fundamental separation between parts. It is the abandonment of commonly held "truths" that has propelled science forward. It is now time to go back and understand that perennial philosophies also challenged the (limited) views of separate, everyday, individual selves. The future science of wholeness will introduce back the centrality of individual awareness which itself is inseparable from universal awareness. As the quantum and the universe are ultimately and intimately interconnected, so are the individual and the universal consciousness. As such, the universe may verily be the conscious universe.

2. Cosmology, Arrow of Time, Quantum, and Complementarity

2.1 Scales and Levels of the Universe: Cosmology and Models of the Universe

In cosmology, one faces the unusual situation that the observer (contained within the universe) and the observed (a part of the universe, which, by definition is also contained within the universe) are part of the same universe. As such, theories of cosmological import must ultimately account for the structure and evolution of the entire system or universe, utilizing experiments carried out in the present that are used to deduce the state of the large-scale universe in the distant past. The most accepted theory of the large-scale structure of the universe is big bang cosmology, which has achieved impressive results (Silk, 1989).

However, big bang cosmology requires extremely fine tuning. This fine tuning is most remarkable as related to the so-called flatness problem: If the universe is close to being flat today, it was exactly equal to flat to one part in 10^{50} near the time of the big bang. This may indeed be related to other applicable coincidences, rather than being a case in itself. The usual interpretation of the flatness problem has been given in terms of the inflationary model of the universe, which occurred at time scales $\sim 10^{-35}$ sec after the beginning. The inflationary model of Guth and others (cf. Guth and Steinhardt, 1984) accounts for the flatness of the universe and is also proposed to solve another challenge, the so-called horizon problem, or apparent isotropy of the 2.73 K black body cosmic microwave background radiation or CMBR seen by the satellite COBE (Smoot, 1996).

Although the 2.73 K radiation was emitted $\sim 10^5$ years after the beginning, opposite sides of the sky at that time were out of causal contact, separated by $\sim 10^7$ light years. What caused the observed isotropy of the CMBR? Other correlations in the large-scale structure of the universe exist such as very large structures (superclusters or extended filaments or sheets of galaxies) in the distribution of matter (Geller and Huchra, 1989) which may persist at all scales extending to the scale of the universe itself.

However, any general relativistic Friedmann- Robertson-Walker big bang model, as well as any other non-big bang cosmological model, cannot be considered outside the process of cosmological observation itself and is ultimately intricately interwoven with limits imposed by observation itself (Kafatos, 1989, 1996, 1998). Any theoretical construct predicts horizons of knowledge at some ultimate, faint observational limit. For the big bang theory, since photons are used to study the universe, the evolving universe becomes opaque to its own radiation at redshifts $z \sim 10^3$, or $\sim 10^5$ years after the big bang. Ultimately, observational limitations prohibit verifying cosmological theories to any degree of accuracy for any observational test. Moreover, as Kafatos (1989) showed, ultimately source position and spectra from sources would become confused due to the existence of very few photons from distant sources and the wave-particle duality which forces experiment choices (see Fig. 1).

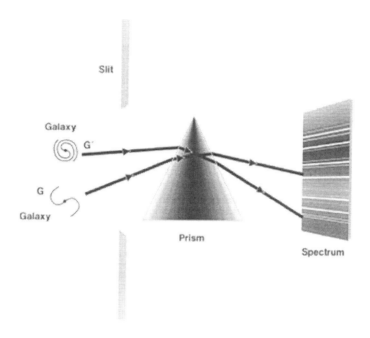

Figure 1. Cosmological Realm: Complementarity as a scale-bridging foundational principle .

For all practical purposes, the big bang galaxy formation theory runs into verification problems at much smaller redshifts, $z \sim 4^{-10}$, close to distances discerned by the Hubble Space Telescope and future space telescopes. The reason is that the type and evolutionary history of the "standard candles" (such as galaxies) used to measure the Hubble expansion rate and overall structure of the universe cannot be unequivocally determined independently of the cosmology itself (Kafatos, 1989). Even recent views of an accelerating universe ultimately depend on understanding very distant sources and the characteristics of the distant Type I supernovae. Although elegant and in many ways supported by evidence, the big bang, of the inflationary kind, cosmology has progressively become ensnarled by current evidence and by its own strong predictions.

However, before such efforts to describe the universe succeed, we need to look at both the very large and very small (cosmology and quantum) realms. Cosmological theories and theories of fundamental physics must ultimately not only account for the structure and evolution of the universe, the physics of fundamental interactions but also lead to an understanding of why this particular universe follows the physics that it does. Such theories must lead to an understanding of the values of the fundamental constants themselves. Moreover, the understanding of universe has to utilize experimental data from the present to deduce the state of the universe in distant regions of the past and also account for certain peculiarities (such as the distribution of matter in the universe) or coincidences (such as the flatness problem) observed.

2.2 The Arrow of Time in Cosmology– an Alternate View

The question of time is equally important. In ordinary physics (including "one vector' quantum theory) time flows in one direction. Aharonov et al. (1964) proposed instead a two vector theory, which is in total agreement with ordinary quantum theory: time also flows from the future to the past, providing a completeness in the description of physical phenomena. Departing also from ordinary ideas about the one vector "flow of time", Kafatos, Roy and Roy (2005) took a different approach than the usual evolutionary picture where the physics itself is assumed invariable.

Kafots et al. (2005) showed that these coincidences could be re-interpreted in terms of relationships linking the masses of elementary particles as well as the total number of nucleons in the universe (or Eddington's number) to other fundamental "constants" such as the gravitational constant, G, the charge of the electron, e, Planck's constant, h, and the speed of light, c. They studied some numerical relations among fundamental constants starting from relationships first proposed by Weinberg (1972), which turn out to be equivalent to the relations found by Dirac (1937) and Eddington (1931), and explored a new scaling hypothesis relating the speed of light c and the scale of the universe R. They conclude that scale-invariant relationships result, e.g. all lengths are then proportional to the scale of the universe R, etc. Note, however, that we cannot deduce the actual variation or the initial value of c and other constants from observations: The relationship that they found, $c \equiv R$ is not enough to tell us the actual variation or even over "how long" it takes place. It is a scale invariant relationship. If we re-write it as a scale-invariant relationship, $c(t_*)/c(t_o) = R(t_*)/R(t_o)$ where t_* and t_o could be conveniently taken as the Planck time and the present "age" of the universe, then this relationship is not enough to give us the evolution of or even the values of t_* and t_o. Hence it cannot tell us how c itself is varying or even if it is varying. If we wanted to insist that c is constant, then all the other "constants" like G and h are really constant as well. But if c is not constant, then all the other "constants" are varying as well. In both cases, however, the number of particles is changing, the ratios of masses are changing and the ratios of scales or lengths are also changing. An arrow of time could, therefore, be introduced. In this picture, invariant relationships hold and from unity, there is evolution into diversity. As such, the arrow of time is introduced in an observer-dependent universe as these fundamental "constants" change (e.g. Eddington's number varies from $Np=1$ at the time of big bang to $= 10^{80}$ today, etc). Time does not exist independently of conscious observers. This approach is equivalent to an axiomatic approach which results in an apparent expanding universe, yielding the same successes as present big bang cosmology but without the need to postulate inflation, cold dark matter, cosmological constant or any of the artificialities of current theory.

Time is strictly a parameter that can be introduced in the above scale-invariant relationships. It has no meaning by itself . The universe appears to be evolving as the number of particles and ratios are varying.

2.3 The Quantum Universe

One can notice that we still don't have a quantum theory of gravity, and hence cannot properly describe theoretically the universe. Nevertheless, quantum processes are fundamental in the universe and prevalent at all times (the basic nature of matter and energy is described in terms of quantum theories such as QED, QCD, Supersymmetry & String Theories). Moreover, according to the Big Bang theory, the universe was in quantum state early-on (at the Planck time and at high energies/densities in such an evolving universe).

If QM is so important to the universe, particularly in the early eras, perhaps it plays an even more fundamental role, through the act of observation itself, which only properly is part of modern QM. The remarkable correlations exhibited at cosmological scales are reminiscent of Bell-type quantum correlations (Bell, 1964) that were so abhorrent to Einstein (Einstein, Podolsky and Rosen, 1935) and yet confirmed by the Aspect and Gisin experiments (see Fig. 2).

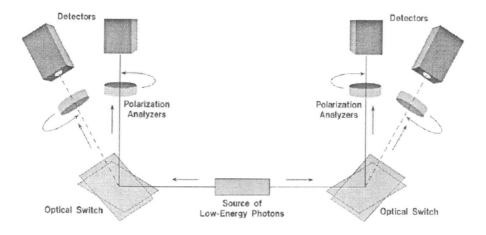

Figure 2. Illustration of the Aspect Experiment.

Kafatos (1989) and Roy and Kafatos (1999b) proposed that Bell-type correlations would be pervasive in the early universe arising from the common electron-positron annihilations: Binary processes involving Compton scattering of the resultant gamma-ray photons with electrons would produce

N-type correlations (Fig. 3).

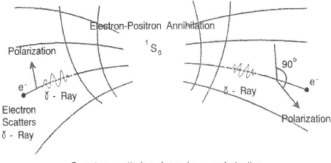

Figure 3. Bell-type correlations in the early universe.

In these conditions, the outcome of the cascade of processes (even in the absence of observers) would produce space-like correlations among the original entangled photons. Kafatos and Nadeau (2000) and Kafatos (1998) have in turn proposed three types of non-localities: Spatial or Type I; temporal or Type II (or Wheeler's Delayed Choice Experiment), wherein the "path" of a photon is not determined until a delayed choice is made.

In some strange sense, the past is brought together (in the sense that the path is not determined) by the experimental choice. This non-locality confirmed in the laboratory could also occur over cosmological distances (Wheeler, 1981; Roy and Kafatos, 2000). Type III non-locality (Kafatos and Nadeau, 2000) represents the unified whole of space-time revealed in its complementary aspects as the unity of space (Type I) and the unity of time (Type II non-10 locality). It exists outside the framework of space and time and cannot, therefore, be discerned by the scientific method although its existence is implied.

The Bell correlations in the early universe may prove to provide that non-local link in a natural way, as the outcome of QM processes themselves. As such, the universe would be quantum at a very fundamental level and not just near the beginning.

The deep underlying wholeness of the universe is revealed in a series of Universal Diagrams (UD) (Kafatos, 1986; Kafatos and Nadeau, 2000). These can be constructed by placing various physical quantities of many different objects in the universe on common, multidimensional plots. 2-D diagrams have been constructed involving the mass, size, luminous output, surface temperature and entropy radiated away (see Fig. 4) of different objects in the universe. These diagrams originally constructed for astronomical objects (Kafatos, 1986) have been revised and extended to all scales including biological entities, industrial and man-made objects, living organisms, etc. The overall appearance of the UDs does not change as more objects are introduced, rather the specifics of smaller regions within a UD become more refined. Over smaller regions, different power laws can be found to fit the data, while more global relationships can be found that approximately fit many different classes of objects (such as an approximately linear relationship between entropy radiated away and mass).

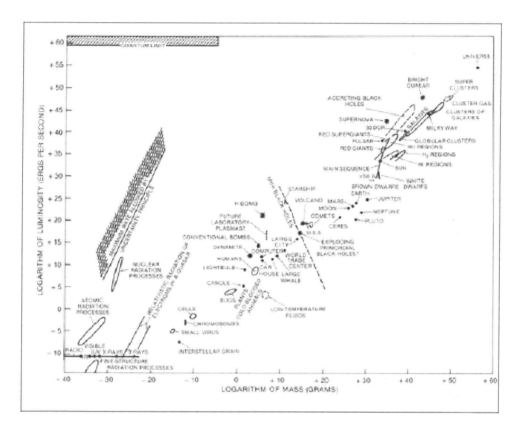

Figure 4. Universal Realm: Universal Diagram.

It is found that black holes provide boundaries in the UDs and often cut across the main relationships in these diagrams. The values of the constants (and their ratios) and the laws of physics are determining the overall relationships and as such the diagrams must be related to cosmological coincidences. There are large scale correlations revealed in these diagrams among different dimensions (other than space and time examined above) or parameters which extend beyond the quantum or cosmological realms, to realms such as living organisms, etc. It follows that non-locality in the sense of global multidimensional correlations, is revealed by the UDs to be a foundational principle of the structure of the cosmos along with complementarity (Kafatos and Nadeau, 2000).

It has become clear that quantum non-locality related to Bell's Theorem and revealed by the Aspect and Gisin experiments (Stapp, 1979; Aspect, Grangier & Roger, 1982; Tittel, Brendel, Zbinden & Gisin, 1998; Kafatos & Nadeau, 2000; Nadeau and Kafatos, 1999) has demonstrated the inadequacy of classical, local realistic theories to account for quantum-like correlations and the nature of underlying reality. The epistemological and ontological consequences are far-reaching (Kafatos and Nadeau, 2000) and imply a non-local, undivided reality. Moreover, Drăgănescu and Kafatos (2000), Kafatos and Drăgănescu (2003), explore the possibility that foundational principles operate at all levels in the physical as well as beyond the physical aspects of the cosmos. These foundational principles are meta-mathematical or pre-mathematical in the sense that mathematical constructs of the physical universe emerge from them. Such generalized principles include a generalized principle of complementarity.

In the generalized complementarity framework (Kafatos and Nadeau, 2000; Nadeau and Kafatos1999), complementary constructs need to be considered to formulate a complete picture of a scientific field under examination (e.g. the large-scale structure of the universe) as a horizon of knowledge is approached. This means that as a horizon is approached, ambiguity as to a unique view of the universe sets in. It was precisely these circumstances that apply at the quantum level, which prompted Bohr to affirm that complementary constructs should be employed (Bohr, 1961).

If truly universal, these principles should apply at all scales. Non-locality also appears to be prevalent at different scales. Quantum theory has shown that the whole is not just the sum of its constituent parts. For example, the quantum vacuum is much richer and complex than any system of particles interacting among themselves. Studying particle interactions, no matter how complex, will not tell us much about the vacuum as the latter is unaffected by such interactions. These developments are indicative of the need to develop a new way to approach problems that have so far eluded ordinary physical science and cosmology in particular. We will see that such generalized principles may also apply at biological levels and as such are truly universal.

3. Integrated Bioscience, Quantum and Consciousness

3.1 The Challenge of Consciousness

The issue of consciousness remains a major challenge for science. Despite great success in several fields including neuroscience, psychology; as well as developments in the philosophy of science and foundations of quantum theory, the basic challenge remains that science is based on the dichotomy between subject and object. Traditionally, science has studied objective reality, assuming in principle that there is an objective world that can be studied independently of the existence of observers. Yet, quantum theory has opened the door to the issue of consciousness in the sense that objective reality cannot be disentangled from the act of observation. The EPR experiment and Bell's Theorem have demonstrated that whatever "reality" might be, it is non-local and tied to the act of observation.

3.2 Quantum Biology

The understanding of how the fundamental physical interactions of inanimate matter and electromagnetic radiation, give rise to cellular dynamics of living organisms and the perceptual experience of human beings, is one of the most challenging problems (cf. Szent-Györgi, 1960) facing science today (for a review of material in this section and section 3.3, see Ceballos et al., 2009). Information is an essential component in the study of living entities, as there exists a fundamental relationship between the dynamic organization of energy and the processing of biological information. It is essential to understand the type of information, e.g. quantum vs. classical, that is involved, particularly in regards to the human brain, but not just applied to human conscious processes. The human brain represents a particularly major challenge to describe and understand the multitude of processes applicable over a vast range of spatio-temporal domains (e.g. Bernroider and Roy, 2004). Fig. 5 shows this vast range of space-time.

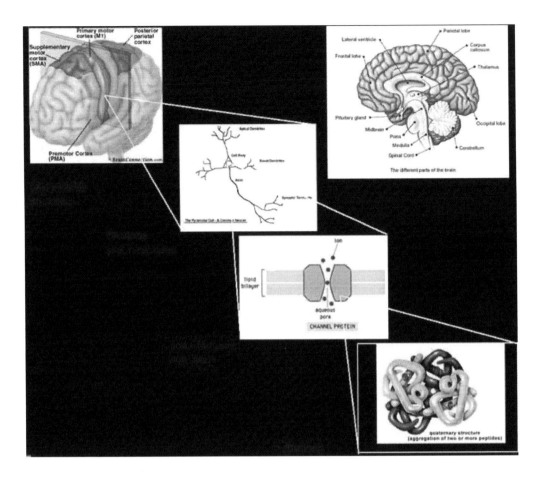

Figure 5. Range of spatio-temporal domains found in the human brain.

The old paradigm of bottom-up approach in increased complexity of living organisms to try to explain the phenomena of life, may not be applicable (i.e. complexity is simply a result of putting together structures from lower levels to higher levels, see Fig. 6).

Bottom up Approach

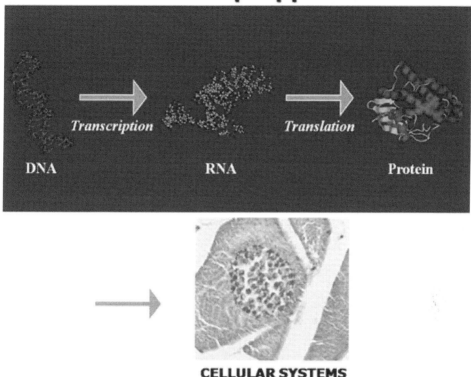

CELLULAR SYSTEMS

Figure 6. The old paradigm of increased complexity in living organisms.

It is becoming increasingly clear that the overall structures, requiring often global relationships, and extreme efficiency with which biological organisms operate, requires the use of quantum mechanical formalisms at biologically, and neurophysiologically, relevant space and time scales (cf. Bernroider and Roy, 2005; Ceballos et al., 2009; Davies, 2004, 2005; Frohlich, 1983; Hagan et. al., 2002; Hameroff et. al., 2002; Hammeroff and Tuszynski, 2003; Hunter, 2006; Mesquita et. al., 2005; Rosa and Faber, 2004; Roy and Kafatos, 2004; Stapp, 2004). The issue of quantum entanglement has become a strong debatable issue particularly as it applies to the brain (e.g. Tegmark, 2000). However, accumulating evidence suggests that quantum interference and entanglement are much more robust than had previously been accepted, and may indeed turn out to be fundamental to a rigorous understanding of biomolecular and brain dynamics (e.g. Bernroider and Roy, 2004; 2005; Prokhorenko et al., 2006; Parson, 2007; Engel, 2007). For example, macroscopic quantum entanglement has been discovered to exist at room temperature (e.g. Fillaux et. al., 2006); quantum coherent spin transfers between quantum dots bridged with benzene molecules are observed to be more efficient at room temperature than at near absolute zero temperatures (e.g. Ouyang and Awschalom, 2003); long-lived macroscopic entanglement between two distinct objects (e.g. Julsgaard, et. al., 2001); and quantum superposition of distinct macroscopic states, have all been experimentally found (cf. Friedman et. al., 2000). These developments mirror progress in quantum experiments, where quantum entanglement has been proven to affect macroscopic observables (e.g. Ghosh et. al., 2003; Brukner, Vedral, and Zeilinger, 2006).

However, despite progress in the lab, the theoretical application of QM to biological problems is in its infancy, even given the understanding of its importance to the fields of bio-molecular dynamics and quantum chemistry (e.g. Bernroider and Roy, 2005; Ceballos et al., 2009; Davies, 2004; 2005; Engel, 2007; Hunter, 2006; Parson, 2007; Shemella et. al., 2007; van Mourik, 2004;). QM calculations are integral for modeling and understanding fundamental biochemical reactions and dynamics (e.g. Engel et. al., 2007). Living organisms have achieved a quantum level of sensitivity to different types of external stimuli (e.g. Angioy et al., 2003; Bialek, 1987; Field et. al., 2005; Hudspeth, 1997; Nobili et. al., 1998). For example, brains of some fish are sensitive to electric fields as low as 1 microV/cm (Bullock, 1977), whereas electroreceptors have been shown to be sensitive to voltage gradients on the order of 10 nV/cm (Kalmijn, 1982).

In addition to their quantum-level sensitivity to external stimuli, Engel et al. (2007) has obtained direct evidence that remarkably long-lived electronic quantum coherence in energy transfer processes within photosynthetic systems is occurring, resulting in the complexes to sample vast areas of phase space to find the most efficient path. Non-locality also is suspect in protein folding (Klein-Seetharaman et. al., 2002).

Other quantum (or "quantum like") effects have been discovered in vision (e.g. Kim et al., 2001; Prokhorenko et al., 2006), QM tunneling of electrons (e.g. Berlin et. al., 2004; Stuchebrukhov, 2003); molecular and chemical bond processes (e.g. Matsuno, 1999, 2001); as well as hypothesized in the brain (e.g. Hammeroff et. al., 2002; Jibu et. al., 1994; Mershin et. al., 2004).

A theory has been proposed for the allometric scaling relations within biological organisms through the quantum nature of energy transfer in electron flow and proton translocation (Demetrius, 2003). Quantum coherence has even been shown to persist within living cells, despite the seemingly "noisy" and "chaotic" cellular environment at room temperature, as quantum spins from biochemical radical pairs have been seen to retain their correlation within the cytoplasm, even after they become separated (Walleczek, 1995). Moreover, squeezed quantum states of light have been observed within biological systems (e.g. Popp, 2002). Finally, it is possible to develop a QM circuit description of voltage fluctuation within neural membranes (reducing to the Hodkin-Huxley equation macroscopically, e.g. Mitra and Roy, 2006).

3.3 Quantum Mechanics and the Brain

The issue of quantum processes in the brain has received a lot of interest. Neuronal decoherence processes have only been calculated while assuming that ions, such as K+, are believed to undergo quantum Brownian motion (e.g. Tegmark, 2000). Extremely short decoherence timescales of 10^{-20} seconds, result. Such arguments though assume that the system in question is in thermal equilibrium with its environment, which is not typically the case for bio-molecular dynamics (e.g. Frohlich, 1986; Mesquita et. al., 2005; Porkony and Wu, 1998). Also, the ions themselves do not move freely within the ion-channel filter, but rather their states are pre-selected, leading to possible protection of quantum coherence within the ion channel for a time scale on the order of 10^{-3} seconds at 300K, $\sim$ time scale of ion-channel opening and closing (e.g. Bernroider and Roy, 2005). Entangled states of K+ ions and oxygen atoms within the channels are likely occurring.

More general, such new quantum ideas applicable to the fields of molecular cell biology and biophysics will have a profound impact in modeling and understanding the process of decoherence within neuro-molecular systems. Quantum coherence within neuro-molecular biological systems may indeed be applicable, for systems that are not in thermodynamic equilibrium with their environments.

It seems clear that a successful representation of neuro-molecular dynamics should include a rigorous understanding of complex, mixed quantum states of entanglement, far-from-equilibrium quantum thermodynamics with non-linear potential terms (i.e. due to strong 17 interaction with a heat bath, electron-phonon coupling, etc.), appropriately modeled water and bio-molecular environments, and perhaps should even include mesoscopic elements of quantum chaos which have been shown to enhance the stability of quantum computations (e.g. Prosen and Znidaric, 2001), as well as describe mathematical structures exhibited by inter-spike train intervals (e.g. Bershadskii et. al., 2003).

As a specific example of the applicability of quantum-like processes at mesoscale levels, and the operation of underlying principles, Roy and Kafatos (1999b) have examined the response and percept domains in the cerebellum and have built a convincing case that complementarity or quantum-like effects may be operating in brain processes. As such, complementarity may be applicable to neuroscience as well, or to conscious processes, to living structures in general. They do not, however, speculate about quantum processes themselves operating at specific brain sites. Rather, they assume that quantum-like processes deriving from deeper principles operate. The difference is important.

From a large series of experiments in cats and monkeys it was found that neurons with similar receptive field axis orientation are located on top of each other in discrete columns, while we have a continuous change of the receptive field axis orientation as we move into adjacent columns. Granlund (1999) discussed the possibility of implementation of filters in the visual cortex as related to the orientation selectivity of neurons. We can define the notion of distance between the "filters" or the orientation selective neuronal clusters or columns, similar to the statistical distance between quantum preparations. The statistical distance is most easily understood in terms of photons and polarizing filters (Roy and Kafatos, 1999a), which illustrates our view that quantum formalism may be introduced for brain dynamics.

It is generally believed that the cerebellum's function is to help the brain to coordinate movements but the recent neurophysiological evidence challenges this theory. Apart from being considered a specialized control box, the cerebellum participates in many activities of the brain including cognition. Now the problem is to find out an integrating principle operative in the brain so as to describe both motor function and cognitive activities. Roy and Kafatos (1999) have proposed that a generalized complementarity principle can be thought of as operative as integrating principle in the cerebellum. More generally, we imagine a measurement process with a device that selects only one of the eigenstates of the observable A and rejects all others. This is what is meant by selective measurement in quantum mechanics. It is also called filtration because only one of the eigenstates filters through the process.

It must be emphasized that we are taking the idea of quantum filter at the conceptual level only for better understanding of the cerebellum function. We are not considering any quantum process that may or may not be operating in some regions of the cerebellum at least at the present state of our understanding of the brain function.

The motive of this work was to show that concepts like the principle of complementarity, non-locality, etc. may play an important role not only in quantum mechanics but also in other branches of science. It is clear from the above analysis that set of dynamical principles are necessary for the description of physical as well as cognitive activities. Indeed, a set of principles is necessary for the description of different levels of cognitive activities and consciousness.

4. Synthesis and Conclusions

In following the above discussion, perhaps we are not yet at the stage to describe life, mind or even begin to understand the underlying underpinnings of consciousness. Nevertheless, we may have to explore the foundational framework for all reality. We firmly believe that any such attempt, has to ultimately be mathematical, involving mathematics as the fundamental language of Nature . A mathematical framework, utilizing category theory, proposed by Kato and Struppa, is in fact appropriate to embody the principles established by Kafatos and Drăgănescu. In a series of papers, Kato and Struppa (1999a; 1999b; 1999c; 1999d), developed a mathematical formalism, which was based on the theory of categories with Grothendieck topologies (Kato and Struppa, 1999a) to describe and interpret a general theory of consciousness.

Moving to more bold steps, the fundamental current description of physical reality may find a place in this general mathematical framework, and we can even explore the connections of perennial philosophies in these new terms. It should be noted that the category theory not only can describe the various levels of consciousness but even the activities of the neurons (Ehresmann and Vanbremeersch, 1987) a fact which may or may not be connected with the framework of awareness or consciousness. Therefore category theory may be a candidate formalism to be used at various levels of reality.

Because of its wide applicability, category theory can be further explored from our previous work (Drăgănescu. and Kafatos, 2003). The relevance here is that quantum theory has revealed a much richer structure to reality and as such, any mathematical language that would have general applicability would have to first and foremost apply to quantum theory. Along the same line of thinking, the two vector quantum theory of Aharonov et al. (1964) has revealed an even richer (and as well elegant) structure and as such, a fundamental mathematical language should fit it and allow further developments to be developed.

In trying to understand where biology and consciousness fit vis-à-vis physics and physical theories in general, one may attempt to utilize the same universal language. Rather than pursuing different paths in trying to understand them, the different realities ought to be considered together, an undivided whole. It may be the case that we cannot explain life, mind and consciousness without knowing the nature of the underlying reality and this may necessitate exploring the foundational framework for this underlying reality (Kafatos and Drăgănescu, 2003). Such an axiomatic approach may allow the question "is consciousness the deepest underlying foundational level of existence?" to be posed, which presently appears to be beyond the reach of science. Related questions such as "does the deepest existence possess the ingredients necessary for the emergence of life and mind as we know it?"; "how are energy, substance and information related to the principles of underlying reality?", etc., may be the deep questions that need to guide future development of science. Developments from quantum theory (Roy & Kafatos, 1999a; 2003) provide plausibility that certain principles apply to different fields of natural sciences and may be considered to hold universal validity. From the early quantum universe, it is likely that quantum-like effects are frozen into the structure of the universe and, therefore, pervasive at all scales in the universe. Complementarity, and non-locality are two principles that apply beyond quantum microphysical scales (Kafatos, 1998; 1999) and as such may be considered to be universal foundational principles applying at all scales. It follows that fundamental foundational principles should be applicable to other fields such as brain dynamics, ecosystems and planetary science (Drăgănescu and Kafatos, 1999; Kafatos, 1999; Kafatos and Drăgănescu, 2003). In the same way, one can search for analogous universal principles that hold in realms beyond physical and biological sciences. Let's ascertain the possibility that consciousness is the foundational substratum of the universe, principles developed in perennial philosophical systems should be even more universally applicable and cut across all levels of the cosmos, "internal" (e.g. individual mental and psychic, etc.) as well as "external" (e.g. collective unconscious, physical, etc). A possible prescription starting from the weak measurements in quantum theory of Aharonov et al. (1964), and the equivalent EEG and other measurements in brain dynamics, leading to increased levels of unification, and ultimately to a common mathematical formalism, is illustrated in Fig. 7. This should be viewed as one of many possible paths for unification.

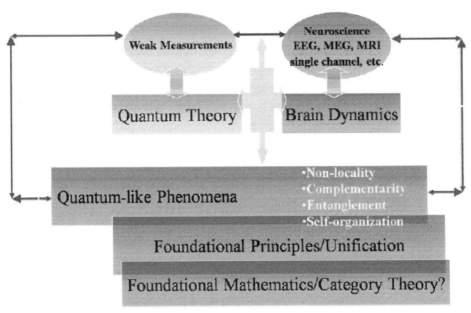

Figure 7. An approach towards unification.

One may then sketch a possible new prescription for a unified "science", beyond even mathematical foundations, that will encompass ordinary natural science and extend it to be able to address the issue of consciousness. In this new prescription one would start from the whole and then study the parts, a reversal of the way that ordinary science proceeds. To assist in this approach, if we start from the premise that consciousness is the underlying foundation of the physical, mental, psychic and all possible realms, one needs to look at the systems of philosophy dealing with consciousness.

As such, universal statements of the different perennial philosophies, which are directly applicable to consciousness, from both the East and the West might be the starting point for a dialogue between hard sciences and philosophical systems (Kafatos and Kafatou, 1991). This dialogue is difficult but can be bridged (Kafatos and Nadeau, 2000; Nadeau & Kafatos, 1999) leading towards a new science of unified knowledge. One can examine principles and statements found in schools of thought such as Vedanta (Swami Prabhavananda and Isherwood, 1975; Swami Vimuktananda, 2005) and Shaivism (Singh, 1979) to seek their "reflection" or analogy at the physical realm. Then one can look at the insights gained to seek new developments in the science of wholeness, which includes the physical world. This is certainly a reversal of the usual scientific method, here we start from the whole, from the general, from the universal, from the unlimited, and we end up going to the individual, the particular, the limited. Two monistic perennial Indian philosophical systems, Kashmir Shaivism and Shankaracharya's Vedanta provide complete systems on ultimate reality, or Absolute (Brahman in Vedanta; Paramashiva or Supreme Shiva in Shaivism), and its nature. Both accept the Absolute as the ultimate, underlying reality but with some important differences in emphasis: Vedanta emphasizes that Brahman is the only reality and the universe is illusory; while Shaivism accepts the universe as real in the sense that it is part, albeit the physical and mental parts, of the great underlying sea of Consciousness. Shaivism accepts a static (Sat) aspect and a dynamic (Chit or Shakti) aspect of Consciousness, whose' nature is Bliss (Ananda). These are all aspects of the One, undivided sea of Consciousness (samvit) which is a dynamic (spanda), creative and intelligent Reality. Reality is then identical to Consciousness. In its practical aspects, Shaivism also holds the view that everything is still part of the fundamental Reality which continuously undergoes creative process in the unfoldment of the universe from the levels of Paramashiva, to the first movement towards differentiation (Shiva-Shakti) all the way down to the creation of the physical universe.

Inherent in these steps is the continuously unfolding object-subject division which "projects" ultimate Reality onto levels of increasingly grosser and grosser experience. As such, Shaivism provides some profound insights to the mysterious problem of subjective experience and parallels the ideas expounded here on generalized principle of complementarity.

To recapitulate, in attempting to understand the connection of the large scale realm (namely the universe, presumably starting in a big bang) to the realm of biology and biosphere, the connection to the realm of microscale or microphysics (particles, atoms, molecules, on which all life and the universe itself and all it contains are composed of), the issue of a common framework to ground different scales and endeavors is a central challenge. The problem is clearly compounded when one brings in the issue of consciousness, whatever one's beliefs on the subject might be, as not only the field of consciousness is vast and rapidly expanding, it is also subject to many different schools of thought. Interdisciplinary approaches combining philosophical and scientific views, utilizing intuition (Kak, 2003) may point to the direction that science needs to be changed, perhaps seriously taking into account what monistic perennial philosophies hold. It has been proposed that future integrative science will contain elements of perennial philosophies, perhaps adopting the fundamental view of monism. The present work has presented a synthesis, following ideas published before by the author and his co-workers in numerous publications. Although in these ideas by themselves, much of what we are saying here has appeared before, the brief synthesis presented here gives the vision of future attempts to integrate these ideas into a coherent whole. As such, the present treatise can be considered to be forging the way forward in a bold attempt to "see over the horizon" future that awaits science and, we believe, humanity's understanding of itself and its role in the cosmos. This has become even more imperative as we are now collectively facing great challenges in the survival of modern societies and perhaps even the Earth's biosphere as it presently is. Perhaps we need to be armed with new understanding and tools, dating to the dawn of civilization, as to who we really are and what science we need in order to evolve collectively and consciously. This is certainly not a minor task but nevertheless an imperative task .

References

Aharonov, Y., Bergmann, P.G., and Lebowitz, J. (1964). Time Symmetry in the Quantum Process of Measurement, Phys. Rev., 134, B1410.

Aharonov, Y., Albert, D., and Vaidman, L. (1988). How the Result of a Measurement of a Component of a Spin ½ Particle Can Turn Out to Be 100? Phys. Rev. Lett., 60, 1351..

Angioy, A.M., Desogus, A., Barbarossa, I.T., Anderson, P., Hansson, B.S. (2003). Extreme sensitivity in an olfactory system. Chem. Senses, 28, 279–84.

Aspect, A., Grangier, P. and Roger, G. (1982).

Experimental Realization of Einstein-Podolsky-Rosen gedankenexperiment; a violation of Bell's inequalities, Phys. Rev. Lett., 49, 91.1.

Bell, J.S. (1964). On the Einstein-Podolsky-Rosen Paradox, Physics, 1, 195.

Berger, D., Pribram, K., Wild, K., and Bridges, C. (1990). An analysis of neural spike-train distributions: Determinants of the response of visual cortex neurons to changes in orientation and spatial frequency, Expt. Brain Res., 80,129-134.

Berlin, Y.A., Kurnikov, I.V., Beratan, D., Ratner, M.A., Burin, A.L. (2004). DNA electron transfer processes: Some theoretical notions, Long-Range Charge Transfer in DNA, Topics in Current Chemistry, G. B. Schuster (Ed.), v. 237, pp. 1-36, Springer-Verlag, Heidelberg.

Bernroider, G. and Roy, S. (2004). Quantum-classical correspondence in the brain: Scaling, action distances and predictability behind neural signals. FORMA, 19, 55–68.

Bernroider, G. and Roy, S. (2005). Quantum entanglement of K+ ions, multiple channel states, and the role of noise in the brain. In: Fluctuations and Noise in Biological, Biophysical, and Biomedical Systems III, Stocks, Nigel G.; Abbott, Derek; Morse, Robert P. (Eds.), Proceedings of the SPIE, Volume 5841-29, pp. 205-214.

Bershadskii, A., Dremencov, E., Bershadskii, J., Yadid, G. (2003). Brain neurons as quantum computers: {in vivo} support of background physics. Int. J. Mod. Phys., C, 14, #7.

Bialek, W. (1987). Physical limits to sensation and perception. Annu. Rev. Biophys. Biophys. Chem., 16, 455–78.

Bohr, N. (1961). Atomic Theory and the Description of Nature, p. 34, Cambridge, Cambridge University Press.

Brukner, C., Vedral, V., and Zeilinger, A. (2006). Crucial Role of Quantum Entanglement in Bulk Properties of Solids. Phys. Rev. A, 73, 012110.

Bullock, T. H. (1977). Electromagnetic sensing in Fish, Neuroscience Res. Prog. Bull. 15, 17-22.

Ceballos, R. (2009), Kafatos, M., Roy, S., and Yang, S., preprint.

Chaplin, M. (2006). Do we underestimate the importance of water in cell biology? Nature Reviews Molecular Cell Biology, 7(11), 861. Davies, P. (2004). Does Quantum Mechanics play a non-trivial role in Life? Bio-

Systems, 78, 69– 79

Davies, P. (2005). A Quantum Recipe for Life. Nature, 437, 819.

Demetrius, L. (2003). Quantum statistics and allometric scaling of organisms. Physica A, 322, 477-490.

Dirac, P.A.M. (1937). The Cosmological Constants, Nature, 139, 323.

Drăgănescu, M., Kafatos, M. (1999). Generalized Foundational Principles in the Philosophy of Science. The Noetic Journal, 2, No. 4, Oct., 1999, p.341-350; published also in the volume Science and the Primacy of Consciousness, Intimation of a 21stCentury Revolution, pp. 86-99, Richard L. Amoroso et al., (Eds.), Orinda: The Noetic Press (2000).

Drăgănescu, M. and Kafatos, M. (2003). Community and Social Factors for the Integrative Science, Noesis, 28, 9-26, 2003.

Eddington, A.S. (1931). M.N.R.A.S., 91, 412.

Ehresmann, A.C. and Vanbremeersch, J.P. (1987). Hierarchical Evolutive Systems: A Mathematical Model for Complex Systems, Bull.Math. Biol. 49, 13.

Einstein, A., Podolsky, B., and Rosen, N. (1935). Can Quantum-Mechanical Description of Physical Reality Be Considered Complete?, Phys. Rev., 47, 777.

Engel, G.S., Calhoun, T.R., Read, E.L., Ahn, T.K., Mancal, T., Cheng, Y.C., Blankenship, R.E., and Fleming, G.R. (2007). Evidence for wavelike energy transfer through quantum coherence in photosynthetic systems. Nature, 446(7137), 782-786.

Field, G.D., Sampath, A.P., and Rieke, F. (2005). Retinal Processing Near Absolute Threshold: From Behavior to Mechanism. Annu. Rev. Physiol., 67, 15.1–15.

Fillaux, F., Cousson, A., and Gutmann, M.J.

(2006). Macroscopic quantum entanglement and 'super-rigidity' of protons in the KHCO3 crystal from 30 to 300 K. J. Phys.: Condens. Matter, 18, 3229–3249.

Flores, J., Kun, S.Y., and Seligman, T.H. (2005). Slow phase relaxation as a route to quantum computing beyond the quantum chaos border. Physical Review E., 72, 017201.

Freeman, W J. (1991). The Physiology of Perception, Scientific American, 264, 78-85.

Freeman, W.J. and Vitiello, G. (2006). Nonlinear brain dynamics as macroscopic manifestation of underlying many-body field dynamics. Physics of Life Reviews, 3, 93-118.

Friedman, J.R., Patel, V., Chen, W., Tolpygo, S.K., and J.E. Lukens. (2000). Quantum Superposition of Distinct Macroscopic States. Nature, 406, 43-46.

Fröhlich, H. (1983) Coherence in Biology. In: Coherent Excitations in Biological Systems, Fröhlich, H. and Kremer, F. (Eds.), Berlin, Springer-Verlag, pp. 1-5.

Fröhlich, H. (1986). In: Modern Bioelectrochemistry, F. Gutman and H. Keyzer (Eds.) Springer- 27 Verlag, New York.

Geller, M.J. and Huchra, J. (1989). Mapping the Universe, Science, 246, 897.

Ghosh, S, Rosenbaum, T.F., Aeppli, G., Coppersmith, S.N. (2003). Entangled quantum state of magnetic dipoles. Nature,425, 48 - 51 (04 Sep) Letters to Nature.

Grandlund, G.H.(1999). Signal Processing, 74, 101-116.

Guth, A. H., and Steinhardt, P. J. (1984). The Inflationary Universe. Scientific American, 250, No. 5, p. 116-128.

Hackermuller, L., Hornberger, K., and Brezger, B. (2004). Decoherence of matter waves by thermal emission of radiation. Nature, 427, 711-714.

Hagan S, Hameroff, SR, and Tuszynski JA (2002). Quantum computation in brain microtubules: Decoherence and biological feasibility. Physical Review E., 65(6), Art. No. 061901 Part 1 June.

Hameroff, S., Nip, A., Porter, M. and Tuszynski, J. (2002). Conduction pathways in microtubules, biological quantum computation, and consciousness. Biosystems, 64(1-3), 149-168.

Hameroff, S. and Tuszynski, J. (2003). In: Bioenergetic organization in living systems. Franco Musumeci, and Mae-Wan Ho (Eds.), World Scientific, Singapore.

Hornberger, K. and Sipe, J.E. (2003). Collisional decoherence reexamined. Physical Review A, 68, 012105.

Hubel, D. (1995). Eye, Brain and Vision, Scientific American Library.

Hudspeth, A.J. (1989). How the ear's works work. Nature, 341, 397–404.

Hunter, P. (2006). A quantum leap in biology. One inscrutable field helps another, as quantum physics unravels consciousness. EMBO Rep., October, 7(10), 971–974.

Jibu, M., Hagan, S., Hameroff, S.R., Pribram, K.H., Yasue K. (1994). Quantum Optical Coherence in cytoskeletal microtubules – implications for brain function. Biosystems, 32 (3), 195-209.

Julsgaard, B., Kozhekin, A., and Polzig, E. (2001). Experimental long-lived entanglement of two macroscopic objects. Nature, 413, 400–403.

Kafatos, M. (1986). In: Astrophysics of Brown Dwarfs, M. Kafatos et al. (Eds.), Cambridge, Cambridge University Press.

Kafatos, M. (1989). In: Bell's Theorem, Quantum Theory and Conceptions of the Universe, M. Kafatos (Ed.), 195, Dordrecht, Kluwer Academic Publishers.

Kafatos, M. (1996). In: Examining the Big Bang and Diffuse Background Radiations, M. Kafatos and Y. Kondo (Eds.), 431, Dordrecht, Kluwer Academic Publishers.

Kafatos, M. (1998). Non-locality, Complementarity and Cosmology. In: Causality and Locality in Modern Physics, G. Hunter et al. (Eds.), Dordrecht: Kluwer Academic Publishers, p. 29.

Kafatos, M. (1999). Non locality, Foundational Principles and Consciousness. The Noetic Journal, 2, 21-27.

Kafatos, M., and Drăgănescu, M. (2001). Toward an Integrative Science, Noesis, XXVI, 2001.

Kafatos, M. and Drăgănescu M. (2003) Principles of Integrative Science, Editura Tehnica, Bucharest.

Kafatos, M., and Kafatou, Th. (1991). Looking In, Seeing Out: Consciousness and Cosmos, Wheaton, ILL: Quest Books.

Kafatos, M. and Nadeau, R. (1990; 2000). The Conscious Universe: Parts and Wholes in Physical Reality, New York: Springer-Verlag.

Kafatos, M., Roy, S. and Roy, M. (2005). Variation of Physical Constants, Redshift and the Arrow of Time. Acta Physica Polonica, 36, 3139-3161.

Kak, S. (2007). The Prajna-Sutras, Aphorisms of Intuition, New Delhi, D.K. Printworld.

Kalmijn, A.J. (1982). Electric and magnetic field detection in elasmobranch fishes. Science, 218, 916–18.

Kato, G., and Struppa, D.C. (1999a) Fundamentals of Microlocal Algebraic Analysis, Marcel Dekker.

Kato, G., and Struppa, D.C. (1999b). A Sheaf Theoretic Approach to Consciousness, The Noetic Journal, 2(1), 1..

Kato, G., Struppa, D.C. (1999c), Category Theory and Consciousness. Proceedings of Tokyo '99 Conference: Toward a Science of Consciousness – Fundamental Approach, International conference at United Nations University, Tokyo, May 25–28, 1999.

Kato, G. and Struppa, D.C. (1999d). Category Theory as the Language of Consciousness, Proceedings of Fairfax Conference, October 1999.

Kim, J.E., Tauber, M.J., and Mathies, R.A. (2001). Wavelength Dependent Cis-Trans Isomerization in Vision, Biochemistry, 40, 13774-13778.

Klein-Seetharaman, J., Oikawa, M., Grimshaw, S.B., Wirmer, J., Duchardt, E., Ueda, T., Imoto, T., Smith, L.J., Dobson, C.M., Schwalbe, H. (2002). Long-range interactions within non-native protein. Science, 295, 1719-1722.

Matsuno, K. (1999). Cell motility as an entangled quantum coherence. Biosystems, Jul, 51(1), 15-9.

Mershin, A., Kolomenski, A.A., Schuessler, H.A., and D. V. Nanopoulos. (2004). Tubulin dipole moment, dielectric constant and quantum behavior: computer simulations, experimental results and suggestions. Biosystems, Nov, 77(1-3), 73-85.

Mesquita, M.V., Vasconcellos, A.R., Luzzi, R., and Mascarenhas, S. (2005). Large-Scale Quantum Effects in Biological Systems, Int. Journal of Quantum Chemistry, 102, 1116–1130

Mitra, I., Roy, S. (2006). Relevance of Quantum Mechanics in Circuit Implementation of Ion Channels in Brain Dynamics. Phys. Rev. E., arXiv:q-bio/0606008v1.

Nadeau, R., and Kafatos, M. (1999). The Non-local Universe: The New Physics and Maters of the Mind, Oxford, Oxford University Press.

Nobili, R., Mammano, F., Ashmore, J. (1998). How Well Do We Understand the Cochlea? Trends Neurosci., 21, 159–167..

Ouyang, M., and Awschalom, D.D. (2003). Coherent spin transfer between molecularly bridged quantum dots. Science, 301(5636), 1074-1078 Aug 22.

Parson, W. W. (2007). Long Live Electronic Coherence. Science, 316, No. 5830, 1438-1439.

Pokorny, J., and Wu, T.M. (1998). Biophysical Aspects of Coherence and Biological Order. Springer, New York.

Pollack, G.H., Cameron, I.L., and Wheatley, D.N. (2006). Water and the Cell. Springer-Verlag.

Popp, F.A., Chang, J.J., Herzog, A., Yan, Z., and Yan, Y. (2002). Evidence of non-classical (squeezed) light in biological systems. Physics Letters A, 293, 98-102.

Pribram, K., Lassonde, M., and Ptito, M. (1981). Classification of receptive field properties in cat visual cortex, Exp.Brain Res., 43, 119-130.

Pribram, K. (1998). The History of Neuroscience in Autobiography, 2, 335.

Prokhorenko, V.I. et al. (2006). Coherent Control of Retinal Isomerization in Bacteriorhodopsin. Science, 313, 1257.

Prosen, T., and Znidaric, M. (2001). Can Quantum Chaos Enhance the stability of Quantum Computation? J. Phys. A: Math. Gen., 34, L681–L687.

Rosa, L.P., and Faber, J. (2004). Quantum models of the mind: Are they compatible with environment decoherence? Phys. Rev. E, 70, 031902.

Roy S., and Kafatos, M. (1999a). Complem-

etarity Principle and Cognition Process, Physics Essays, 12, 662-668.

Roy, S., and Kafatos, M., (1999b). Bell-type Correlations and Large Scale Structure of the Universe. In: Instantaneous Action at a Distance in Modern Physics: Pro and Contra. In A. E. Chubykalo, V. Pope, & R. Smirnov-Rueda (Eds.), New York: Nova Science Publishers.

Roy, S., and Kafatos, M., (2000). Quantum correlations, large scale structure of the universe and temporal non-locality. In: Studies on the Structure of Time: From Physics to Psycho(path)logy, Buccheri et al.(Eds.), Kluwer Academic/Plenum, New York.

Roy, S., and Kafatos, M. (2004). Quantum processes and functional geometry: new perspectives in brain dynamics. FORMA, 19, 69.

Shemella, P., Pereira, B., Zhang, Y., Van Roey, P., Belfort, G., Garde, S., and Nayak, S.K. (2007). Mechanism for Intein C-Terminal Cleavage: A Proposal from Quantum Mechanical Calculations. Biophys. J., 92, 847-853.

Silk, J. (1989). The Big Bang, New York, W. H. Freeman.

Singh, J. (1979). Shiva Sutras, Delhi, Motilal Banarsidass.

Smoot, G.F. (1996). In: Examining the Big Bang and Diffuse Background Radiations, M. Kafatos and Y. Kondo (Eds.), 31, Dordrecht, Kluwer Academic Publishers.

Stapp, H. P. (2004). Mind, Matter and Quantum Mechanics (2nd edition). Heidelberg: Springer-Verlag.

Stapp, H.P. (1979). Whiteheadian Approach to Quantum Theory and the Generalized Bell's Theorem. Found. of Physics, 9, 1-25.

Stuchebrukhov, A.A. (2003). Long-distance electron tunneling in proteins. Theor. Chem.

Acc., 32 110, 291–306.

Swami Prabhavananda, and Isherwood, C. (1975). Shankara's Crest-Jewel of Discrimination, Vedanta Press, Hollywood, CA.

Swami Vimuktananda (2005). Aparokshanubhuti, Shankara's Self-Realization, Kolkata, Advaita Ashrama.

Szent-Györgi, A. (1960). Introduction to a Submolecular Biology. New York, Academic Press.

Tegmark, M. (2000). Importance of quantum decoherence in brain processes. Phys Rev E Stat Phys Plasmas Fluids Relat Interdiscip Topics, 2000 Apr, 61(4 Pt B), 4194-206.

Tittel, W., Brendel, J., Zbinden, H. and Gisin, N. (1998). Violation of Bell Inequalities by Photons More Than 10 km Apart. Phys. Rev. Lett., 81, 3563.

van Mourik, T. (2004). First-principles quantum chemistry in the life sciences. Phil. Trans. A. Math. Phys. Eng. Sci., Dec 15, 362(1825), 2653-2670.

Walleczek, J. (1995). Magnetokinetic effects on radical pairs: a possible paradigm for understanding sub-kT magnetic field interactions with biological systems. In: Biological Effects of Environmental Electromagnetic Fields, M Blank (Ed), Advances in Chemistry, No 250, American Chemical Society Books, Washington D.C.

Weinberg S. (1972). Gravitation and Cosmology: Principles and Applications of the General Theory of Relativity, Wiley, New York.

Wheeler, J.A. (1981). In: Some Strangeness in the Proportion, H. Woolf (Ed.), Reading, Addison-Wesley Publishing Co.

Neoclassical Cosmology and Menas Kafatos's "Cosmos and Quantum: Frontiers for the Future"

Theodore Walker Jr., Ph.D.

Southern Methodist University, Perkins School of Theology, Dallas, Texas, USA.

Abstract

A possible mechanism by which mental acts may be synchronized with physical states is postulated. In "Cosmos and Quantum Frontiers for the Future," Menas Kafatos (2009) prescribes a "future science" of "undivided wholeness" incorporating insights from quantum physics and perennial philosophies. For the sake of advancing this future science, we should observe that some of these insights (including the importance of process and relativity, universal mind, universal individuality, and cosmic indeterminacy) have also been well developed in the process-relational and neoclassical philosophies instructed by the works of Alfred North Whitehead and Charles Hartshorne.

keywords: quantum universe, process, relativity, process-relational philosophy, neoclassical philosophy, neoclassical theology, consciousness, panpsychism, psychicalism, universal psychicalism, psychical variables, cosmic variables, universal undivided wholeness, universal individual, quantum indeterminacy, cosmic indeterminacy, future science, neoclassical cosmology

1. The Future and the Importance of Process and Relativity

In his "Cosmos and Quantum: Frontiers for the Future," Menas Kafatos (2009) prescribes the development of a "future science" of "undivided wholeness". Here Kafatos calls for a science incorporating insights from quantum physics, including the insight that the quantum universe evidences the "interconnectedness of everything" via "non-local interactions," that "process is much more important than "building blocks", and that "the whole is not just the sum of its constituent parts". And, he calls for incorporating insights from perennial philosophies, including the insight that "the universe may verily be the conscious universe".

For the sake of advancing this future science, we should observe that insights into the importance of "process" have also been well developed in the "process philosophy" instructed by Alfred North Whitehead's Process and Reality: An Essay in Cosmology (Gifford Lectures, 1927-28), and in the closely related and substantially overlapping "neoclassical philosophy" and "neoclassical metaphysics" instructed by Charles Hartshorne's (1953)Reality As Social Process.

Interconnectedness and relativity are also essential to Hartshorne's social conception of reality, including divine reality. For example, in The Divine Relativity: A Social Conception of God Hartshorne (1948) describes divine social relations as "supremely-relative" and "surrelative" (p. 1). For Hartshorne, "relativity" is not less important than "process." And in the interest of not favoring "process" over "relativity, " Hartshorne prefers to employ the term "neoclassical" because "neoclassical" implicitly embraces both "process" and "relativity" while providing explicit contrast with "classical. " Accordingly, Hartshorne-instructed process philosophers frequently speak of "process-relational philosophy."

2. Consciousness and "Universal Psychicalism"

Kafatos (2009) prescribes that "if we start from the premise that consciousness is the underlying foundation of the physical, mental, psychic and all possible realms, one needs to look at the systems of philosophy dealing with consciousness ". Neoclassical and process philosophies are among the systems one needs to study for advancing inquiry into the full range of mental-psychic processes.

Concerning the conscious universe: Neoclassical philosophers affirm that "the one all-inclusive whole of reality" (Ogden, 1984, p. 21) is the supremely sentient (omniscient) "ultimate reality" that some religious people rightly identify as "God" [as the one reality that is so great that "none greater can be conceived" (Anselm)]. In fact, this affirmation distinguishes neoclassical theology from all of the many classical theologies that identify "God" (or "gods") with some less-inclusive part(s) of reality. The idea of a supremely conscious universe is essential to, and fully developed in, neoclassical theology.

Furthermore, inquiry into "the possibility that consciousness is the foundational substratum of the universe" and cuts "across all levels of the cosmos"

(Kafatos, 2009) has also been advanced by Hartshorne. In Beyond Human-ism: Essays in the Philosophy of Nature Hartshorne (1975 [originally 1937]) advances a doctrine he called "panpsychism" in 1937, and "psychicalism" or "universal psychicalism", a doctrine which holds that "psychical variables" —such as "sensations or feelings" (p. 118) and "memory" --are "cosmic vari-ables" that apply in varying degrees throughout the cosmos, throughout "the whole scale of beings" (p. 121)— "running from the least particle of inorganic matter to the great universe itself" (p. 112).

"Universal psychicalism" witnesses against the existence of wholly insen-tient, wholly inanimate, and totally mindless physical matter. In "The Physi-cal and the Spiritual," a chapter in Omnipotence and Other Theological Mis-takes (1984), Hartshorne argues that, rather than being two separate realities (dualism), the physical-material and the spiritual-mental-psychical are dis-tinct aspects of one reality (monism). Contrary to both classical "universal materialism" (another monism) and classical mind-body/mind-matter dual-ism, neoclassical "universal psychicalism" ("the more intelligible monism," says Hartshorne) holds that "all nature is in some sense life-like, that there is no absolutely new principle of life that comes in at some point in cosmic evolution " (Ibid, p. 62-63, italics added). Here and in numerous other more technical books and articles, Hartshorne makes important contributions to inquiry into "psychical variables" on all levels of reality.

3. Universal "Undivided Wholeness" and the Universal Individual

Kafatos writes of the "undivided wholeness". However, he does not explic-itly indicate if that universal "undivided" whole is "individual." For instance, Kafatos writes, "As the quantum and the universe are ultimately and inti-mately interconnected, so are the individual and the universal conscious-ness" (Kafatos, 2009). Notice that here Kafatos contrasts "individual" con-sciousness with "universal consciousness." Similarly, Kafatos writes, "This is certainly a reversal of the usual scientific method, here we start from the whole, from the general, from the universal, from the unlimited, and we end up going to the individual, the particular, the limited". Therefore, Kafatos ap-pears to contrast whole, general, universal, and unlimited, on the one hand, with "the individual," "the particular," and "the limited" on the other. Accord-ing to neoclassical thinking, unlike with "the particular" and "the limited," "the individual" should not be included in a contrast with universal whole-ness. Instead, it is argued that "individual" and universal wholeness go to-gether. Insofar as the word "individual" (in-divide -ual) implies "not divided" into separate parts, to speak of an actual universal "undivided" whole is to speak of a universal "not divided" whole, a universal "individual" whole—

"the one universal individual" (Hartshorne, 1953, p. 176).

Instead of applying to only one of two hands (the one universal/all-inclusive individual on the one hand, and many variously less-inclusive individuals on the other hand), individuality can be applied to both: Individuality applies strictly, and eternally, to the one universal individual. And, by contrast, individuality applies only loosely, and for only segments of time, to less-inclusive individuals, including human individuals from whom parts can be divided-separated (departed). Though parts of reality can be divided-separated from other parts of reality; no part of reality can be divided-separated from the all-inclusive whole of reality. Hence, according to neoclassical theology, the all-inclusive divine whole of reality is strictly individual, the one and only "strictly universal individual" (Ogden, 1984, p. 27, italic added).

4. Quantum Indeterminacy and Cosmic Indeterminacy

In accordance with Kafatos's call for applying indeterminacy beyond the quantum level, even to the point of conceiving of a quantum universe; neoclassical theology holds that the "strictly universal individual" sometime identified as "God" is the one and only individual that makes a partly determinative difference to all events, and the one and only individual to which all events make a partly determinative difference (Ogden, 1989). Contrary to absolute determinism in classical physics, and contrary to absolute determinism in classical theology, process philosophy and neoclassical theology deny that any real thing or event can be wholly determinative of any other(s), or wholly determined by any other(s). All real things and all real events are functions of both partial freedom and partial determinism. According to process-relational and neoclassical philosophies, at all levels (cosmic, intermediate, and quantum), reality admits no absolute determinism.

5. The Future and Neoclassical Cosmology

We should accept Kafatos's quantum universe inspired calls for viewing "process" as fundamental, for appreciating indeterminacy at all levels, and for viewing all "parts of reality" as interconnected-related parts of the undivided [individual] conscious whole of reality. As scientists advance into this frontier, in addition to encountering insights from perennial philosophies, they will encounter process philosophers, process theologians, neoclassical philosophers, neoclassical metaphysicians, and neoclassical theologians. And perhaps together, unencumbered by classical materialist and classical mind-matter/mind-body dualist presumptions, we can develop a new science of undivided wholeness, a new neoclassical cosmology.

References

Hartshorne, C. (1975). Beyond Humanism: Essays in the Philosophy of Nature. Gloucester, Massachusetts: Peter Smith, originally 1937.

Hartshorne, C. (1948). The Divine Relativity: A Social Conception of God. New Haven: Yale University Press, 1948, 1964, 1983.

Hartshorne, C. (1984). Omnipotence and Other Theological Mistakes. Albany, New York: State University of New York Press.

Hartshorne, C. (1953). Reality As Social Process: Studies in Metaphysics and Religion, edited by James Luther Adams. Glencoe, Illinois: Free Press; Boston, Massachusetts, Beacon Press: Boston.

Kafatos, M. (2009). Cosmos and Quantum: Frontiers for the Future. Journal of Cosmology, 2009, 3, 511-528.

Ogden, S.M. (1989). Faith and Freedom: Toward a Theology of Liberation: Revised and Enlarged Edition. Eugene, Oregon: Wipf and Stock, originally Nashville, Tennessee, Abingdon Press, 1979.

Ogden, S.M. (1984). Process Theology and the Wesleyan Witness. Perkins School of Theology Journal, Vol. 37, No. 3, Spring 1984, pages 18-33.

Whitehead, A. N. (1978). Process and Reality: An Essay in Cosmology: Gifford Lectures Delivered in the University of Edinburgh During the Session 1927-28: Corrected Edition, edited by David Ray Griffin and Donald W. Sherburne. New York, New York: The Free Press, 1978, originally 1927-28.

Can Discoverability Help Us Understand Cosmology?

Nicholas Beale, MA FRSA Director of Sciteb:
One Heddon Street, London.

Abstract

The discovery of the laws and constants of nature with increasing degree of verisimilitude requires that these laws are not only compatible with the evolution of intelligent beings, but also that these beings should have a sufficiently long period of cooperative existence and intellectual freedom. This leads to the formulation of a "Discoverability Principle" – more exacting in its conditions than the classic account of the Anthropic Principle. Furthermore if one adopts, at least as a thought experiment, a closely related "Discoverability Postulate", which can be expressed symbolically as a simple equation, then in addition to "explaining" the many anthropic features of the universe, it suggests a possible explanation of why the range of allowed parameters is so narrow. It also offers a basis for simplifying the highly profligate ontologies that occur in discussions of cosmology, and suggests some in-principle testable predictions. I also discuss some of the difficulties of attempted evolutionary explanations of the anthropic features of the universe, such as Smolin's Cosmological Natural Selection.

1. "Introduction

Hydrogen has been described as "a colorless, odourless gas that, given enough time, turns into people" (S. Rasmussen, quoted in Balazs & Epstein 2009). Of course it is not that simple. According to the seminal book by Barrow & Tipler (1986), the initial conditions required for life to be able to evolve, anywhere in the universe, are very special indeed. At present we have a Standard Model of particle physics which describes, with extraordinary accuracy, all the known elementary particles and their interactions, but has about 20 adjustable parameters which have to be fitted to the data. Similarly there is a standard model of Cosmology with about 15 parameters. How are these 35-or-so parameters determined?

It's well known that one strong constraint on the values of these parameters is the possibility of the existence of intelligent life anywhere in the universe. Even at the crudest level, assuming that life needs carbon and other similar elements and a reasonable amount of time to evolve (c 3bn years after heavier elements have been produced) imposes very strong constraints on some of the fundamental parameters. For example, the parameter which defines how firmly atomic nuclei bind together, is about 0.007: if it were 0.008 or 0.006 there would be no intelligent life. Similarly (the relative importance of gravity and expansion energy) has to be within 1 part in 10^{15} of 1 in the early universe. There are plenty of other examples: (the coefficient in the Einstein Equation now associated with "dark energy") has to be within about 10^{-100} of 0 (see eg Rees, 1999, Polkinghorne & Beale 2009).

Following Barrow & Tipler (1986) it has become common to use "anthropic" considerations to select initial conditions for the universe, though this has been strongly criticised by Lee Smolin (2007) and others, who proposed an alternative of Cosmological Natural Selection. Although I have some sympathy with Smolin's concerns, there are fundamental difficulties with explanations of the type he proposes. Instead I want to draw attention to two additional constraints which strengthen the "anthropic principle" and suggest a "Discoverability Postulate". This can be expressed as a simple equation, and offers the prospect of explaining a number of puzzling features of the universe as presently perceived, as well as some in-principle testable predictions.

To avoid this looking too much like a mathematical paper I won't give formal definitions, but I will bold a term when it is first defined, and I will number my observations and conjectures for ease of reference.

2. L, X and PI

Let's think about a set of laws of nature L and a set of initial conditions X (cf eg Hartle 2002). Let's assume that there exists some laws (L*) and initial conditions (X*) of that actually obtain in the Universe – this is impossible to prove but a reasonable working assumption if we are to do science. Why do these laws and these initial conditions obtain? If we define PI(L, X) as the probability that intelligent life will come into being somewhere in a universe with laws L and initial conditions X, we can note that PI(L*, X*) must be >0 otherwise we wouldn't be here to ask these questions.

It became clear in the last 50 years that PI(L,X)>0 was a non-trivial constraint: many values of X would not give universes that lasted long enough, or produced carbon, or in some other way were highly inimical to intelligent life. Furthermore it became clear in the last 35 years or so that, at least with the Standard Model, there is an element of "fine-tuning" involved. In other words, if (L^c, X^c) are the Laws and Initial Conditions that we currently think we have.

Observation O1 ("Fine-Tuning"): $PI(L^c, X^c + \delta X) = 0$ for a significant fraction of possible values of X

That $PI > 0$ may not be too surprising but O1 really is. There seem to be two possibilities:

- There are some more accurate laws and initial conditions ($L^+ X^+$) which are better approximations to (L^*, X^*), and from which L^c and X^c derive (at least to a very good approximation: aspects of the standard model have been verified to enormous accuracy) for which $PI(L^+, X^+ + \delta X)$ is usually > 0, indeed if fine-tuning is to be avoided, we would ideally want $PI(L^+, X) > 0$ for a wide range of parameters X.

- One can always artificially re-scale a parameter space and a set of laws. But we are reluctant to accept arbitrary re-scalings, which make the elegant mathematics of the Standard Model horribly ugly. Inflation and String Theory address aspects of the problem, but are examples of the Exploding Free Parameter Postulate (Polkinghorne and Beale 2009): "a theory that seeks to explain the fine-tuning of the Standard Model eventually has more free parameters than are explained".

- There is some principle at work which selects (L^*, X^*) or at least selects X^* from its neigbours.

One possibility is that X^* represents some kind of maximum, so either:

Conjecture C1: X^* is such that it maximises (or nearly maximises) $PI(L^*, X)$ or:

C2: X^* is such that it maximises/nearly maximises the probability $P(W|(L^*,X))$ of some quality W where $P(I|W) >> 0$.

Again C2 will always be true for suitably artificial definitions of W, but we would like to find a quality W which is both plausible and ideally one for which there is some conceivable mechanism. But one fundamental problem with any attempt on these lines is that the value of x which maximises the abundance $A(x)$ will usually have neighbouring values that give almost as large values of A:

O2: if x1 maximises $A(x)$ and A is differentiable at x1 then $A(x1+\delta x)$ &cong $A(x1) - a''(x1)|\delta x|^2$ with $a'' > 0$

since the derivative will be zero at a maximum, and this tends to contradict O1. Although it is possible for A not to be differentiable this is unlikely with an evolutionary process. For example if we are considering evolution in discrete time then $A_{t+1}(x) = \int A_t(y)f_t(y)Q_t(y,x)dy$ where f(y) is the fitness function and Q(y,x) is the mutation function giving the probability density that an entity with parameter values y will result in one with parameter values x (c/f Nowak 2006 p273). If Q is differentiable – as commonly-used continuous probability distributions are – then (subject to a few technicalities) then A_{t+1} will be differentiable even if A_t and f are not. And even if Q is not differentiable, A_{t+1} may still be. For example if Q is a finite sum of the form $\sum_i w_i \delta(y-k_i,x)$ then A_{t+1} will be differentiable if A_t and f are. Thus rather careful fine-tuning of the assumptions about fitness and mutation are required for any evolutionary "explanation" of O1 to escape O2.

3. Digression: The Trouble with CNS

An interesting example of the kind of thing envisaged by C2 is Lee Smolin's idea of Cosmological Natural Selection (CNS). Smolin (2007) suggested that:

- Universes might be "born" mainly from black holes in other universes,

- There might be small random variations in their fundamental constants, and

- The fine-tuning of the parameters required for life might also sharply maximize the production of black holes.

- By a process analogous to Natural Selection therefore, the probability that a "random" universe drawn from the "multiverse" of all existing universes would be high.

Unfortunately there are problems with all of these (see Polkinghorne and Beale 2009, and Silk 1997 for more details). Some of these are specific issues about physics, which I do not want to repeat here, but there are more general points which seem to apply to all attempts of this type.

Firstly, natural selection and Evolutionary Dynamics depend on having a common timescale. This is very problematic with sets of universes. Consider for example a "multiverse" in which there were 2 types of universe: Type A produced 10^{10} Type A "children" and Type B had 2 Type B children. It is intuitively obvious that Type A would dominate the population. But if Type B produced children after 10^6 years and Type A required 10^{10} years then of course by the time Type A had produced its 10^{10} children, about 10^{300} Type Bs would have been produced. The relative dominance of Type A and Type B in the overall population would therefore depend entirely on how you projected each universe's time onto a hypothetical multiversal time.

Secondly, specifying random variations in a parameter X requires more information than is contained in the parameter X: you need at minimum to specify a distribution and some kind of variance parameter. Although Evolutionary Dynamics will generally iron out the details of this choice, it will generally be possible to disrupt an Evolutionary Dynamical process with sufficiently strange distributions or high variances. If "explaining" the value of a parameter X requires postulating a distribution D and a variance V, then you end up with more postulates than explanations.

Thirdly, Evolutionary Dynamics works well because population sizes are constrained, generally by resources, and there is some effective competition between individuals and types, often mediated by physical proximity or other constraints. In typical multiverse theories these constraints are absent.

Fourthly, the most likely outcome of a randomised process may still be very unlikely, especially in the absence of constraints. If we tossed a coin 10^6 times and got exactly 5×10^5 Heads we would be very suspicious. Even if there were a plausible random process that generated values of X with a distribution $S(X)$ and a maximum likelihood outcome X_M such that $PI(X_M) \gg 0$, this would not entail that the expected value of $PI(X)$ given the distribution $S(X)$ was $\gg 0$. Nor would such mechanisms explain the observation $PI(X_M + \delta X) = 0$ unless $S(X)$ was itself very finely tuned so that $S(X_M + \delta X) = 0$, and we have discussed some of the problems about this in O2 above.

Smolin advocated CNS to demonstrate the possibility of developing a genuinely scientific theory about why the universe is likely to be anthropic—one that makes specific predictions that can, in principle, be falsified. It is highly commendable that he offers specific falsifiable predictions and engages in detail with the actual physics of black hole formation, and whether or not his ideas are right, his pursuit of them, in the teeth of a fashionable consensus, is admirable. But the problems mentioned above suggest that there are serious difficulties for all these types of theories, in addition to the specific problems with CNS.

4. Discoverability, Cooperation and Freedom

The view I want to suggest here is that (L*, X*) are constrained by a strengthened version of the Anthropic Principle, which we might call the Discoverability Principle, and would be highly constrained by a Discoverability Postulate.

Suppose that at time t it is believed, with good supporting evidence, that the laws and initial conditions are (L_t, X_t). (L*, X*) must be such that it is possible at time t that persons in the universe could have discovered (L_t, X_t). Let us write $D_t(L,X)$ as the set of possible laws and initial conditions that could have been discovered by beings in a (L,X) universe at time t. $D_t(L,X)$ is of course empty if there could be no intelligent life in such a universe at time t. We can then observe:

O3 ("Discoverability Principle"): If (L_t, X_t) has been discovered at time t then $(L_t, X_t) \in D_t(L^*, X^*)$

This is a non-trivial constraint. Not only does (L*, X*) have to allow for the emergence of intelligent life, it has to allow for a sufficient degree of cooperation between these intelligent life forms, and for enough creative thinking by them, to be able to do the necessary science. These are quite strong conditions:

O4: Critical levels of cooperation are needed between intelligent beings in order for them to do science for a sustained period of time. In particular, when technology has become sufficiently advanced for a set of intelligent beings to trigger their mass extinction (Elewa, 2009; Jones, 2009), then these beings need to achieve high enough levels of cooperation to avoid this for a substantial period of time (McKee, 2009; Tonn, 2009).

We need only mention the dangers of nuclear proliferation and extreme global warming to realise that it is not a foregone conclusion (Levy and Sidel, 2009; Rees 2004). The conditions under which cooperation will emerge in populations are becoming much better understood, and although the relationships between these and fundamental physics are beyond presently feasible calculation, it is clear that different physical conditions on otherwise habitable planets could influence the likelihood of highly cooperative advanced societies evolving. There are typically critical thresholds in terms of the ratio of benefits to cost of cooperation (b/c). For example if players have a probability w of having to play another round against each other, and the driving force for cooperation is "direct reciprocity" (I'll cooperate if you do) then cooperation becomes an Evolutionary Stable Strategy if b/c > 1/w (Nowak et al. 2006, Nowak 2006). Therefore conditions which tended to reduce the number of days in which individuals in a society could interact would tend to prevent the emergence of certain cooperative strategies. Much fascinating work is being done in this area (eg Rand et al 2009) and it seems likely that in 10-20 years we will have detailed quantitative understanding of many of these thresholds and mechanisms. It is therefore worth considering the extent to which they are fundamental to the possibility of sustained development of knowledge or scientific understanding.

Sustained cooperation is necessary for scientific progress, but not sufficient. Robot scientists might systematically try possible laws of nature and experiments (c/f King et al 2009), but we have a strong, well-motivated, intuition that they would not be very good at producing fundamental new creative ideas (eg Anderson & Abrahams 2009). Proverbial "Monkeys with typewriters" have no chance of producing Shakespeare within the lifetime of the universe. Large combinatorial problems are intractable if attacked by "brute force" and it is known that randomised algorithms can be much more time-efficient. Genuine creative thought seems to require genuine intellectual freedom, both in the sense of not thinking and acting on wholly deterministic lines and having a society which allows individual dissent – even though this is somewhat in tension with the cooperation needed per O4.

We can thus conjecture:

C3: Substantial sustained conscious intellectual freedom is necessary for the timely development of science.

This is also becoming, at least in outline, scientifically tractable. Siegelmann showed that sufficiently complex analog recurrent neural networks were not Turing machines (Siegelmann, 1995), underpinning John Lucas' famous argument (Lucas, 1951) that the human brain cannot be a Turing machine. It is also clear that the release of neuro-transmitters is triggered by the docking of single Ca^{2+} ions with a synaptotagamin molecule, which means that its timing is subject to genuine quantum uncertainties. Standard simulations show that when the neuron is on the cusp of firing, small changes in the time of an input make a large change in the time of the output, and thus can make the difference between whether a subsequent neuron will fire or not (Polkinghorne & Beale, 2009). There are many other sources of stochasticity in the human brain, which, unless the whole universe is deterministic, is clearly a non-deterministic system. At the level of societies, the number of creative scientific ideas that are accepted into the scientific community will be a function of the number of members of that community, their ability to generate ideas, the extent to which they think independently, and the propensity of the community to accept them. Populations of intelligent conscious beings could be too small, too conformist or too limited in their ability to communicate to make substantial scientific progress in a reasonable time.

In short, C3 if true it further limits the possibilities for (L*, X*), and together with O2 imposes a deep and subtle set of constraints which, although well beyond our present ability to calculate, are worth recognising.

5. The Discoverability Postulate

It is widely supposed that, as time advances, scientific uncertainty will reduce, decisions will be made between previously conflicting scientific theories (either one is falsified or both subsumed into a larger integrated whole), and that the process will be essentially convergent. So we can think about $D^*(L, X)$ as the convergent limit, in a suitable sense, of the sets $D_t(L, X)$ as t tends to infinity. If no single convergent limit exists we will set $D^* = \varnothing$ by definition.

Since there will be an infinite set of equivalent reformulations of a given set of laws, with rescaled parameters, the "output" of D^* would technically be an equivalence class, but the abuse of notation is I think justified for readability: the technical details of the convergence are beyond the scope of this paper. This allows us to formulate:

C4 ("Discoverability Postulate"): $(L^*, X^*) = D^*(L^*, X^*)$

In words: the actual laws and initial conditions will be the convergent limit of what can be discovered. As with all postulates, it could be false, and I can see little prospect of a mechanistic explanation. However it could be read as a statement about the kinds of laws and constants under which it would be possible to do science in a satisfying way, eventually converging towards a true understanding. Arguably we should restrict ourselves to exploring scientific theories for which C4 is true, provided they are sufficiently consistent with experimental observation, and only abandon this postulate if forced to do so, since it would be an admission that we will never be able to get the convergent scientific understanding we seek and appear so far broadly to be achieving. Some motivation for C4 comes from:

O5: If (L,X) is compatible with all known observations and satisfies C4, there is an infinite set of $\{(L', X')\}$ which are not discoverable but are equally compatible with all known observations.

Consider for example the idea of parallel universes, causally disconnected from our own with different laws and/or initial conditions. There are infinitely many such hypotheses, and no way of distinguishing them empirically from (L,X). But C4 can act as a quantified Occam's Razor, focusing our attention only on those laws and initial conditions which have demonstrable empirical consequences in our universe. This also leads us to:

C5: If (L,X) is compatible with all known observations and stateable with a sequence of mathematical symbols small enough to be comprehensible to the human mind, there exists a similarly compatible and stateable (L',X') for which $(L',X')=D^*(L',X')$.

If $(L,X)=D^*(L,X)$ then C5 is clearly true. But if (L,X) has some parameters which are not discoverable then either these parameters make no observable difference, or they make an observational difference but only when combined with other parameters, in such a way that you could never observe the underlying value but only the value of these combinations. In either case we should be able to formulate an (L', X') which is observationally equivalent and discoverable. If for example it turned out that the only evidence for inflation was the Harrison-Zel'dovich spectrum (perhaps because some form of cosmic censorship prevented observation of inflatons), then one could replace inflationary hypotheses with a direct hypothesis about the initial conditions. I want to emphasise the if in the last sentence because we should never underestimate the ability of outstanding physicists like Smolin to find subtle experimental tests for effects which one would have thought experimentally inscrutable (see Abdo et al 2009, Amelino-Camelia & Smolin 2009).

6. Suggestively Implies Fine Tuning

C4 is a fixed point condition, which in principle imposes very tight constraints on (L*, X*). For this to be true the universe described by (L*, X*) must be such that intelligent beings with sufficient ability for sustained cooperation and, if C3 is right, intellectual freedom, can arise for long enough. Furthermore, for D* to exist Dt, which is itself an extremely complex and delicate operator and the function of many complex iterations of "lower level" factors, has to be convergent. The sets of values under which such operators are convergent tend to have a fractal character. It is therefore quite understandable in principle why small changes in X would tend to lead to divergence and an infeasible region. Hence we can suggest:

C6: If (L, X) = D*(L, X) for plausible values of (L, X) then in general D*(L, X+ δX) = ∅

Note that this can in principle be explored at least for Lc (the laws we have at present) and a deeper understanding of the structure of D* might lead to a more general result. Indeed if we define D**(L,X) as the set of X for which D*(L,X)=(L,X) then we can restate C6 as: D**(L,X) will tend to be fine-tuned and have a fractal, or quasi fractal character.

Now admittedly D**(L,X) will be a subset of the set of values of X for which PI(L,X)>0, and the fact that a subset of a set S is fine-tuned does not imply that S is fine-tuned. But given the extreme subtlety with which the laws of physics are likely to influence the conditions of cooperation in O4 and freedom in C3, it is plausible to suggest that there may not be very large differences between the two sets. Hence the Discoverability Postulate offers, plausibly, an "explanation" of the very puzzling O1. Note that in this respect C4 differs significantly from:

C7 ("Strong Anthropic Principle"): PI(L*,X*) >> 0

Clearly C4 implies C7 but it is not at all clear why C7 should imply O1. Note of course that all the fine-tuning conditions which are entailed by assuming C7 (and thus in some sense "explained") are also entailed by C4.

7. Other Suggestive Implications

Although it is not easy to see how C4 could be falsified, one could imagine a result like Gödel's theorem that showed that laws of nature beyond a certain level of complexity had the property of non-convergence so that D* was not well-defined. In conjunction with C3, C4 suggests a number of predictions that are at least in principle testable, eg:

C8: any plausible deterministic algorithm for discovering the laws and constants of nature would have an expected time to completion which is large compared to the age of the universe.

This is another prediction that is not a prediction of C7. In fact C8 may be too weak. Discovering the laws and constants of nature is, intuitively, a harder version of the problem of learning a language, and it has been known since (Gold, 1967) that there is no general algorithm for learning an arbitrary language. Vapnik and Chervonenkis (1971) demonstrated that a set of languages is learnable if and only if it has a finite VC Dimension and Valliant (1984) showed that there are sets of languages that are learnable in principle but no algorithm can do them in polynomial time. Note that these results extend into statistical learning theory and not just the deterministic cases. Exploring all this in detail is beyond the scope of this paper, but these considerations at least strongly suggest that we have to posit some limitations on the sets of possible scientific laws if we are to do science at all.

Accepting C4 would allow us at least in principle to dispense with the highly profligate multiverse hypothesis, by providing another explanation for the fine-tuning. It also offers the prospect of dealing in an orderly way with the "string landscape" problem: rather than having up to 10^{500} possible string theories which are considered as in some sense describing existing universes, and then selected against, such theories are considered as possible values of L, which do not obey C4 and thus do not obtain in the real world. C4 might also allow us to dispense with Inflation which, although it provides a nice explanation for the flatness of the initial universe (which is probably also required by C4), postulates inflationary fields/inflatons which have not been observed. The main observational evidence for inflation seems to be the observation from the Cosmic Background Radiation that there was a nearly-scale invariant Gaussian distribution of matter/energy in the early universe with a present day spectral index c. 0.96, and observations suggest that the value of 0.96 is significantly different from 1, which might be a natural expectation (Komatsu et al 2009 give an overview of the whole field in the light of the latest observations). But perhaps we can boldly offer:

C9: C4 will favour a nearly-scale invariant Gaussian distribution of matter/energy in the early universe with a present day spectral index c. 0.96.

Some of this may be a pure anthropic effect (C7) but it is at least plausible that the large-scale homogeneity of the universe is necessary for reasonably timely discoverability of the fundamentals of cosmology. Intuitively changes in the spectral index might be expected to have a significant effect on discoverability, but as yet I can't find papers about this: the focus seems mainly on confirming inflation by finding fits with the data: in this context (and others) the remarks in (Efstathiou 2008) seem very pertinent.

These are also benefits offered by C7, but superficially at least C7 is a much "fuzzier" condition than C4: how big does PI have to be and why is that value chosen? Admittedly the D* operator is well beyond the possibility of exact calculation but at least we can begin to approximate to it by noting that we need Sufficient Sustained levels of Intelligence, cooperation and intellectual freedom (O3 and C3). Then the probability that $(X,L)=D^*(X,L)$ is the probability that there is sufficient sustained intelligence (SI), times the probability, given SI, of sufficient sustained intellectual freedom (F) times the probability given SI and F of sufficient sustained cooperation (C) times the probability given SI, F and C that $(X,L)=D^*(X,L)$ – assuming that an exact evaluation of D* is not possible. In symbols:

O6: $p(\ (X,L)=D^*(X,L)\ ) = p(SI)\ .\ p(F|SI)\ .\ p(C|\ SI \wedge F)\ .\ p(\ (X,L)=D^*(X,L)\ |\ C \wedge SI \wedge F)$

One can certainly imagine how one might start to estimate some of these terms, to provide some reasonable upper and lower bounds on the probabilities and hence get some sense of how likely C4 is to be fulfilled. It is also clear that this would be related to the number and distribution and lifetime of stable habitats in the universe where intelligent life might evolve. This would be highly inexact to start with, but the history of science in general and cosmology in particular suggests that once people start focusing on quantities that could usefully be estimated, ingenious researchers usually find ways of reducing the error bands. Whether such intelligent life-forms evolved completely independently or via some form of panspermia (Hoyle & Wickramasinghe 1985, 2000; Joseph 2000, 2009) would influence the detailed calculations (for example a civilisation that destroyed itself might nevertheless have seeded life on other planets) but not the basic principle.

C4 also suggests that theories under consideration should be discoverable, ie:

C10: For sufficiently large t, $(L_t, X_t)=D^*(L_t, X_t)$

This would allow us to explore the Discoverability Postulate in the context of currently understood scientific theories. It suggests the additional testable predictions:

C11: $D^{**}(L_t,X)$ will have a fine-tuned character (ie usually $X+ \delta X \notin D^{**}(Lt,X)$).

C12: As the conditions under which the levels of cooperation mentioned in O3 and intellectual freedom required by C3 become better understood, it will become clearer that small changes in some aspects X will have substantial effects on p(C) and p(F), even within the domain under which PI(L,X) is high.

For example, if it turns out that delay amplification of timing uncertainties due to the binding of Ca^{2+} ions is an important mechanism in the emergence of adequate intellectual freedom then C10 suggests that some perturbation of the fundamental parameters is likely to change the magnitude of that effect without significantly changing the probability of carbon-based life.

8. Conclusions

In this paper I have sketched out a "Discoverability Principle" [O3], which appears to be a nontrivial strengthening of the Anthropic Principle, especially if [C3] is accepted. I also offer a "Discoverability Postulate" [C4], which if it is accepted, can deal with some significant philosophical problems about multiverses and string landscapes, offering a possible explanation of the fine-ness of anthropic fine tuning, and a number of in-principle testable predictions [C8, C9, C10, C11 and C12], none of which (except perhaps C9) are entailed by the Strong Anthropic Principle [C7]. Although the operators defined here are far too complex for present calculation, it is clear that at least a start could be made on some quantitative aspects [O6]. Thus I would suggest that discoverability can help us advance cosmology, and that these would be fruitful avenues for research.

Acknowledgements: I am very grateful to John Polkinghorne for his helpful comments and advice on earlier drafts of this paper, to Rose Beale for discussions that led to O4, to a helpful discussion with Corina Tarnita and to the anonymous referees.

References

Abdo A. A. et al (2009). A limit on the variation of the speed of light arising from quantum gravity effects Nature 462, 331-334

Amelino-Camelia, G. & Smolin, L. (2009). Prospects for constraining quantum gravity dispersion with near term observations Phys.Rev.D 80:084017,2009

Anderson P.W. & Abrahams, E. (2009). Machines Fall Short of Revolutionary Science Science 324 1515-1516

Balazs, A. C. & Epstein I. R. (2009). Emergent or Just Complex? Science 325 1632 – 1634

Barrow J .D. & Tipler F. J. (1986). The Anthropic Cosmological Principle Oxford University Press, Oxford

Barrow J. D. (2007). New Theories of Everything 2nd Edition, Oxford University Press, Oxford

Carr, B (2007). ed Universe or Multiverse? Cambridge University Press, Cambridge

Efstathiou, G (2008). The Future of Cosmology, arXiv:0712.1513v2

Elewa, A. M. T. (2009). The History, Origins, and Causes of Mass Extinctions, Journal of Cosmology, 2, 201-220.

Gold, E. M. (1967). Language Identification in the Limit Inform. Control 10:447-474.

Hartle, J. B. (2002). The State of the Universe, arXiv:gr-qc/0209046

Hoyle, F., and Wickramasinghe, N.C. (1985). Living Comets, University College Cardiff Press, Cardiff.

Hoyle, F., Wickramasinghe, N. C. (2000). Astronomical origins of life – Steps towards panspermia, Klewer Academic Publishers. 1–381.

Joseph, R. (2000). Astrobiology, the origin of life, and the death of Darwinism. University Press, San Jose, California.

Joseph, R. (2009). Life on Earth came from other planets. Journal of Cosmology 1, 1-56.

Jones, A. R. (2009). The Next Mass Extinction: Human Evolution or Human Eradication. Journal of Cosmology, 2, 316-333.

King et al (2009). The Automation of Science Science 324 85-89

Komatsu, E. Et al (2009). Five-Year Wilkinson Microwave Anisotropy Probe Observations: Cosmological Interpretation Astrophysical Journal Supplement Series, 180:330–376

Levy, B., and Sidel, V. (2009). The Threat of Nuclear War. Journal of Cosmology, 2009, 2, 309-315.

Lucas J. R. (1961). Minds, Machines and Godel. Philosophy, XXXVI

McKee, J. K. (2009). Contemporary Mass Extinction and the Human Population Imperative. Journal of Cosmology, 2, 301-308.

Nowak M. R. et al (2006). Five Rules for the Evolution of Cooperation Science 314, 1560-1563

Nowak, M. R. (2006). Evolutionary Dynamics: Exploring the Equations of Life Harvard University Press, Cambridge.

Polkinghorne, J.C. & Beale, N.C.L. (2009). Questions of Truth (Appendix A). Westminster John Knox, Louisville.

Rand, D. G. & al. (2009). Positive interactions Promote Public Cooperation Science 325: 1272- 1275

Rees, M. R. (1999). Just Six Numbers: The Deep Forces that Shape the Universe Weidenfeld & Nicolson, London.

Rees, M. R. (2004). Our Final Century? Arrow Books

Siegelmann, H. T. (1995). Computation Beyond the Turing Limit Science, 238, 632-637

Silk, J. (1997) Holistic Cosmology Science 277 644

Smolin, L. (2007). Scientific Alternatives to the Anthropic Principle, in Carr (2007).

Tonn, B. (2009). Preventing the Next Mass Extinction, Journal of Cosmology, 2009, 2, 334-343.

Valliant, L. G. (1984). A Theory of Learnable Comm. ACM 27:436-445

Vapnik, V. and Chervonenkis, A. (1971) On the uniform convergence of relative frequencies of events to their probabilities. Theory of Probability and its Applications, 16(2), 264–280

On Meaning, Consciousness and Quantum Physics

Yair Neuman, Ph.D.[1] and Boaz Tamir, Ph.D.[2]

[1]Office for Interdisciplinary Research Ben-Gurion University of the Negev; [2]Israel Institute for Advanced Research Rehovot, Israel.

Abstract

The Mind is a machine that computes "difference of similarities" and "similarity of differences". In this context, the basic unit of the Mind is a "difference that makes a difference", a sign, a unit of meaning. We argue that as a Machine of Interaction and under the constraint imposed by the Principle of Least Efforts, the mind must compute signs that exist in a superposition. Self-consciousness is explained through this conceptualization and the paper concludes by introducing the idea of the Mind as a hybrid machine that combines classical and quantum computations.

Key Words: consciousness, meaning, quantum physics/computation, semiotics, interdisciplinary research

1. "WHY THERE IS SOMETHING RATHER THAN NOTHING"?

Philosophers have bothering questions that cannot be easily addressed. For example, Leibniz (1646-1716) has asked the famous question: "Why is there something rather than nothing?" Surprisingly an experiment conducted by the Gestalt psychologist Wolfgang Köhler (1887-1967) provides an answer, albeit to a slightly different question. This low tech experiment (described in Luria, 1976) involved a hen, grains and two sheets of paper. The hen was presented with grains on the two sheets of paper, one light gray and the other dark gray. On the light gray sheet, the grains simply rested on the surface of the paper, so that the chicken could peck at them, whereas those on the dark gray sheet of paper were glued in place so that the chicken could not peck at them. After being exposed to the sheets at several trials, the chicken learned the trick. It pecked at the light gray sheet and avoided the dark gray sheet. At this phase, Köhler turned to the crucial phase of the experiment and presented the hen with a new pair of sheets, one of which was the same light gray sheet and the other a new white sheet. Now the interesting question was how would the chicken behave in this case and to which of the sheets would she positively react. In most of the cases, the chicken … approached the new white sheet! Köhler's explanation is that the hen had been directed not to the absolute darkness or lightness but to the relative darkness. In other words, what triggered the hen's response was a difference.

In this context, we may amuse ourselves by imagining Köhler's hen answering Leibniz by explaining to him that only an intelligent being can ask a question such as: "Why is there something …", and for such a creature the nature of the world cannot be artificially demarcated from the nature of his contemplating mind. In this context, the "Why" question should be replaced by a "How" question: How Mind comes into being? The hen could have also answered this question by explaining that the basic unit of the mind, whether the mind of a chicken, the mind of the immune system or the mind of a human being, is a "difference that makes a difference" (Bateson 1979/2000). The chicken could have also advised Leibniz to study quantum physics in order to better understand the mind and self-consciousness. Following the hen's advice we may turn to the next section.

2. A DIFFERENCE THAT MAKES A DIFFERENCE

The hen's response has been triggered by a difference. However, in itself a difference (or a bit of information) is meaningless. As proposed by David Bohm (1998), order appears as the interplay of "similarity of differences" and "difference of similarities". The difference turns into a difference that makes a difference (i.e. a unit of meaning) if it is mapped, for instance, into another difference. The difference between the light gray sheet and the dark gray sheet is mapped into the difference between the pleasure of eating the grains and the "pain" of pecking the glued grains. See next figure 1.

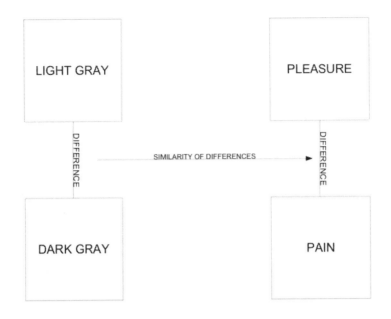

Figure 1. A similarity of differences.

What we see is that the mapping function between the differences involves a similarity of differences that establishes a correspondence between two different realms: the physical realms of colors and the mental realm of pleasure and pain. In this context, the difference between the two sheets functions as a sign, "something which stands to somebody for something in some respect or capacity" (CP 2.228, c. 1897). This generic definition of the sign has been introduced by C. S. Peirce and it is applicable to different systems from natural language to the immune system (Neuman, 2008a).

A sign, whether in the human mind or in the immune system, establishes a semantic unit, a unit of meaning, which is always about something whether it is a sign in natural language that corresponds to a concept or an antigen that signals 'danger' to the immune system. This "aboutness" is the source of some difficulties presented in the next section.

3. THE HAPTIC DANCE OF LIVING SYSTEMS

The Principal of Least Efforts (PLE) suggests that the minimization of energy expenditure is a force motivating the behavior of living systems. The PLE is the parallel of the well-known principle of least action known in classical and quantum physics (Feynman, 1964). In the behavioral sciences, the principle has been intensively discussed by Zipf (1949) and in order to illustrate it, we will use Zipf's example that concerns a verbal interaction.

A verbal interaction between two people involves the exchange of linguistic signs (i.e. words). The PLE may motivate the speaker to use only a single word in order to denote all possible objects in the world. In other words, the speaker's interest is to minimize his/her efforts and therefore s/he may use a single word vocabulary. The speaker's selfish strategy would put enormous cognitive load on the listener who would have to decide in a specific context what the meaning of the word is.

On the other hand, the listener has a contrasting interest that the speaker will use a different word for each different object in the world. This interest may lead to an absurd situation in which each different object in the world, whether the external or the internal, has a distinct sign. For instance, instead of regarding myself as an object with permanence, I may use different signs to denote each different experience of the self such as "I" at the age of 3, "I" at this particular moment etc. The listener's interest will overload the speaker in a way that would probably seize any form of interaction. The situation is much more complex as verbal interaction is reciprocal and at this game, the roles of speaker and listener are changed by turn-taking. Therefore, the conflicting interests exist both between and within the subjects.

Each person as a selfish Turing machine would fail to maintain sign mediated interactions under the constraints imposed by the PLE. However, a living system is a Machine of Interaction (Bassingthwaighte et al., 2009; Neuman, 2008a) that like a dancer performing haptic dance must coordinate its behavior under certain constraints. How is it possible to coordinate a sign mediated interaction under the constraint of the PLE? Here Quantum physics gets into the picture. We would like to argue that the only economical solution for managing this coordination-under-constraints is that the signs exist in a superposition and that the listener determines their meaning by quantum measurement. One should notice that the act of measurement is usually regarded as external to the theory of quantum physics. However, the act of measurement which is an act of "meaning making" (Neuman, 2008a) must be an internal part of any theory of the mind.

Many superpositions of signs may interfere with each other to cancel some of the interpretations and to enhance the others. The interferences are done by some apparatus that we cannot yet specify. Its Hamiltonian (time evolution rule) checks every possible path (option of interpretation) leaving only the minimal action path. Therefore using superpositions (with complex amplitudes) enable them to interfere with each other. In this way the PLE of behavioral science is being realized through the principle of least action in physics. It's not the superposition itself that is motivated by the PLE but the interference of superpositions. Therefore, we can use the same signs in different context and get different meanings. Let us illustrate this idea by using a simple example. The sign 'Cat' is polysemous; has several potential senses. It can be used to denote 'Guy' or to denote 'Feline mammal'. The sign 'Bass' can be used to denote 'Musical instrument' or a kind of fish (sea bass). Suppose now we treat both signs as superpositions: so

$$\text{Cat} = a \cdot \text{Guy} + b \cdot \text{Feline mammal}$$

$$\text{Bass} = c \cdot \text{Musical instrument} + d \cdot \text{Fish}$$

By the sign + we mean 'a superposition of' in the quantum sense. Therefore, 'Cat' may sometimes collapses into 'Guy' and sometime into 'Feline mammal' with amplitudes a and b respectively. The same is true for 'Bass'. Now consider the sentence: "The Cat played the Bass". First, looking at the tensor of both 'Cat' and 'Bass' we get the following superposition of four possible options:

$$\text{Cat x Bass} = \{a \cdot \text{Guy} + b \cdot \text{Feline mammal}\} \{c \cdot \text{Musical instrument} + d \cdot \text{Fish}\}$$
$$=$$
$$a \cdot c \{\text{Guy} \cdot \text{Musical instrument}\} + a \cdot d \{\text{Guy} \cdot \text{Fish}\} + b \cdot c \{\text{Feline mammal} \cdot \text{Musical instrument}\} + b \cdot d\{\text{Feline mammal} \cdot \text{Fish}\}$$

Clearly when considering the meaning of the sentence "The Cat played the Bass" some of the options are peculiar and some are reasonable. In building the sentence, some of the above options are stressed and others are discarded. In a sense, we 'compute' the meaning of the sentence. Suppose we are left now with only two possible options:

$$\text{The Cat played the Bass} = a \{\text{Guy} \cdot \text{Musical instrument}\} + b \{\text{Feline mammal} \cdot \text{Fish}\}$$

We can say that these two options constitute an entanglement in the following sense: If 'Cat' is a 'Guy' then 'Bass' is a musical instrument, and if 'Cat' is a mammal then 'Bass' is a fish. If you know one of the senses you know the other because they are entangled. When the reader "measures" the above sentence, the superposition collapses into a single value; It is probably a sentence about a guy who played a musical instrument.

Excavating the meaning out of a tensor of signs may be easily described in terms of quantum computation. A quantum computer starts with a simple tensor and ends up with a superposition that constitutes the answer to a computational problem. In fact the construction of the superposition or the entanglement is in itself a computation. In a sense we (quantum) compute part of the context of the sentence by building the possible entanglements between the different signs. This operation is conducted by reducing the amplitudes of all absurd interpretations and enhancing all amplitudes of reasonable interpretations. All interpretations get interfered in this process of computation leaving only paths that has 'least action' (Feynman, 1964). Those 'least action' paths constitute the reasonable interpretations. This process is done immediately when introducing such a sentence such as "The Cat played the Bass". Still, some part of the context is revealed by the last stage of the computation which is the measurement process, when the receiver collapses the computed entanglement into one of its branches.

The idea that linguistic signs exist in a superposition before a measurement takes place is the only economical solution to the need to coordinate the use of signs under the constraint imposed by the PLE. Any assumption that the communicated unit (i.e. the word) has only one definite value before being observed would result in the impossibility of interaction as the sign would have to either signify all of the objects in a given universe (i.e., the speaker's interest) or will have to correspond to a unique singular object (i.e., the listener's interest). In other words, our novel explanation why signs have to exist in a superposition is that in a mental world constituted by communicated signs under the constraint of the PLE, this is the only reasonable option that may support an interaction between two interactive systems with conflicting interests.

The quantum leap we have made is in using a concept that describes the behavior of physical particles at the micro-scale of analysis for describing the behavior of signs at a higher level of analysis. This move is theoretically justified at least as it presents a novel explanation for old problems (Neuman, 2008b). Moreover, we are sensitive to the fact that formalism such as the one of Quantum Physics cannot by itself be a substitute for a theory of the mind. The theory of the mind as an interactive machine that is constituted through differences/similarities under the constraints imposed by the PLE, bridges the gap between the use of quantum physics and the mental phenomenal world.

4. SELF-CONSCIOUSNESS

Consciousness is a term covering a scope of seemingly unrelated phenomena from a sense of being to the process of reflecting on one's thoughts (Shanon, 1990). As argued by Brentano (1995), a defining characteristic of consciousness is intentionality, the fact that it is always about some object in the world whether the external world or the internal world. For instance, the taste of an apple constitutes the subjective experience – the quale – of tasting an apple. When we are self-conscious, our "self" whatever it is, is the "intentional object" of our consciousness. However, the phenomenon of self-consciousness is different from other forms of conscious experience that have an intentional object. When we look inside and introspect our attention floats as if there is no object. This phenomenon has been well-documented and the explanation we may provide, based on the above theorization is as follows. The mind as a measuring device is trying to measure itself. It extends its own boundaries.

To recall, the Mind is a machine constituted by similarity of differences and difference of similarities. In this context, a difference that makes a difference, the basic unit of the mind, is actually a sign. Each sign is in a sense "floating" and has no defined meaning before a measurement takes place. Under the constraint imposed by the PLE a sign is in a superposition before it is measured. Therefore, the measurement of the "self" is possible only through the use of signs that function as both our measurement device and as the object we attempt to measure. This idea resonates with the finding that self-consciousness is heavily mediated by inner-speech – the internalized use of natural language – and that inner-speech is crucial for overcoming difficulties in self-consciousness (Neuman & Nave, 2009). By measuring itself through signs the mind is collapsing the same particles responsible for the measurement process i.e. the signs. This is the place where uncertainty gets into the picture. The mind, cannot measure and being measured at the same time. This is probably the reason why self-observation or self-consciousness results in two common insights. First, that the self is "No-thing", a vanishing point (Neuman, 2009) or the blind spot of our Mind. Second, that the "self" emerging from self-observation is not a monolithic object but an artifact constituted through inner speech and the use of signs. In other words, it is an invention that through symbolic processes and memory integrates the fragmented pieces of our experience. According to this interpretation the self is the vertex of knowledge, but self-knowledge in its ultimate form is impossible.

5. "WE ARE TWO LOST SOULS SWIMMING IN A FISH BOWL"

The Turing Machine exists "in and for itself" as it does not include any feature which is specifically attunes to interaction with other machines under real world constraints.

It is an information-processing device rather than a "meaning-making" device (Neuman, 2008a). If this machine aims to serve as a model of the human mind then we can describe it, by paraphrasing Pink Floyd's poem, as a lost soul swimming in a fish bowl. It is doubtful whether such a lost soul may know itself and the world outside the fishing bowl. However, the world is imbues with interactions that shape the emergence of the mind and the mind is a fascinating device that observes itself and extends its limit line. Indeed, in itself each of us is a lost soul swimming in a fish bowl and as such it is hard to imagine the possibility of extending the limit line of our mind beyond the "bowl" in which we live. However, when we add the idea of sign-mediated interaction, the way in which we extend the limit line of our mind seems more comprehensible. Two lost souls swimming in a fish bowl can know better as a second person perspective is introduced into the game, and three lost souls swimming in a fish bowl know even more as a third person perspective is introduced. We know the world and ourselves through sign-mediated interactions with other minds.

These interactions seem to involve some characteristics of quantum physics such as superposition, quantum entanglement and quantum measurements. However, this analogy between the human mind and quantum computer should be qualified. The human mind involves irreversible computation while a quantum computer is necessarily reversible, besides the measurement process, which is usually regarded as alien to the quantum theory. Moreover, living systems are constantly involved in self-measurement, where there is no such thing in quantum mechanics. It is possible to imagine a hybrid model of the mind that integrates classical Turing and quantum machine processes. However, such a hybrid model would have to take into account the unique characteristics of the mind. Can we explain the way consciousness emerges from the interaction between minds working along such a hybrid model? We chose to close this paper by introducing this challenge. Therefore, the paper concludes by inviting other "souls" to swim with us in the same fish bowl with the aim of addressing this grand challenge.

References

Bassingthwaighte J., Hunter, P., & Noble, D. (2009). The Cardiac Physiome: perspectives for the future. Experimental Physiology, 94, 597-605.

Bateson, G. (1979/2000). Steps to Ecology of Mind. The University of Chicago, Press Chicago.

Bohm, D. (1998). On Creativity (L. Nichol, Ed.). Routledge, New York.

Pierce, C.P. (1897). Collected papers. Collected Papers of Charles Sanders Peirce (Vols. 1-8). Cambridge, MA: Harvard University Press. (Vols. 1-6, C. Hartshorne & P. Weiss, Eds.; Vols. 7-8, A. W. Burks, Ed.)

Brentano, F. (1995). Psychology from an Empirical Standpoint. Routledge.

Feynman, R. (1964). The Feynman Lectures on Physics. Addison-Wesley Publishing Company, California Institute of Technology.

Luria, A. R. (1976). Cognitive development: Its cultural and social foundations. Harvard UP, Cambridge, Mass.

Neuman, Y. (2008a). Reviving the living: Meaning making in living systems. Elsevier, N.Y.

Neuman, Y. (2008b). The polysemy of the sign: From quantum computing to the garden of the forking paths. Semiotica, 169, 155-169.

Neuman, Y. (2009). On love, hate and knowledge. The International Journal of Psychoanalysis, 90, 697-712.

Neuman, Y., & Nave, O. (2009). Why the brain needs language in order to be self-conscious. New Ideas in Psychology, 28, 37-48.

Shanon, B. (1990). Consciousness. Journal of Mind and Behavior, 11, 137–152.

Zipf, G. K. (1949). Human Behavior and the Principle of Least Efforts. Hafner Publishing Company, N.Y.

Semiotica, 169, 155-169.

Neuman, Y. (2009). On love, hate and knowledge. The International Journal of Psychoanalysis, 90, 697-712.

Neuman, Y., & Nave, O. (2009). Why the brain needs language in order to be self-conscious. New Ideas in Psychology, 28, 37-48.

Shanon, B. (1990). Consciousness. Journal of Mind and Behavior, 11, 137–152.

Zipf, G. K. (1949). Human Behavior and the Principle of Least Efforts. Hafner Publishing Company, N.Y.

Quantum Reality and Evolution Theory

Lothar Schäfer, Ph.D.

Department of Chemistry and Biochemistry, University of Arkansas, Fayetteville, AR

Abstract

I describe some aspects of quantum theory and the current paradigm change in physics and chemistry, which are neglected in modern (neo-Darwinian) evolution theory. In the quantum phenomena physical reality has revealed the nature of an indivisible wholeness, in which everything is interconnected. Thus, it is unlikely that the evolution of life has been driven by segregative principles, such as competition and selfishness, as the primary principles of processes of marginalization and extinction. Instead, emerging views of symbiosis are supported, which propose that the evolution of complex life forms needs biological cooperativity and the sharing of information. Because of the quantum nature of DNA molecules the possibility of spontaneous mutations, which have no material-energetic causes, must be accepted, It is argued that complex order in molecular systems emerges by actualization of transempirical, virtual quantum states that already exist, before they are manifest in the empirical world. Since quantum phenomena reveal a transempirical aspect of physical reality, one must suppose that evolution of life is also informed by transempirical order.

1. Introduction

Darwin's theory of evolution was conceived in the age of classical physics and it is an expression of the materialist-mechanistic worldview of its time. Like Newton's mechanics, Darwin's theory describes the visible surface of things, but it misses out on important phenomena at the molecular basis (Joseph, 2009). As a consequence, modern evolution theory, which is largely based on Darwinian ideas, is completely left out of the current paradigms of physics and chemistry, even though biology is based on their laws. It is the purpose of this paper to describe this inconsistency and some of its consequences.

2. The Ontology of Quantum Theory

Our new understanding of natural sciences is based on quantum theory. According to the standard interpretation of this theory a transempirical domain of reality exists, which does not consist of material things but of transmaterial forms. Even though these forms are transempirical, they are real, because they have the potential – Aristotelian potentiality – to manifest themselves in the empirical world. Thus, physical reality appears to us in two domains: potentiality and actuality. Physics posits that the forms in the realm of potentiality are waves – potentiality waves (Villars, 1987). Since the waves are contiguous, the nature of reality is that of an indivisible Wholeness, in which all things are interconnected.

The claim that a transempirical part of physical reality exists seems at first sight self-contradictory. However, it is suggested by numerous empirical phenomena. Since I have given detailed descriptions elsewhere (Schäfer 1997, 2004, 2006, 2008, 2009; Schäfer, Valadas-Ponte und Roy, 2009a,b), only a short summary shall be presented here.

3. Potentiality Waves

The concept of Aristotelian potentiality was first introduced into the description of quantum reality by Werner Heisenberg (([1958] 2000; 1962). This view suggests that the quantum mechanical state vector represents a network of potentialities governed by Schrödinger dynamics. Accordingly, a microphysical object can exist in a state that is not a state of actuality, but potentiality, where the state vector introduces something "standing in the middle between the idea of an event and the actual event" (Heisenberg 1962, 41). In such a state a particular property of a system, such as the position in space, does not have a single actual value but a multiplicity of potential values (Villars 1984, 1987). The actuality emerges out of the potentiality by controlled or uncontrolled acts of measurement – that is, irreversible interactions of a microphysical potentiality state with a macroscopic object or environment. As Heisenberg described it (1962, 54): "The observation … selects of all possible events the actual one that has taken place. … Therefore, the transition from the 'possible' to the 'actual' takes place during the act of observation." Thus, in the act of observation a transition is made between two different modalities of being; i.e., from potentiality to actuality. Since, in the very act needed to observe it, a state of potentiality ceases to exist, it follows that potentiality states are transempirical.

As an example, consider the state of an electron in a double-slit single-particle interference experiment immediately prior to its detection by a position sensitive detector, say a photodiode array. In this state, the electron has a certain freedom of choice, where to hit the detector, so that its position on the detector has many potential values. Villars' terminology (1987) can be applied, stating that this electron is a "potentiality wave", that is, "microphysical objects are waves of potential observation interactions" (Villars 1987, 148). When the measurement is actually performed, one of the potential observation interactions contained in the potentiality wave becomes the actual one; the particle appears in a specific channel, and the potentiality wave has ceased to exist.

The principle that actuality emerges out of potentiality by interactions of potentiality states with the environment applies to everything: The visible world is an actualization out of a realm of potentiality that exists in physical reality. That is, reality appears to us in two domains: potentiality and actuality.

4. Virtual States.

Another class of transempirical entities is found in the empty states of material systems. Under normal conditions, atoms and molecules exist in stationary states. Quantum theory posits that every system consists not only of the state that it occupies when it is observed, but also of countless other states that are empty. Quantum chemists call empty states virtual. When a given atom or molecule is in its ground state, the higher states also exist, but not as empirical entities, because they are empty: there is nothing there to see. They exist in the sense that their mathematical order is part of the constitution of the system, contains its empirical possibilities, and is a priori predictable. Virtual states are mathematical forms, patterns of information, but they are more than mere formulae, because they have the potential to manifest themselves in the empirical world.

I will not enter into the discussion here, as to whether or not virtual states are real, since I have presented a detailed analysis elsewhere (Schäfer, 2008). In short, it can be proposed that virtual states are real because they participate in and control empirical phenomena – such as spectroscopic transitions and chemical reactions – before they are actual states. Thus, even though they are transempirical, virtual states are real and elements of the realm of potentiality in physical reality.

5. Transempirical, Transmaterial and Transpersonal Wholeness.

The nature of the entities of the realm of potentiality cannot be known to us, because they are transempirical, like Kant's noumena. We have to rely on intuitions that arise from various constellations in quantum physics, in order to contemplate, what the realm of potentiality might be like. Important indications derive, for example, from quantum chemistry, where Schrödinger's mechanics is currently the only quantum formalism that allows one to calculate the properties of polyatomic molecules. In Schrödinger's mechanics, the electrons in atoms and molecules are not material particles, but standing waves. The nature of these waves is that of potentiality waves and their squared magnitudes determine probabilities of presence. For this reason Heisenberg ([1958] 2000, 78) has called them "probability functions". Probability functions are empty; carry no matter or energy, just information on numerical relations. Thus, if one pursues the nature of matter to its roots, at the level of atoms and molecules all of a sudden one finds oneself in a realm of mathematical forms where the notion of matter begins to be lost and actuality turns into potentiality. In this way one is led to the view that transempirical reality is also transmaterial.

The non-classical coherence of states in the realm of potentiality suggests that the nature of reality is that of indivisible Wholeness. Everything that comes out of the Wholeness belongs to the Wholeness, including our consciousness. This aspect of physical reality has led countless physicists, among them Arthur Stanley Eddington (1929, 276; 1939, 151), James Jeans (1931, 158), David Bohm ([1980] 1981, 11), Menas Kafatos and Robert Nadeau (1990), Hans-Peter Dürr (2000, 18; 2004, 102), Hans-Jürgen Fischbeck (2005), and others, to the conclusion that spirit or consciousness is a cosmic property. "Matter is not made up of matter," writes Hans-Peter Dürr, long-time coworker of Werner Heisenberg, "basically there is only spirit" (Dürr 2000, 18). If one adopts this view, it follows that transempirical and transmaterial wholeness is also transpersonal; transcending, that is, our personal consciousness.

From the nature of reality, as it appears to us in the quantum phenomena, several conclusions follow for the nature of life and its evolution, which contradict basic hypotheses of modern neo-Darwinian evolution theory. Here I refer specifically to a complex of neo-Darwinian principles, which can be summarized in the following way: New species emerge gradually in the accumulation of small genetic changes in existing life forms, and never in jumps (Darwin, 1859, 1971). Genetic changes are random; that is, driven by chance, and neither an organism nor factors outside of it exert any control over what kind of mutation is made, and when it is made. Genetic changes are tested by natural selection, which is based on segregative principles, such as selfishness and competition, as primary principles of processes in which the struggle for survival among competing genes, individuals and species leads to the marginalization or extinction of the less successful participants. Finally, the central dogma (Crick 1970) of molecular biology holds, which states that the character of an organism is the result of the actions of its genes.

6. The Importance of Virtual States.

From the summary given above it is apparent that physics and chemistry are undergoing a paradigm change. In this situation it is puzzling that biology, which is based on the laws of physics and chemistry, completely excuses itself from this process. For example, even though quantum theory has shown that a mechanistic and materialistic description of reality is impossible, biologist Kenneth R. Miller writes in the context of a discussion of the theses of Douglas Futuyama (1999, 168): "Science, by this analysis, is mechanism and materialism. And all that Darwin did was to show that mechanism and materialism applied to biology, too. As I hope the preceding chapters have shown, there is something very right about this."

The basis of life is molecular, molecules are quantum systems, they exist in quantum states and their chemical reactions involve transitions from occupied states to empty states. Important aspects are missed when such simple conditions are disregarded. For example, when Richard Dawkins writes that "mutations are caused by definite physical events; they don't just spontaneously happen" (Dawkins [1986] 1996, 306), he omits an important degree of freedom that molecules have; i.e., the ability to undergo spontaneous changes of state.

Mutations that are caused by mutagens – material or energetic factors – can be called stimulated. But the quantum properties of molecules show that there must also be mutations not caused by such factors, in which a group of nucleotides populates one of their virtual states for no empirically discernible reason. We call such a process spontaneous, meaning that it is not caused by a factor in the empirical domain of reality. The important aspect here is that, when mutations depend on the properties of virtual states, the center of biological evolution is shifted away from the realm of material objects, i.e., the genes, to the transmaterial realm of potentiality, where entirely new possibilities arise. Nobody can state a priori that such factors are not relevant for biology.

In his paper, Three Levels of Emergent Phenomena, Terrence Deakon writes (2001, 4): "Biological evolution presents us with some of the most dramatic cases of … spontaneous order from chaos." Similarly (2001, 8): "Creating something from nothing is an important part of what the universe is about, and some of the most intriguing examples of this curious process are what define us as living thinking beings."

Such views are widely accepted among neo-Darwinians, but they neglect completely the fact that molecular systems cannot jump out of an occupied state into nothing, but only into other, already existing virtual states. Thus, the emergence of complex order in the biosphere is not out of nothing, but due to the actualization of a virtual order that already exists before it is manifested as an empirical order.

In his paper, The Unknown, the Unknowable, and Free Will as a Religious Obligation, Robert Pollack writes (2001, 7): "Facts from science tell us ... that our species – with all our appreciation of ourselves as unique individuals – is not the creation of design, but the result of accumulated errors." In contrast to this view is the fact that, in living cells, the synthesis of genes – DNA molecules – is a quantum process; that is, the outcome of a particular event is unpredictable. Thus, when a particular stretch of DNA is synthesized, the probability may be overwhelming that the product is the same as the starting material, but this outcome is not necessary. If the product is different than expected, this does not mean that an error was made. Jacques Monod's characterization of the process, in terms of chance and necessity (Monod, 1972), is completely off the mark: in the synthesis of a single molecule there is no necessity.

7. The Evolution of Life in a holistic Reality

Life is not evolving in a vacuum but within the order of the universe. Thus, it is a manifestation of universal order and not a violation of it. Specifically, if the nature of reality is that of an indivisible Wholeness, it is unlikely that the evolution of life is driven by segregative principles, such as competition and selfishness, as primary principles in processes of marginalization and extinction (Joseph, 2009). In this regard, too, the neo-Darwinian worldview is unrealistic.

Indeed, details are increasingly becoming known (Bauer, 2008; Lipton, 2005; Woese 2002), which show that the evolution of complex life forms is based on symbiotic principles, such as communication and biological cooperativity (Joseph, 2009). Not the ploys of "selfish genes" come into play, as Richard Dawkins claims (Dawkins [1976] 1999), but the fundamental biological principles of the genome are "cooperativity, communication, and creativity" (Bauer, 2008, 17).

The driving force in early cellular evolution was not the rivalry of "replicators", as Dawkins claims – "There was a struggle for existence among replicator varieties. ... These proto-carnivores simultaneously obtained food and removed competing rivals." (Dawkins [1976] 1999, 19) –, but different systems shared information in gene transfer processes (Joseph, 2009). Innovation was not the achievement of a few ruthless operators, which eliminated the competition, but a communal project. "The high level of novelty required to evolve cell designs is a product of communal invention, of the universal

HGT (horizontal gene transfer) field, not intralineage variation. It is the community as a whole, the ecosystem, which evolves" (Woese, 2002, 8742).

In all advances of the complexity of life, cooperativity and the sharing of resources were the primary principles, not strife and combat among cannibals. For example, eukaryotes evolved from Archaean Cells, when the latter accepted prokaryotic bacteria inside their system as organelles (mitochondria and chloroplasts) in order to cope with the rising oxygen content of the atmosphere (Bauer, 2008, 52). In this process both, respiratory (oxygen consuming) and photosynthetic (oxygen producing) organisms were formed. Thus, this development was not that of "lone warriors (neither lone-warrior individuals, nor lone-warrior species)," as the neo-Darwinians claim, but it was the development "of biological systems" (Bauer, 2008, 54). Cooperativity and the willingness to share were in all developments of complexity necessarily involved; for example, when multicellular organisms evolved from single cells, and when individuals formed social groups. And we will need these principles even more intensely, when we want to establish on this planet a truly globalized social order.

It is true that Darwinism and its modern versions do not deny the importance of cooperativity and altruism. But, in Darwinism, altruism is not the primary principle of a holistic reality, but it evolves in secondary processes as "optimized strategies in the struggle for survival" (Bauer, 2008, 15). As Richard Dawkins writes ([1982] 1999, 291) on altruism: "Biologists use the word in a restricted (some would say misleadingly so) sense, only superficially related to common usage. An entity, such as a baboon or a gene, is said to be altruistic if it has the effect (not purpose) of promoting the welfare of another entity, at the expense of its own welfare."

The coherence of natural phenomena in a holistic reality is also apparent from the fact that mutations are not entirely random and driven by chance – that is, disconnected from any coherent order – but "cells may have mechanisms for choosing which mutations will occur" (Cairns, Overbeck and Miller, 1988, 142). The experiments of Barbara McClintock revealed "programmed responses to threats that are initiated within the genome itself," indicating that "a genome may reorganize itself when faced with a difficulty for which it is unprepared" (McClintock, 1983, 180). Therefore, the evolution of life does not proceed by way of gradual, stepwise, and completely random mutations, whose accumulation leads to new species in a linear process, but it proceeds in "surges" (Bauer 2008, 16) – quantum leaps (Gould, 2002), as it were – in which "the self-modification of organisms follows identifiable principles, which are laid out in the biological system itself" (Bauer, 2008, 66), and not in randomness and chance. "Species formations are the work of an inherent dynamic, which is laid out in a given genome. Living systems are not just victims of evolution, but they act in it" (Bauer, 2008, 188).

In this context Bauer (2008, 72) characterizes biological processes in a way, that is reminiscent of quantum processes: "On the one hand, biological processes are subject to laws … On the other, all biological systems display considerable tolerance – within the limited bandwidth set by the structure of a given species – so that processes in the single case can take a varied course." These are exactly the properties of quantum processes. On the one hand, quantum leaps, for example, are subject to certain lawfulness; on the other, they depend on chance in the sense that they can occur without any actual causes that exist in the empirical world. As a consequence, the outcome of a single quantum event is unpredictable, but the appearance of a multiplicity of repeated events follows a quasi-deterministic, pre-determined order. The quantum indeterminacy of single molecular processes – like the synthesis of a gene – allows precisely the "tolerance" which seems a characteristic of the evolution of life.

The behavior of material particles in a double-slit experiment can serve as an instructive example. When an electron passes a double-slit, it has a certain freedom of choice as to where it will impact a position sensitive detector: the position of a single, specific impact is unpredictable. Nevertheless, the seemingly random and unpredictable single impacts are not completely arbitrary, because they follow a hidden order that demands for a multiplicity of them the buildup of an interference pattern. Even though apparently isolated, the single impacts are connected in a hidden order.

In the same way, each one of us appears in the pattern of life as an isolated dot with a certain freedom and individuality, apparently unaffected by countless other, unrelated appearances. But, perhaps, the seemingly unrelated appearances of many individuals, too, are somehow connected in a hidden order. In that case, the intrinsic laws by which cells can change their genome have to be seen in a cosmic context. Even though single mutations in different individuals seem completely disconnected from each other, they may be coherent in a hidden order that demands for a multiplicity of them a quasi-deterministic pattern, like the interference pattern in single-particle double slit experiments. The progression of evolution towards higher complexity and mentallization may be the manifestation of such an order.

The connection of a life form with the entire biological system is also suggested by the fact that the chemistry of cells is not determined by its genes, but by the interaction of a cell with its environment. Although the central dogma of molecular biology (Crick 1970) dictates that by controlling the synthesis of proteins, genes determine the character of an organism, it has been shown by epigenetics that while the biochemistry of cells is controlled by the genes, the genes are controlled by the reactions of a cell to signals which it receives from its environment (Joseph, 2009).

8. The Interplay of Potentiality and Actuality

From considerations of the kind presented above one conclusion that follows is easy: neo-Darwinian theory is, like Newton's mechanics, an incomplete description of reality. A second conclusion is more difficult to accept: a completely new approach is needed to understand the nature of life, which will bring transempirical and transmaterial aspects into play, which seem to violate the very basis of science.

In section 5 I have described, how the quantum phenomena have led a number of physicists to propose that consciousness is a cosmic principle. The reaction to such a hypothesis should not be to shrug it off as a sign of sloppy thinking, but to try to explore what it would mean for the evolution of life, if such a principle really existed.

Potentiality and actuality are two different modalities of being in the wholeness of reality. The distinctive character of living organisms lies in their ability to be simultaneously active in both domains. For example, one of the characteristic properties of living cells is their intelligence. Even single cells are endowed with the ability of a planning control or intelligence, which is reminiscent of the intentionality of a self-conscious mind. "Each cell is an intelligent being that can survive on its own" writes cell biologist Bruce Lipton (2005, 7). And Barbara McClintock writes about cells (1983, 184): "They make wise decisions and act upon them." The science of Epigenetics shows that the decisions of cells are essentially reactions to chemical or physical signals in their environment, which lead to regulations of the activities of the genes (Joseph, 2009). If a realm of potentiality in physical reality exists, we have to consider the possibility that the receptors in cell walls are sensitive not only to chemical and physical signals, but also to signals emanating out of the realm of potentiality, in the same way in which a measuring instrument in physics is sensitive to microphysical objects in a potentiality state. Perhaps this sensitivity is at the basis of the ability of organisms to construct themselves.

Informatics engineer Karl Goser views such processes as the defining difference between machines and biological systems: "Machines cannot receive information from a transcendent world" (Goser, 2005, 2007).

9. Conclusion

The hopelessness of a meaningless life in a mechanistic-materialistic-Darwinian universe has often been described. "Man must at last wake out of his millenary dream," writes Jacques Monod (1972, 160) "and discover his total solitude, his fundamental isolation. He must realize that, like a gypsy, he lives on the boundary of an alien world; a world that is deaf to his music, and as indifferent to his hopes as it is to his suffering or his crimes." And Richard

Dawkins writes about replicators and the rationale of our existence: "They are in you and me; they created us, body and mind; and their preservation is the ultimate rationale for our existence. They have come a long way, those replicators. Now they go by the name of genes, and we are their survival machines" (Dawkins [1976] 1999: 20).

In this situation the appearance, in physics, of a transempirical part to physical reality is of utmost significance. We live in this physical reality which is a wholeness, its nature is our nature, and it makes a difference whether our humanity is an accidental emanation of complex material structures, or perhaps it is rooted in a deeper order.

In his book, "For a civil society," Hans-Peter Dürr (2000) describes how the awareness of quantum reality can help us build a kinder world and a more humane society, whose order is based on community, not adversity; on cooperation, not competition (2000, 29). Indeed, the point can be made that even the understanding of ethics depends on our understanding of reality, so that the wrong view of the world can easily lead to the wrong life (Schäfer, Valadas Ponte, and Roy, 2009).

The phenomenon of epigenetics shows that the behavior of a living organism can change without concomitant changes in its genome, because a cell's interaction with its environment affects its biochemistry. Within the framework of psychosomatic medicine Hanne Seemann (1988) has described the same effect for human beings: our perceptions of the world affect the physiology of our bodies to the extent that errors in our perceptions can lead to psychosomatic disorders. The primary motivation of human beings is not the repression and annihilation of others, but "the search for social acceptance and bonding" (Bauer, 2008, 154). Acceptance and bonding with other human beings will lead to a different body chemistry than the constant engagement in conflict and the readiness to aggression. Similarly, the belief to live in a purely materialistic world will give the cells in our body different signals than the belief that a higher order exists in a transempirical reality.

The Darwinian world view and that of its modern syntheses has become untenable as a metaphysic of human values. The time has come to restore a realistic view of life and to arrange human order in accordance with the nature of reality.

References

Bohm, D. [1980] 1981, Wholeness and Implicate Order. London: Routledge and Kegan Paul.

Bauer, J. (2008). Das Kooperative Gen. Hamburg: Hoffmann und Kampe.

Cairns, J., Overbaugh, J., Miller, S. (1988). The origin of mutants. Nature 335, 142-145.

Crick, F. (1970). Central Dogma of Molecular Biology. Nature 227, 561-563.

Dawkins, R. [1986] (1996). The Blind Watchmaker. New York: Norton.

Darwin, C. (1859). The origin of species by means of natural selection. London, Murray.

Darwin, C. (1871). The origin of species and the descent of man. New York, Random House.

Dawkins, R. [1976] (1999). The Selfish Gene. Oxford: University Press.

Dawkins, R. [1982] (1999). The Extended Phenotype. Oxford: University Press.

Deakon, T. (2001). Three Levels of Emergent Phenomena, in Science and The Spiritual Quest Boston Conference, Conference Papers, Boston: Harvard University. Dürr, H-P. (2004). Auch die Wissenschaft spricht nur in Gleichnissen. Freiburg: Herder.

Dürr, H-P. (2000). Für eine zivile Gesellschaft. München: Deutscher Taschenbuch Verlag.

Eddington, A. S. (1929). The Nature of the Physical World. New York: Macmillan.

Eddington, A. S. (1939). The Philosophy of Physical Science. New York: Macmillan.

Fischbeck, H-J. (2005). Die Wahrheit und das Leben—Wissenschaft und Glaube im 21. Jahrhundert. München: Utz Verlag.

Goser, K. (2005). persönliche Mitteilung (September).

Goser, K. (2007). Von der Information zur Transzendenz – vom Wissen zum Glauben in: Martin R., Beuttler, U. (Hg.), Glaube und Denken. Jahrbuch der Karl-Heim-Gesellschaft 20. Jahrgang 2007, Peter Lang GmbH, Frankfurt/Main, 177-196.

Gould, S. J. (2002). The Structure of Evolutionary Theory. Belknap Press of Harvard University Press.

Heisenberg, W. [1958] (2000). Physik und Philosophie. Stuttgart, Germany: Hirzel.

Heisenberg, W. (1962). Physics and Philosophy. New York: Harper Torchbook.

Jeans, J. (1931). The Mysterious Universe. New York: Macmillan.

Joseph, R. (2009). Extinction, Metamorphosis, Evolutionary Apoptosis, and Genetically Programmed Species Mass Death. Journal of Cosmology, 2, 235-255.

Kafatos, M., and Nadeau, R. (1990). The Conscious Universe. New York: Springer.

Lipton, B. H. (2005). The Biology of Belief. New York: Hay House.

McClintock, B. (1983). The Significance of responses of the genome to challenge. Nobel lecture, December 8: 180-199.

Miller, Kenneth R. 1999. Finding Darwin's God. New York: Cliff Street Books.

Monod, J. (1972). Chance and Necessity. London: Collins.

Pollack, R. (2001.) The Unknown, the Unknowable, and Free Will as a Religious Obligation, in Science and The Spiritual Quest Boston Conference, Conference Papers, Boston: Harvard University.

Schäfer, L. (1997). In Search of Divine Reality. Fayetteville, AR: Univ. of Arkansas Press.

Schäfer, L. (2004). Versteckte Wirklichkeit-Wie uns die Quantenphysik zur Transzendenz führt. Stuttgart: Hirzel.

Schäfer, L. (2006). "Quantum Reality, the Emergence of Complex Order from Virtual States, and the Importance of Consciousness in the Universe." Zygon, Journal of Religion and Science 41: 505–31.

Schäfer, L. (2008). Nonempirical Reality: Transcending the Physical and Spiritual in the Order of the One. Zygon, Journal of Religion and Science 43: 329–52.

Schäfer, L. (2009). "Paraklase der Weltsicht – Paraklase der Gottessicht. Wie Umwälzungen in den Naturwissenschaften globale, politische, soziale und religiöse Umwälzungen anzeigen und nach sich ziehen." Grenzgebiete der Wissenschaft 58: 3-48.

Schäfer, L., Ponte, D. V., and Roy, S. (2009a). Quantum Reality and Ethos: A Thought Experiment Regarding the Foundation of Ethics in Cosmic Order. Zygon, Journal of Religion and Science 44: 265–87.

Schäfer, L., Ponte, D. V., and Roy, S. (2009b.) Quantenwirklichkeit und Weltethos. Zur Begründung der Ethik in der Ordnung des Kosmos. Ethica 17: 11-54.

Seemann, H. (1998). Freundschaft mit dem eigenen Körper schließen. Stuttgart: Klett-Cotta.

Villars, C. N. (1984). Observables, states and measurements in quantum physics." European Journal of Physics 5:177–83.

Villars, C. N. (1987). Microphysical objects as 'potentiality waves.'" European Journal of Physics 8:148–49.

Woese, C. R. (2002). On the evolution of cells. Proceedings of the National Academy of Science. 99: 8742-8747.

Four Perspectives on Consciousness

Varadaraja V. Raman, Ph.D.

Rochester Institute of Technology, Rochester, NY

Abstract

This paper presents different views on the puzzle of consciousness from the spiritual, the physical, the biological and the neuroscientific perspectives. It gives glimpses of these different views to remind us of how complex the phenomenon is, and how varied its interpretations are. There is as yet no bridge linking the random permutation of letters in a sonnet to the meaning that permeates it.

1. Introduction

Many religions and cultures assign a non-physical entity to the core of every living human. Named variously as soul, spirit, âtman, etc., this entity is what thinks, feels and creates. It does all this through the instruments of perception. In this view, the human body is living as long as a soul is within; it becomes a corpse when the soul departs. The disembodied soul goes elsewhere, perhaps to a realm transcending space and time. This view of the soul is satisfactory in explaining the phenomenon of dynamic life and inert death at a subjective level but it does not constitute a scientific theory.

2. Spirituality in the Indian Framework

In the Indian traditions the world has a physical as well as a spiritual dimension. The physical dimension includes everything that is matter and energy. Our perceptions and minds bring to our knowledge many of the world's tangible aspects. As per the spirituality thesis, beneath and beyond the physical universe there is a spiritual undercurrent that cannot be analyzed through logic, detected through instruments, or verbalized in language. But facets of it can be experienced through spiritual disciplines.

The universal spirituality cosmos is not unlike the ether of classical physics permeating every nook and niche of the world and the universe. The vacuum of current physics would be an even better analogy: that void is no longer inert nothingness, but a dynamic sea of fluctuations, like the heart-throb of the cosmos. In the Hindu framework, every individual consciousness is a spark of a cosmic consciousness Brahman that stretches across the span of space and time.

Moreover, individual consciousness is our spiritual dimension. Spirituality is infinite and eternal. However, we are finite in breath and body and our finiteness is painted on a cosmic canvas. Though we may die and turn to dust, the protons and electrons that subtend our physical frame will exist for ever and this may be considered analogous to spirituality. This is no more obvious than the supernova origins of our physical being.

There are levels of consciousness, experienced in various states of awareness: while awake, while dreaming, and in deep sleep, in all of which consciousness is only vaguely experienced. There is a state called samadhi in which one experiences consciousness in its dismantled, fragmented glory. Yoga is an effort to seek union between the individual and the cosmic consciousness. In its full potential, samadhi is the ultimate goal.

Hindu insights on spirituality arose from meditative probing, instead of from philosophical speculations or external observations. Some have pointed out that this is an important difference between Indian experiential appraisals and Western empirical theories of consciousness. As one scholar said, "the focus is on the person having the experience…(In the West) the focus is on the object of experience, the emphasis is on the physical, and the preferred method is third person based on observation and experiment (Rao, 2005, 8). While this is true at the mystical level, there have also been analytical approaches to the problem in various Hindu philosophical schools.

3. Physics and Consciousness

According to modern physics/science every aspect of the experienced world arises from complex configurations of matter and transformations of energy. Physics holds that this can be unraveled through the methodology of science: careful observation and data analysis, instruments, mathematics, and conceptual constructs.

Until the first quarter of the twentieth century, the focus of physics was on the material world, from atoms to astronomy. The discovery of electromagnetic waves uncovered an insubstantial aspect of the physical universe. Quantum physics revealed an inevitable interaction between observer and observed in the microcosm. Thus, human consciousness entered the realm of physics. Physicists began to consider the role of humans in the appraisal of the physical world, not simply as interpreters but also as participants. John

Wheeler famously said, "We are not only observers. We are participators."

Whereas the early quantum physicists spoke in broad terms about a conscious observer and an insentient objective reality, later ones began to propose theories to explain how this comes about, by appealing to specific quantum phenomena and to neuroscience. David Bohm was one of the first to suggest that consciousness is intrinsic to matter at a deeper level (implicate order) of which mind and matter are different manifestations (explicate order) (Bohm and Hiley, 1993).

Roger Penrose argued that that the human brain is capable of discovering truths which cannot be derived through logic alone. His thesis was that "the brain's organization would have to be geared to take advantage of non-computable action in physical laws, whereas ordinary materials would not be so organized (Penrose, 1994, 216). With Stuart Hameroff, he proposed a theory of consciousness involving microtubules which are important elements of the cytoskeleton. In this theory, consciousness arises when the microtubules induce collapses of quantum coherence. (Hameroff and Penrose, 1996).

Henry Stapp (1992) has developed quantum mechanical consciousness theories. He regards consciousness as resulting from the fact that the brain determines itself in a way that defies external representation. Every neural excitation is a quantum code, and consciousness arises when one of the codes is selected. If and when one zeroes in on the neurons that are responsible for the top-level code, that could be an experimental confirmation of Stapp's theory.

In the view of Amit Goswami (1995), there are 'archetypes of mental objects" in the mind which are subject to the laws of quantum physics. He formulates a series of equivalences between position and momentum in physics on the one hand and content and association in the world of thought.

The materialistic view of consciousness was expressed in no uncertain terms by Daniel Dennett (1995, 203) when he wrote: "An impersonal, unreflective, robotic, mindless little scrap of molecular machinery is the ultimate basis of all the agency, and hence meaning, and hence consciousness in the universe."

By contrast, Freeman Dyson (1979) published calculations to the effect that consciousness may not be subject to entropy increase and energy conservation, and could therefore exist ad infinitum in the universe. He wrote, in fact, that in his view, "the world of physics and astronomy is also inexhaustible; no matter how far we go into the future, there will always be new things happening, new information coming in, new worlds to explore, a constantly expanding domain of life, consciousness, and memory" (Dyson, 1979).

4. Biology and Consciousness

There are two opposing scientific views on the origin of life. Adherents to "panspermia" hold to the position that life is everywhere throughout the cosmos (Hoyle and Wickramasinghe 2000; Wickramasinghe et al., 2009) and that life on Earth came from other planets (Joseph, 2009). Hoyle, Joseph, and Wickramasinghe believe the universe may be infinite and eternal, and that life may have no origins, and is an intrinsic feature of the living, infinite universe.

Yet others subscribe to the theory of "abiogenesis" where life emerges from non-life (Burns, 2009; Istock, 2009). According to this scenario, life arose some three and a half billion years ago through a chemical mix caused by a propitious set of physical conditions. Since then, self-replicating molecules have been morphing in myriad ways provoked by ambient variations and through intrinsic urges to survive and propagate. This proliferation in forms and peculiarities is what one calls evolution: a perspective which explains the panorama of plants and animals, insects, birds, and beasts that populate the earth.

Adherents of panspermia tend to view consciousness as an integral feature of the cosmos; as a collective consciousness, which may come to be fragmented and individualized within the brain (Joseph, 1988a,b).

Therefore, be it panspermia or abiogenesis, human consciousness can be viewed as an offshoot of the evolution of the human brain. Consciousness can evolve. As summed up by Mayr, "it is quite certain that human consciousness did not arise full-fledged with the human species, but is only the most highly evolved end point of a long evolutionary history" (Mayr, 2001, 282).

Tremlin (2006, p.54) offers a machine metaphor of consciousness, when he says: "as a biological machine… the human central nervous system has much in common those other living organisms, designed, as all are, to control bodily function and to interpret and respond to signals received from the outside world." And yet he concedes, "the human brain, however, is different from that of any other creature on Earth in displaying the higher-order mental activities we label with names like 'intelligence' and 'consciousness.'"

In evolutionary terms, consciousness is one of many techniques that arose for fruitfully processing external stimuli. As one biologist put it (Wilson, 2002, 121): "Conscious intentional thought is only the latest gadget in a toolkit of psychological mechanisms that evolved to transform environmental information into adaptive behavior, many of which operate beneath conscious awareness." In other words, there were many factors involved in the evolution of consciousness in the creature called human being.

According to Lovejoy (1981, 326), "evolution of cognition is neither the result of an evolutionary trend nor an event of even the lowest calculable probability, but rather the result of highly specific evolutionary events whose ultimate cause is traceable to selection for unrelated factors such as locomotion and diet."

With all that, what Crick (1995, 255) wrote many years ago is still valid: "I believe that the correct way to conceptualize consciousness has not yet been discovered, and we are merely groping our way toward it."

5. Neuroscience and Consciousness

From the neuroscientific perspective, consciousness is essentially an overall effect of neuronal activities, a consequence of the incessant transformations of chemical and electrical signals in the human brain. The challenge is to uncover which neurons do what and how, to create this extraordinary phenomenon in the entire universe. To the neuroscientist, consciousness is associated with feelings and expressions of pain and pleasure, with seeing and hearing, touching, and self-awareness (Joseph, 1988a,b).

A unique feature of the brain is functional localization, with specific areas of the brain processing and expressing unique aspects of the human experience. For example, the left frontal area of the brain, known as "Broca's Area" is associated with the expression of human speech. The left temporal area, known as "Wernicke's Area" processes the sounds of speech and comprehends human language.

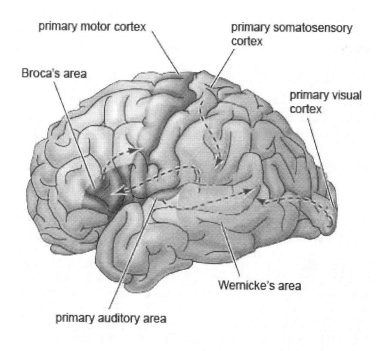

The Left Half of the Brain

Therefore, according to some neuroscientists the left hemisphere is linked with the language-dependent aspects of consciousness (Joseph 1988a,b). The right hemisphere is more concerned with body language, visual-spatial analysis, and social-emotional information processing. Thus, different areas of the brain are associated with different types of conscious experience. In consequence, if the brain is injured, consciousness may be fractured.

For example, it is well known that with severe right cerebral injuries a patient (or rather his/her left hemisphere) might ignore the left half of the body, and even deny ownership of the left arm or leg (which is controlled by the right hemisphere). If the ignored left hand is shown to them the undamaged left hemisphere (which controls language) may claim it belongs to the doctor or a person in the next room (Joseph, 1988b). What this means is that the verbal consciousness associated with the left half of the brain is very limited and is unable to recognize the half of its body that is governed by the right half of the brain; and this is because, when the right is damaged, right (and left) cerebral awareness of the left half of the body is erased.

When the right and left hemisphere's are surgically disconnected the two halves of the brain actually display two independent forms of consciousness.

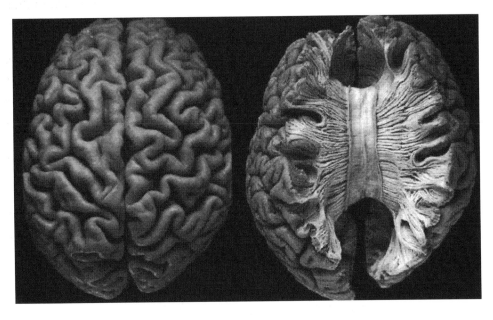

The Right and Left Hemisphere and the Corpus Callosum

As described by Joseph (1988a): split-brain patient, "2-C complained of instances where his left hand would act in a manner completely opposite to what he expressively intended, such as turn off the T.V., or change channels, even though he (or rather his left hemisphere) was enjoying the program, or perform socially inappropriate actions (e.g. attempting to strike or even strangle a relative). On at least one occasion, his left leg refused to continue going for a walk and would only allow him to return home."

Based on an analysis of dozens of "split-brain" cases, Joseph (1988b) concluded that the verbal aspects of consciousness are associated with the left hemisphere, and the awareness maintained by the right half of the brain, makes self-awareness possible.

Research on split-brain patients, and the duality of consciousness, parallel discoveries in quantum physics, such that the observer observes himself, giving rise to self-awareness, which is the result of an interaction between observer and observed in the microcosm.

Research along these lines has led to the popularization of neurotheology which attributes religious and spiritual experiences to the activation of and interactions between different areas of the brain. Consider, for example, the classic "near death" experience, where the patient may experience themselves detached from and looking down on their dead body. Again, this can be construed as a splitting of consciousness and the result of an interaction between observer and observed in the microcosm.

Andrew Newberg and Eugene D'Aquili (1994) identified clear differences in brain activity between benign spiritual experiences and pathological brain-states. Nevertheless, neurotheology implies that the God to whom people pray is ultimately only an idea formed in the brain.

An extreme version of this is the psychologist Michael Persinger's idea that "electromagnetic fluctuations – produced by solar flairs, seismic activity, radio and microwave transmissions, and other external sources, or originating in the brain itself – can trigger disturbances resembling epileptic seizures which generate a wide range of altered states, including religious and mystical visions, out-of-body-experiences, and even alien-abduction episodes (Persinger 2002a,b).

On the other hand, some philosophers are convinced that mental processes "are not reducible to the neurobiological level. … [M]ental properties, properly understood, are higher-level properties relative to neural events and structures. They are contextualized brain events, co-constituted by their role in action-feedback-evaluation-action loops in the environment" (Murphy & Brown, 2007, 195). In this view consciousness is beyond the scope and purview of neurophysiology.

6. Concluding Thoughts

Of late, scientists from different disciplines such as cognitive science, linguistics, computer science, anthropology, and neurscience have attacked the problem of how the brain – a mere mass of tissue, from the materialist perspective – acquires information, interprets it, experiences awareness, and does a thousand other things that could well be described as miraculous. They have gained many insights and much technical/mechanistic information on the phenomenon, but we are still far from deciphering how this inner light seems to make all the difference in the world between mute matter and measuring mind, between rhythmic heart-beat and the joy of love, between the pneumatics of pulmonary bellow and sighs of sorrow.

It is satisfying to many to regard love and laughter, acts of kindness, and the quest for truth as among the peak performances of neuron firings, as evolutionary upshots of cerebral chemistry, as readable scripts from genetic programming. It may well be that we are essentially sophisticated carnal robots which compose music, write poetry, and make jokes. But it is also plausible that some kind of transcendence is at work in the context of value and meaning and whatever else goes with what we call the human spirit.

We cannot deny the biochemical basis in the persistence of personhood. Some day, silicon configurations in plastic casings may acquire feelings and emotions, mimicking the heaves and exhilarations of the human heart. Computers create music today; they may be enjoying it tomorrow. But this is no proof that there is nothing beyond matter and energy in space and time.

Four centuries of modern science have thrown much light on the physical basis of this uncommon wonder which may have parallels in other planetary pockets in the universe. Perhaps some day we will be able to account for it fully in terms of matter-based principles. But as of now, consciousness remains a fantastic anomaly in the mindless arena of mass-energy. No purely material link has as yet been unveiled between alphabetical permutations and sublime sonnets, nor between molecular structure and meaning and value. The tenuous bridge between matter and mind could well be an aspect of transcendence.

The importance of the human species is by no means obvious when viewed in terms of our physical dimensions. No planet, star or galaxy, if they could judge, would attribute to puny humans greater weight than to icebergs or volcanoes. The relative smallness of the human frame is beyond question, even to the most superficial observer. The earth itself, in comparison the sun, is significantly small.

When it comes to sheer physical power, our bodies are but flimsy structures susceptible to instant decimation by nature's fury. A lightning bolt can kill anyone in a brief thunderous flash. Hurricanes and earthquakes can annihilate thousands without a moment's notice. Even tiny bacteria can spell disaster, ruining cities and wiping out civilizations.

When we reckon the age of our species and reflect on the fleeting nature of individual lives, our significance shrinks even further. What are a few hundred thousand years of human survival compared to the billions of years during which the universe has survived, and what is a century of longevity compared to the age of mountains and lakes, of stars and galaxies? If one were to evaluate significance in terms of size or superior strength, longevity or persistence, Homo sapiens is frail, a very recent vulnerable entity in the grand arena of space and time.

Thus, at the purely physical level humans don't have a special place in the universe. But this would be but a partial vision if we don't recognize that we play an unusual role in it. To see this, just imagine a theater-hall that is stark empty while a magnificent play is being performed. What a waste of artistry that would be! Now think of the universe without the human consciousness in it. That world would be dark and dismal. All the light and beauty, grandeur and majesty of the universe are unraveled only in the tiny retinas of human beings, and in those of other living creatures. But for human brains, there would be no formulas for elliptical orbits, no reckoning of space or time, no inverse square law or indeterminacy principle.

Grass and sky have been there for eons, but not green grass or blue skies; there were electromagnetic waves, but no light before the evolution of rods in the retina. Neither the golden sunset nor the patterns butterflies, neither the fragrance of flowers nor the taste of honey would emerge as aspects of the physical world without complex brains. We may imagine a universe that subsisted since the big blast from which it all came. But that pre-life universe was insipid and inert, with no music or melody, no poetry or philosophy.

We compute distance and speed, temperature and density, we conceptualize symmetry breaking and separation of the fundamental forces, we theorize on gravitation, nuclear fusion and the formation of stars. All this reality was somewhat like the tracks of an invisible beast in a vast wilderness: Only the responsive affirmations of noumenal states by brains give meaningful presence to the universe.

We have not been just passive observers. Consider nuclear fusion of hydrogen into helium. This had never occurred anywhere in the universe save in the core of stars. Now it has been brought about here on earth by human ingenuity. All through the eons of cosmic history, planets had never been spied, nor their images captured as photographs until human science and technology. Without human observational and recording devices all this would all be like encyclopedias buried under the sea, away from the reach of any complex system that can decipher. All the stories of stellar birth and death, of galaxies and expansion, remained untold and unknown until humans verbalized them in words and equations. None of the glory and splendor of the universe would have become apparent, if there had been only mute matter and no measuring mind in the cosmos (Raman, 2009, 199 et seq).

This then is the role of the human consciousness in the world. We begin to realize that the emergence of awareness was as great an event in cosmic history as the first big blast of its materialization. That awareness injects meaning into a mechanical and mindless world. It is as if by our presence we have lit up the whole universe which, until our emergence, had been plunged in a stark stillness devoid of joy, meaning, or reflection.

References

Bohm, D., & Hiley, B. J. (1982). The Undivided Universe. London: Routledge, 1993. Elvee, Richard Q. (ed.) Mind in Nature, New York, NY: Harper & Row.

Burns, B. P. (2009). Understanding the Origins of Life on Earth. Journal of Cosmology, 2009, 1, 60-62.

Crick, F. (1995). The Astonishing Hypothesis: The Scientific Search for the Soul, New York, NY: Touchstone, 1995.

Crick, W. and Koch, C. (1998). Consciousness and Neuroscience, Cerebral Cortex, 8, 97-10.

Dennett, D. (1995). Darwin's Dangerous Idea, New York, NY: Simon and Schuster.

Dyson, F. J. (1979). Time Without end: Physics and biology in an open universe, Reviews of Modern Physics, 51, No. 3.

Goswami, A. (1995). The self-aware Universe: How Consciousness Creates the Material World, New York, NY: Putnam's Sons.

Hameroff, S. and Penrose, R. (1996). Consciousnes Events as Orchestrated Space-Time Selection," Journal of Consciousness Studies, 1, 36-53.

Hoyle, F. Wickramasinghe, N. C. 2000. Astronomical Origins of Life – Steps Towards Panspermia, Klewer Academic Publishers, 1–381.

Horgan, J. (2003). Rational Mysticism: Dispatches from the Border Between Science and Spirituality, New York, NY: Houghton Mifflin Co.

Istock, C. (2009). Did Life Originate on Other Planets? Journal of Cosmology, 2009, 1, 57-59.

Jones, R. H. (2008). Science and Mysticism: A Comparative Study of Wedstern Natural Science, Theravada Buddhism, and Advaita Vedanta, London and Toronto: Associated University Press.

Joseph, R. (1988a). Dual mental functioning in a split-brain patient. Journal of Clinical Psychology, 44, 770-779.

Joseph, R. (1988b). The Right Cerebral Hemisphere: Emotion, Music, Visual-Spatial Skills, Body Image, Dreams, and Awareness. Journal of Clinical Psychology, 44, 630-673.

Joseph, R. (2009). Life on Earth Came From Other Planets. Journal of Cosmology, 2009, 1, 1-56.

Lovejoy, C. O. (1981). Life in the Universe, ed. J. Billiongham, Cambridge, MA: M.I.T. Press.

Mayr, E. (2001). What Evolution Is, New York, NY: Basic Books.

Murphy, N. & Brown, W. S. (2007). Did My Neurons Make Me Do it? Philosophical and Neurobiological Perspectives on Moral Responsibility and Free Will, New York, NY: Oxford University Press.

Newberg, A. and D'Aquili, E. (1994). The Mystical Mind, Minneapolis, MN: The Fortress Press.

Penrose, R. (1994). Shadows of the Mind: A Search for the Missing Science of Consciousness, New York, NY: Oxford University Press.

Persinger, M. (2002a). Complex magnetic fields, abiogenesis, and the evolution of living systems In R. Joseph (Ed). Neurotheology. University Press. 221-230.

Persinger, M. (2002b). Experimental simulation of the God experience. In R. Joseph (Ed). Neurotheology. University Press. 279-300.

Raman, V. V. (2009). Truth and Tension in Science and Religion, Center Ossipee, NH, Beech River Books.

Rao, K. R. (2005). Consciousness Studies: Cross-Cultural Perspectives, Jefferson, NC: MacFarland & Co. Inc. Publishrs.

Stapp, H. P. (2006). A quantum theory of consciousness, in B. Rubik ed., The Interrelationship Between Mind and Matter, 207-171, Ohiladephia, PA: enter for Frontier Sciences.

Tremlin, T. (2006). Minds and Gods: The Cognitive Foundations of Religion, New York, NY: Oxford University Press.

Wickramasinghe, N. C., et al., (2009). Astrobiology, Comets And the Origin of Life. World Scientific Publishing Company.

Wilson, D. S. (2002). Darwin's Cathedral: Evolution, Religion, and the Nature of Society, Chicago, IL: The University of Chicago Press.

Synchronicity, Quantum Information and the Psyche

Francois Martin, Ph.D.,[1] Federico Carminati, Ph.D.,[2] Giuliana Galli Carminati, Ph.D.[3]

[1]Laboratoire de Physique Theorique et Hautes Energies, Universites Paris 6 et 7, Place Jussieu, 75252 Paris.
[2]Physicist at CERN, Geneva, Switzerland.
[3] Mental Development Psychiatry Unit - Adult Psychiatry Service, Department of Psychiatry, University Hospitals of Geneva, Switzerland

Abstract

In this paper we describe synchronicity phenomena. As an explanation of these phenomena we propose quantum entanglement between the psychic realm known as the "unconscious" and also the classical illusion of the collapse of the wave-function. Then, taking the theory of quantum information as a model we consider the human unconscious, pre-consciousness and consciousness as sets of quantum bits (qu-bits). We analyze how there can be communication between these various qu-bit sets. In doing this we are inspired by the theory of nuclear magnetic resonance. In this manner we build quantum processes that permit consciousness to "read" the unconscious and vice-versa. The most elementary interaction, e.g. between a pre-consciousness qu-bit and a consciousness one, allows us to predict the time evolution of the pre-consciousness + consciousness system in which pre-consciousness and consciousness are quantum entangled. This time evolution exhibits Rabi oscillations that we name mental Rabi oscillations. This time evolution shows how, for example, the unconscious can influence consciousness and vice-versa. In a process like mourning the influence of the unconscious on consciousness, as the influence of consciousness on the unconscious, are in agreement with what is observed in psychiatry.

Key Words: Synchronicity, quantum entanglement, quantum information, consciousness, unconscious.

1 Synchronicity Effects

Synchronicity phenomena are characterized by a significant coincidence which appears between a (subjective) mental state and an event occurring in the (objective) external world. The notion was introduced by the Swiss psychoanalyst Carl Gustav Jung and further studied together with Wolfgang Pauli (Jung and Pauli, 1955). Jung referred to this phenomenon as "acausal parallelism" which are linked by an "acausal connecting principle." Synchronicity effects show no causal link between the two events that are correlated.

We can distinguish two types of synchronicity phenomena. The first one is characterized by a significant coincidence between the psyche of two individuals. An example of this type is when two friends at a distance simultaneously buy two identical neckties without having consulted each other beforehand. The significant coincidence appears as a correlation between the psyche of the two subjects, suggesting some type of psychic communication. There are many examples of such long range correlations between events which are causally unrelated, or subjects who engage in identical behaviors, often simultaneously: twins, relatives, members of a couple, friends, or scientists who make the same discoveries at around the same time.

For example, in March of 1951, a new comic strip appeared in over a dozen newspapers in the United States, featuring a little blond boy wearing a red and black striped shirt. The boy was called: Dennis The Menace. In the United Kingdom, a new character, a little boy wearing a red and black striped shirt was introduced in a comic book, The Beano. He was also named, Dennis The Menace. The creators of both comics claimed it was a coincidence.

The second type of synchronicity phenomena, which is closer to what was advocated by C.G. Jung, happens when the significant coincidence occurs between a mental state and a physical state. In this case the physical state is symbolically correlated to the mental state by a common meaning. They appear not necessarily simultaneously but in a short interval of time such that the coincidence appears exceptional. Jung referred to these events as "meaningful coincidences."

Another more common example goes as follows: You are sitting at home and begin thinking about an old friend who you had not seen in months, when the phone rings, and its him.

Synchronistic events between mind and matter seem difficult to explain in terms of correlations between conscious or unconscious minds. For Jung, synchronistic events are remnants of a holistic reality - the unus mundus which is based on the concept of a unified reality, a singularity of "One World" from which everything has its origin, and from which all things emerge and eventually return. The unus mundus, or "One World" is related to Plato's concept of the "World of Ideas," and has its parallels in quantum physics. Thus, the unus mundus underlies both mind and matter.

As already stressed, in a synchronicity effect, there is no causal link between correlated events localized in space and time. Synchronicity effects are global phenomena in space and time. They cannot be explained by classical physics. However, in the case of a significant coincidence appearing between the psyche of two individuals one can see an analogy with quantum entanglement (Baaquie and Martin, 2005).

Moreover one can possibly see synchronistic events between the mental and the material domains as a consequence of a quantum entanglement between mind and matter (Primas, 2003). For us mental and material domains of reality will be considered as aspects, or manifestations, of one underlying reality in which mind and matter are unseparated (Atmanspacher, 2004).

Synchronicity phenomena, especially those involving a correlation at a distance between several individuals, lead us to postulate non-localized unconscious mental states in space and time. Although different regions of the brain subserve specific functions (Joseph, 1982, 1992), mental states are not exclusively localized in the human brain. They are correlated to physical states of the brain (possibly via quantum entanglement) but they are not reducible to them.

Since we study the analogy between synchronistic events and quantum entanglement, we treat mental states (conscious and unconscious) as quantum states, i.e. as vectors of a Hilbert space (Baaquie and Martin, 2005). Moreover we treat them as vectors of a Hilbert space of information (Martin, Carminati, Galli Carminati, 2009).

2 Quantum information and the Psyche

We try to apply quantum information to some functions of the Psyche. In classical information, the memory boxes are binary system, called bits, which can take only two values: 0 or 1. A quantum bit (in a shortened form qu-bit) can take all values which are superposition of 0 and 1 (more precisely all superpositions of the states /0 > and /1 >). In other words, a qu-bit can take simultaneously the values 0 and 1. Quantum information studies the monitoring of qu-bits. It studies also the transfer of quantum information from one qu-bit to another one (especially via two-qubit quantum logic gates).

As an example of a binary psychic system we have considered the phenomenon of mourning (Galli Carminati and Carminati, 2006): either mourning is achieved (qu-bit 0), either it is not (qu-bit 1). So quantum mechanics allow the existence of all superpositions of the state in which mourning is achieved with the state in which mourning is not achieved.

Quantum mechanics rests upon two fundamental properties. First it is based on the superposition principle (superposition of vector states of an Hilbert space). Second it is based on a fundamental phenomenon called quantum entanglement. This phenomenon manifests itself by the fact that a system of two, or several, quantum entangled particles is "non-separable". In technical terms this means that the wave-function of the two-particle system does not factorize into a product of a wave-function for each particle. The quantum system describing the two particle system is a global system, a non-local one. Moreover, in such a system, the particles are heavily correlated. Therefore, if we measure a certain property of one of the two particles, destroying in this way the "non-separability" of the system, we can predict with certainty the corresponding property of the other particle, even if this one is at the other extreme of the universe. However, there are caveats: the quantum specificity indicates that this property is not determined beforehand, i.e. before measurement. Quantum physics is a non-local and non-realistic theory. Quantum entanglement and the property of "nonseparability" are properties that are fundamentally quantum, that do not exist in "classical physics".

Assuming, with Belal Baaquie (Baaquie and Martin, 2005), the existence of quantum entanglement between the unconscious of two or several persons, we have proposed an explanation of correlations at a distance that appears between two (or several) individuals having affective links. This would constitute an explanation of synchronicity of the first type. It would be interesting to measure in a quantitative manner those unconscious correlations at a distance. May be those correlations could activate neural circuits that could be visible in nuclear magnetic resonance imaging (NMRI).

We propose to measure quantitatively the existence (or the non-existence) of such correlations during group therapies or group training, via "absurd" tests (Galli et al., 2008; Martin et al., 2007, 2009). Those experiments are currently in progress.

Quantum information applied to Psyche allows to explain a certain number of mental processes (Martin, Carminati, Galli Carminati, 2009). We suppose that the mental systems first proposed by Freud (1900, 1915a,b), i.e. the unconscious, pre-consciousness, consciousness, are made up of mental qu-bits. They are sets of mental qu-bits.

Specifically, Freud (1900, 1915ab), saw the mind as consisting of three mental realms; the unconscious, preconscious, and conscious mind, with the unconscious being the deepest, most inaccessible region of the psyche and which contains repressed memories and unacceptable feelings, thoughts, and ideas. The preconscious serves as a bridge, or passageway between the unconscious and conscious mind, and lies just below the surface of consciousness. Freud believed that unconscious impulses must pass through the preconscious which acts as a double doorway; one door leading from the unconscious to the preconscious, and the other from the preconscious to the conscious mind. In this way, the preconscious can censor information and prevent unacceptable impulses and ideas from becoming conscious. However, the preconscious is also the depository of information which has been pushed out of consciousness, and which may be shoved so deeply underground, so to speak, that the information becomes completely unconscious. Therefore, although separated, these mental realms interact and can influence one another.

Inspired by the theory of nuclear magnetic resonance (NMR), we have built a model of handling a mental qu-bit with the help of pulses of a mental field. Starting with an elementary interaction between two qu-bits we build two-qubit quantum logic gates that allow information to be transferred from one qu-bit to the other. For example, we build the controlled-NOT (CNOT) gate in which, under certain circumstances, the information is transferred from the control qu-bit to the target qu-bit. We also build swapping in which there is a complete exchange of information between two qu-bits. In those manners we build quantum processes that permit consciousness to "read" the unconscious and vice-versa. The most elementary interaction, e.g. between a pre-consciousness qu-bit and a consciousness one, allows us to predict the time evolution of the pre-consciousness + consciousness system in which pre-consciousness and consciousness are quantum entangled. This time evolution exhibits Rabi oscillations that we name mental Rabi oscillations. This time evolution shows how, for example, the unconscious can influence consciousness and vice-versa.

The pulses of the mental field can be emitted either by consciousness (effects of will or freewill) or by the unconscious (individual, group or collective). As we said, together with quantum entanglement, they can explain the awareness of unconscious components. In this case we can say that consciousness measures the unconscious like an experimental physics device records a microscopic process. As we said, quantum entanglement explains also the influence of the unconscious on consciousness and the reciprocal influence of consciousness on the unconscious. We have studied these two types of influences in the case of mourning and we have seen how they could allow mourning to be achieved with time.

A third mental process, already mentionned above, is the quantum entanglement between two (or several) unconscious psyches. The evolution in time of the state of the two quantum entangled unconscious shows the reciprocal influence of each unconscious on the other one. Then through the interaction of their two unconscious, a psychoanalyst named Alice can help Bob to achieve relief from his mourning.

The fundamental characteristic of the most elementary interaction between two mental qubits, e.g. between a qu-bit of pre-consciousness and a qu-bit of consciousness, is to highlight, as a function of time, oscillations between two quantum states made of two correlated qu-bits; i.e. the states /I1 > /C0 > and /C1 > /I0 > (I for "Insight" or pre-consciousness and C for "Consciousness").

Let us notice that at the level of the brain, there is evidence of an alternating activity of the two hemispheres (Joseph 1982, 1988). This oscillation expresses itself in the phenomenon of binocular rivalry (Blake, 1989). When two images are presented to each of the two eyes of a subject, they enter in "competition" so that one image is visible while the other is not. The same happens when the subject is presented with two superposed images, a nice metaphor to represent the superposition of two quantum states.

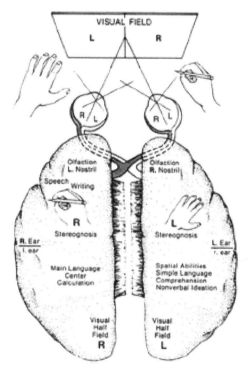

The Right and Left Hemisphere

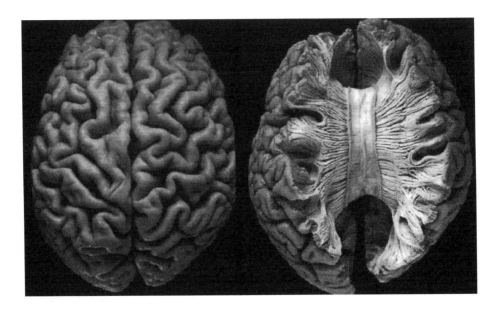

Joseph (1982, 1988) proposed that this oscillating activity and the different functions controlled by the right and left half of the brain, could explain some mental phenomenon associated with the conscious and unconscious mind, with the corpus callosum, a major cord of nerves, linking the two brain halves and thus acting as a bridge between these two mental realms. This is similar to Freud's concept of the preconscious linking the conscious and unconscious mind. Further, Joseph (1982, 1988) linked this oscillating activity to dream recall vs dream forgetting, with the right hemisphere (the domain of visual-spatial imagery and social-emotion) producing the dream during high levels of oscillating activity, and the left (the domain of language and verbal thought) forgetting the dream due to low levels of activity.

Mental (Rabi) oscillations are still to be studied. In particular in the case of the "asleep" consciousness, the unconscious + consciousness system (or at least a part of this system) constantly oscillates between the states $/U1 > /C0 >$ and $/C1 > /U0 >$. A pendulum does not measure time. For this we need a system that keeps the memory of the number of the oscillations of the pendulum. This is a function of a clock, which measures time. In a clock the oscillations of the pendulum have a cumulative effect that allows us to keep the memory of the number of oscillations. In the case of the Rabi oscillations of the unconscious (pre-consciousness)+ consciousness system, we have to imagine a system, correlated to the first one, that is subject to cumulative effects and that allows to memorize the mental Rabi oscillations. In this case, it is only thanks to the storage of the mental Rabi oscillations that consciousness or preconsciousness or the unconscious can be modified.

At the level of the brain this memorization can be actuated by the limbic system, and in particular by the hippocampus (Joseph 1992). To be more specific, the limbic system is the domain of our emotions, and is classically associated with the "four F's:" feeding, fighting, fleeing, and sexual behavior. The amygdala and the hippocampus are some of the main structures of the limbic system, with the amygdala playing a major role in emotional memory, and the hippocampus in storing non-emotional memories. So, in some respects, the limbic system could be compared to the unconscious (Joseph 1992). The limbic system is part of the old brain, and is buried beneath the new brain, which consists of "new cortex," i.e. neocortex. It is the neocortex, particularly that of the left hemisphere, which we associate with human thought, language, rational behavior, and the conscious mind. However, it is the limbic system and the right hemisphere which become most active during dream-sleep (Joseph 1988, 1992).

For an asleep consciousness the perturbations coming from the environment are weak. In these conditions, the mental Rabi oscillations may extend over a time that can be long, probably of the order of several minutes, or more. The situation is totally different for an awaken consciousness. Its interaction with the environment, which operates via the sensory system, perturbs the interaction between pre-consciousness and consciousness and therefore interferes with the oscillations that, as a consequence, cannot last very long. The time for the awaken consciousness to receive an external stimulus being of the order of half a second. The Rabi mental oscillations cannot last more than that.

From a neurological perspective, this can be explained as follows: During dream sleep the left half of the brain is at a low level of activity and it cannot perceive or respond to outside sensory impressions unless they are sufficiently arousing they trigger wakefulness. By contrast, because the right half of the brain and limbic system are at a high level of unconscious-activity during dream-sleep, they can respond to external stimuli (Joseph 1982, 1988). This explains how external stimuli can become incorporated into a dream. A typical example, the dreamer is walking down a strange street when a little boy on a bike rides by ringing a bell. The bell is so loud the dreamer wakes up to discover the alarm clock is ringing. However, upon achieving full awake consciousness, the awake-consciousness may forget the dream; that is, the awake part of the psyche (the left hemisphere) forgets the dream which may remain stored in the limbic system of the right hemisphere. However, later that day, the awake dreamer sees a little boy on a bike ringing his handle-bar bell, and the awake dreamer experiences synchronicity; he remembers his dream.

This same framework can be applied to individuals who engage in the same behaviors. They may respond, unconsciously, to the same stimuli which, for a variety of reasons may not be perceived by the conscious mind. Moreover, these unconscious realms are more closely attuned to the collective unconscious and most probably to the unus mundus, the unified reality from which everything has its origin, and from which all things emerge. Although not perceived by the conscious mind, the unconscious does respond, and then influences the conscious mind of different individuals, who then engage in the same behaviors or come up with the same thoughts or ideas.

3 Conclusions

In summary, some mental phenomena are not explainable in the framework of what we call "classical" mechanics. Let us cite, among others, the phenomenon of awareness, the correlations at a distance between individuals, and more generally the synchronicity phenomena. These three types of phenomena can be explained in the framework of quantum mechanics, particularly, thanks to quantum entanglement for the correlations at a distance between individuals (synchronicity phenomena of type I) and thanks to what we can call the classical illusion of the collapse of the wave-function for the synchronicity phenomena of type II.

Let us notice that the existence of synchronicity phenomena prevents the mental states to be reducible to physical states of the brain. The mental states are correlated to such states, probably via quantum entanglement, but they are not reducible to those states. Therefore this invalidates the materialistic hypothesis.

The projection of our subjectivity in the environment in which we live (synchronicity phenomena of type II), in agreement with quantum mechanics, refutes the local hypothesis ("each individual is in his parcel of space-time") as well as the realistic hypothesis ("the object has a reality well defined independent of the subject who observes it").

As an end let us mention a quantum effect that can have important consequences in mental phenomena, for example for awareness (for the emergence of consciousness). It is the Bose- Einstein condensation, in which each particle looses its individuality in favour of a collective, global behaviour.

References

Atmanspacher, H. (2004). Quantum theory and consciousness: an overview with selected exam- ples, Discrete Dynamics in Nature and Society, 1, 51-73 (2004)

Baaquie, B.E., and Martin, F. (2005). Quantum Psyche - Quantum Field Theory of the Human Psyche, NeuroQuantology, 3, 7-42.

Blake, R. (1989). A neural theory of binocular rivalry, Psychological Review, 96, 145-167

Freud, S. (1900). The Interpretation of Dreams. Standard Edition, 5, 339-622.

Freud, S. (1915a). Repression. Standard Edition, 14, 141-158.

Freud, S. (1915b). Repression. Standard Edition, 14, 159-204.

Galli Carminati, G., and Martin, F. (2008). Quantum mechanics and the Psyche, Physics of Particles and Nuclei, Vol. 39, 560-577.

Galli Carminati, G., and Carminati, F. (2006). The mechanism of mourning: an anti-entropic mechanism, NeuroQuantology Journal, 4, 186-197.

Joseph, R. (1982). The Neuropsychology of Development. Hemispheric Laterality, Limbic Language, the Origin of Thought. Journal of Clinical Psychology, 44, 4-33.

Joseph, R. (1988). The Right Cerebral Hemisphere: Emotion, Music, Visual-Spatial Skills, Body Image, Dreams, and Awareness. Journal of Clinical Psychology, 44, 630-673.

Joseph, R. (1992). The Limbic System: Emotion, Laterality, and Unconscious Mind. The Psychoanalytic Review, 79, 405-456.

Jung, C. G., and Pauli, W. (1955). The Interpretation of Nature and the Psyche, Pantheon, New York, translated by P. Silz (1955); german original: Natureklarung und Psyche, Rascher, Zurich (1952).

Martin, F., and Galli Carminati, G. (2007). Synchronicity, Quantum Mechanics and Psyche, talk given at the Conference on "Wolfgang Pauli's Philosophical Ideas and Contemporary Science", May 20-25, 2007, Monte Verita, Ascona, Zwitzerland; published in Recasting Reality, pp. 227-243, Springer-Verlag, (2009).

Martin, F., Carminati, F., and Galli Carminati, G. (2009). Quantum information, oscillations and the Psyche, to be published in Physics of Particles and Nuclei (2009).

Primas, H. (2003). Time-Entanglement Between Mind and Matter, Mind and Matter, Vol. 1, 81-119.

Speculations about the Direct Effects of Intention on Physical Manifestation

Imants Barušs, Ph.D.

Department of Psychology, King's University College at
The University of Western Ontario, London, Ontario, Canada

Abstract

A possible mechanism by which mental acts may be synchronized with physical states is postulated. It is argued that a layer of deep consciousness, similar to David Bohm's implicate order, underlies and gives rise to both subjective, intentional consciousness and objective, physical manifestation. The influence of volition at the level of intentional consciousness can be conceptualized in the context of the Kochen-Specker theorem as the exercise of the unconstrained choice of observables, and, at the level of deep consciousness, as modulation of the activity of the creation and annihilation operators of a quantum field. The discrete nature of observations in quantum theory leads to the notion of a flicker universe in which temporal continuity of physical structures is maintained by morphic fields.

keywords: consciousness, quantum fields, Kochen-Specker theorem, flicker universe, morphic fields

In order to try to find a mechanism for the direct effects of intention on physical manifestation, I want to bring together four ideas, namely, the primacy of consciousness; the activity of a quantum field; the notion of a flicker universe; and the significance of morphic fields. Let me explain each of these in the sections below after first giving some basis for taking seriously the idea that intention can have direct effects on physical manifestation.

1. Direct Effects of Intention on Physical Manifestation

Over the course of the past 75 years (Radin, 1997), there has been a gradual accumulation of empirical evidence in support of a direct connection between mentally expressed intention and physical manifestation. Much of this research has been done using random event generators (REGs) in laboratory settings (e.g., Jahn and Dunne, 2005). Even when overall effects of intention are not found or are small in size, there are meaningful secondary characteristics in the database revealing the apparent agency of the participant (e.g., Jahn et al., 2000). Large scale effects have been noted under a variety of conditions. For instance, such was the case in the Scole experiment, in which physical manifestation mediums ostensibly communicated with the deceased. Various markings, including drawings and writing in a variety of languages, were found on unopened rolls of photographic film that had been brought to the sessions by independent investigators (Keen, Ellison, and Fontana, 1999). In another case, Ted Owens, whom Jeffrey Mishlove investigated over the course of a decade, successfully produced or predicted anomalous events at least 75 times that had less than one percent probability of occurrence. For example, Owens could apparently direct lightning strikes to locations requested by others (Mishlove, 2000).

There have also been instances of healing that seem to not have followed ordinary biological processes. This would include the remission of cancer in mice following the "laying on of hands"(Bengston and Krinsley, 2000) and cases of spontaneous healing of those who had visited Lourdes (Gesler, 1996). More recently, dramatic changes in physical manifestation have been claimed for Matrix Energetics (ME), a system of transformation and healing developed by Richard Bartlett. For example, Barlett has cited cases of both people and animals in which broken bones have instantaneously healed at least sufficiently to restore function (Bartlett, 2007, 2009). In a formal study of distance healing using techniques derived from ME that I initiated, one of my participants correctly wondered whether I were doing a healing session for her without knowing until afterwards that I had actually been doing so at the time. She said that the distress that she had been feeling had dissipated and that she had felt as though she had been "effortlessly lifted from a state of low energy to a higher more harmonious state." There have been several summaries of evidence for these sorts of phenomena in trade books (e.g., Radin, 1997; McTaggart, 2007). While continuing to be controversial, there is sufficient empirical evidence at this time to take seriously the notion that direct effects of intention on physical manifestation exist.

2. The Primacy of Consciousness

The conventional research programs for understanding consciousness as an emergent property of neurological or information-processing systems have failed to deliver. For example, as one of the developers of functionalist cognitive theories has said, "I would have thought that the last forty or fifty years have demonstrated pretty clearly that there are aspects of higher mental processes into which the current armamentarium of computational models, theories, and experimental techniques offers vanishingly little insight" (Fodor, 2000, p. 2). The hard problem of consciousness, namely, to give an account of why consciousness is conscious (Eccles, 1966), remains intractable (Chalmers, 2007). This suggests that consciousness is ontologically an additional element to matter — or that matter itself is a byproduct of consciousness (Baruss, 2008; Chalmers, 2003). So much quantum weirdness has been uncovered since the end of the nineteenth century that matter no longer resembles our naive intuitions about its nature. "It seems more than time to recognize that quantum entities are neither waves nor particles" (Lévy-Leblond, 1988, p. 20). Matter has literally disappeared, given that elementary particles have no spatial extension. (Otherwise it would seem reasonable to suppose that they would blow up to galactic sizes in expanding spacetimes (cf. Mukhanov and Winitzki, 2007). This opens the possibility that matter could be a particular manifestation of consciousness, a position that has been receiving increasing support (e.g., Pfeiffer and Mack, 2007) and one which I adopt here.

In considering the phenomenological structure of consciousness, two distinct aspects of consciousness can be identified. I have called these subjective consciousness$_2$ and consciousness$_3$.

Subjective consciousness$_2$ refers to the stream of subjective experience characterized by intentionality, whereas consciousness$_3$ is the sense of existence of the subject of mental acts. This is essentially the distinction between the contents of experience and the feeling of experience going on at all (Baruss, 1987). This suggests a natural stratification of consciousness. From a phenomenological perspective, the sense of existence appears to be a prerequisite for any specific existents in the sense that without existence there are no existents. In other words, for there to be contents of experience, there must be experience in the first place. Insofar as transcendent states of consciousness can occur apparently without objective contents (Foreman, 1998) and without objects or a subject (Merrell-Wolff, 1994; 1995), consciousness3 can be thought of as a gateway for an ontologically primitive layer of consciousness that underlies the experiences of the ordinary waking state. I have also called this deeper layer of consciousness deep consciousness (Baruss, 2008).

Perhaps the clearest characterization of deep consciousness is given by

Franklin Wolff's description of consciousness-without-an-object-and-with-out-a-subject, which occurred for Wolff after he turned the stream of outgoing consciousness, so to speak, back to its source. That source, as I conceptualize it, is just consciousness$_3$, the presence of the self. But, upon achieving that reorientation, the distinction between the subject and the object disappeared, leaving Wolff in a fluid realm identified with all that exists (Barušs, 2007; Merrell-Wolff, 1994, 1995). Such non-dual consciousness, in some cases accessed through consciousness$_3$, is what I mean by deep consciousness.

David Bohm suggested that underlying both consciousness and physical manifestation is an implicate order from which both emerge (Bohm, 1983). To my mind, but without accepting Bohm's quantum formalism (Bohm & Hiley, 1993), the implicate order is deep consciousness as well as being the prephysical substrate from which physical manifestation emerges. Volition, at the level of subjective consciousness$_2$ invokes deep consciousness which gives shape to physical manifestation. Or, to put it perhaps more precisely, subjective consciousness$_2$ is synchronized with deep consciousness. Such a mechanism is consistent with Robert Jahn and Brenda Dunne's M^5 model, which itself is supported by the empirical REG evidence (Jahn and Dunne, 2001). And we thereby have a way of conceptualizing the primacy of consciousness.

3. A Little Quantum Field Theory

It seems to me that the most obvious access point within quantum theory for the effects of intention on physical manifestation would be given by the Kochen-Specker theorem, which addresses the consequences of assuming that physical variables have definite values prior to their selection for measurement. Indeed, one way of understanding the theorem is to say that either physical variables have no values before the observables to be measured are selected or that contextuality exists.

Contextuality refers to the idea that the values measured for observables would differ depending upon which other observables were also being measured (Kochen & Specker, 1967). Quantum theory itself does not appear to determine the selection of observables, so that there is room for human intention to act in choosing which of them is to be measured. Henry Stapp, without reference to the Kochen-Specker theorem, uses this as the insertion point for volition in his quantum mind theory (Stapp, 2004, 2007, 2009). Another strategy has been to suppose that intention affects stochastic processes, thereby, in effect, removing actual randomness. Variations of this can be found in the work of Jean Burns (2002), Evan Harris-Walker (1970, 1977, 2000), and Amit Goswami (Goswami, Reed and Goswami, 1993).

In light of such deliberations, let us consider the quantum fluctuations of a quantum field, such as the Klein-Gordon Field on curved spacetime given by:

$$\left(\frac{1}{\sqrt{-\det[g_{\mu\nu}(x)]}} \frac{\partial}{\partial x^{\mu}} g^{\mu\nu}(x) \sqrt{-\det[g_{\mu\nu}(x)]} \frac{\partial}{\partial x^{\nu}} + m^2 \right) \hat{\Phi}(x,t) = 0$$

where Φ represents a scalar quantum field, all other symbols have their usual quantum-theoretic meanings, and Einstein summation convention is being used. Solutions of the appropriate equations of motion yield:

$$\hat{\Phi}(x,t) = \sum_{k} \left(u_k(x,t) a_k + u_k^*(x,t) a_k^+ \right)$$

where the u_k are complex number-valued mode functions, the a_k and a_k^+ are annihilation and creation operators respectively, and the remaining symbols all have their usual meanings. The idea is that volition could be acting through the creation and annihilation operators thereby affecting the number of particles in the appropriate Fock space representing physical manifestation. And, through backreaction, spacetime curvature would change as given by the Einstein equation:

$$R_{\mu\nu}(x) - \tfrac{1}{2} g_{\mu\nu}(x) R(x) + \Lambda g_{\mu\nu}(x) = -8\pi G T_{\mu\nu}(x)$$

where x is a position 4-vector, T_{uv} is the energy-momentum tensor, and the remaining symbols all have their usual meanings (mathematical text based on Kempf, 2008).

4. A Flicker Universe

As I have noted previously, in collapse-type quantum mind theories, the supposition is made that whatever collapses the state vector during measurement in formal experiments in subatomic physics must carry over to the activity of individual people experiencing the reality that they do (Baruss, 2008). The idea is that it is unreasonable to suppose that quantum events can distinguish between the irreversible acts of amplification associated with formal experimentation and everyday observation (Baruss, 1986) and that, hence, they must occur informally for everyone. That means that whatever process collapses the state vector, including any decoherence mechanisms, must be extracted from the notion of observation in the context of subatomic experimentation and applied to the situation of everyday life. And whatever that process is, it cannot just occur once in a while, but must be ongoing. The watched pot never boils theorem states that a quantum system cannot change if it is being continuously observed (Sudbery, 1986), so that these volitional acts of observation must be closely-spaced, iterated, discrete ones. For Henry Stapp, the time-scale of intentional acts is of the order of tens of milliseconds (Stapp, 2007). If, by the Kochen-Specker theorem, observables cannot have fixed values before they are selected for observation, and acts of observation are discrete, then is there anything physically present at all between observations? On a positivist interpretation, the answer is no.

One of the characteristics of transcendent experiences is their noetic quality (Baruš, 2003). And, while we can, of course, question the validity of knowledge stemming from altered states of consciousness, nonetheless it can be fruitful to examine some of the contentions arrived at therein. John Wren-Lewis said of his transcendent experience that ". . . what I perceive with my eyes and other senses is a whole world that seems to be coming fresh-minted into existence moment by moment" (Wren-Lewis, 1988, p. 116). The idea is that perhaps the universe flickers, such that the implicate order re-mains, but its explication as the experiential stream and physical manifesta-tion is constantly being constructed and deconstructed. With regard to the latter, it is not just that the substance of physical manifestation appears and disappears but, given the Einstein equation, so do space (cf. Aerts & Aerts, 2005) and time, as we ordinarily conceptualize them. I have proposed, from the point of view of physical manifestation in spacetime, that the flicker rate could be once per Planck time. Following Jack Ng (2003), we can conceptual-ize a spacetime lattice (with Planck length spacelike separation and Planck time timelike separation) which, in effect, disappears between explications of the implicate order (Baruš, 2008).

William James famously proposed that, for all that there appear to be breaks in them, our thoughts are actually not like a train but, rather, continu-ous as a stream (James, 1890/1983). Reversing James's metaphor, we could say that, because our experience flickers along with physical manifestation, what appears to be a continuous stream is actually more like a train whose individual boxcars become blurred as they occur for us as intentional mental acts.

5. Morphic Fields

From a conventional point of view, the usual problem is to understand how the mind can affect a physically closed material system made up of con-tinuously existent matter. Now the inverse problem presents itself, namely, if physical manifestation flickers on and off, what provides for any continuity at all between its iterations? The answer might lie in the notion of morphic fields, patterns that are not themselves physical, but that physical manifestation follows (Sheldrake, 1988). These can also be regarded as thoughtforms, using more psychological terminology (Barušs, 1996). There is some empirical evidence for the existence of such fields (Sheldrake, 1988). The idea is that the morphic fields are present at the level of the prephysical substrate from whence they shape physical spacetime manifestation. And they can be not only selected, but also created, by volition acting at the level of deep consciousness. Hence, while in the nonmanifest state, a selection of a different morphic field can be made, resulting instantaneously in a different physical outcome through the activity represented by the creation and annihilation operators. This could account for some of the more dramatic instances of radical transformation described in the first section of this paper.

6. Conclusion

There are, of course, many unanswered questions. One is the relation of the flicker rate to changeable rates of observational acts and the consequent timing of intention. My guess would be that intention, at the level of deep consciousness, persists across iterations of the universe, but that changes in intention could be registered within a single Planck time between instances of manifestation. However, intention expressed within the experiential stream of subjective consciousness$_2$ could require longer time periods to synchronize with deep consciousness. But this just raises the problem of the relationship of subjective consciousness$_2$ to deep consciousness and the degree to which it can function autonomously from deep consciousness. My sense is that subjective consciousness$_2$ does not exist on its own, but that its functioning could be largely synchronized with the same "automatic" mechanisms that support morphic fields and only sometimes coincide with creative volitional acts that manipulate the automatic processes. It is also possible that this scheme is too simple and that the mechanisms that maintain the "laws" and patterns of physical manifestation do not stem from the same domain as intentional acts. In particular, creative volitional acts could stem from a deeper level of reality than the automatic processes that sustain morphic fields (cf. Barušs, 1996). Of course, an even more basic concern is the extent to which these speculations can hold up to a more thorough examination of the empirical evidence than that to which allusion has been made in this paper. All that I have done here is to try to suggest a mechanism to account for the empirical observation that intention can apparently directly affect physical manifestation.

Acknowledgements: I thank the editors of the Journal of Cosmology for an invitation to submit a paper, Shannon Foskett for assisting with writing and editing, David Meredith for his comments about the quantum-theoretic text, and King's University College for a research grant that was used for its preparation.

References

Aerts, D., and Aerts, S. (2005). Towards a general operational and realistic framework for quantum mechanics and relativity theory. In: Elitzur, S., Dolev, S., and Kolenda, N. (Eds.). Quo Vadis Quantum Mechanics? Springer, Berlin, Germany. pp. 153–207.

Bartlett, R. (2007). Matrix Energetics: The Science and Art of Transformation: A Hands-on Guide to Subtle Energy and Radical Change. Atria, New York, US.

Bartlett, R. (2009). The Physics of Miracles: Tapping Into the Field of Consciousness Potential. Atria, New York, US.

Baruss, I. (1986). Quantum mechanics and human consciousness. Physics in Canada, 42(1), 3–5.

Baruss, I. (1987). Metanalysis of definitions of consciousness. Imagination, Cognition and Personality, 6(4), 321–329.

Baruss, I. (1996). Authentic Knowing: The Convergence of Science and Spiritual Aspiration. Purdue University Press, West Lafayette, US.

Baruss, I. (2003). Alterations of Consciousness: An Empirical Analysis for Social Scientists. American Psychological Association, Washington, US.

Baruss, I. (2007). Science as a Spiritual Practice. Exeter, UK: Imprint Academic.

Baruss, I. (2008). Characteristics of consciousness in collapse-type quantum mind theories. Journal of Mind and Behavior, 29(3), 255–265.

Bengston, W. F. & Krinsley, D. (2000). The effect of the "laying on of hands" on transplanted breast cancer in mice. Journal of Scientific Exploration, 14(3), 353–364.

Bohm, D. (1983). Wholeness and the Implicate Order. Ark, London, UK.

Bohm, D., and Hiley, B. J. (1993). The Undivided Universe: An Ontological Interpretation of Quantum Theory. Routledge, London, UK.

Burns, J. E. (2002). Quantum fluctuations and the action of the mind. Noetic Journal, 3(4), 312–317.

Chalmers, D. (2003). Consciousness and its place in nature. In: S. Stich & F. Warfield (Eds.), The Blackwell Guide to Philosophy of Mind. Blackwell, Boston, US.

Chalmers, D. (2007). The hard problem of consciousness. In: M. Velmans & S. Schneider (Eds.), The Blackwell Companion to Consciousness, Blackwell, Malden, US, pp. 225–235.

Eccles, J. C. (Ed.). (1966). Brain and Conscious Experience: Study Week September 28 to October 4, 1964, of the Pontificia Academia Scientiarum. Springer-Verlag, New York, US.

Fodor, J. (2000). The Mind Doesn't Work That Way: The Scope and Limits of Computational Psychology. MIT Press, Cambridge, US.

Forman, R. K. C. (1998). What does mysticism have to teach us about consciousness? Journal of Consciousness Studies, 5(2), 185–201.

Gesler, W. (1996). Lourdes: Healing in a place of pilgrimage. Health & Place, 2 (2), 95–105.

Goswami, A., Reed, R. E., and Goswami, M. (1993). The Self-Aware Universe: How Consciousness Creates the Material World. Jeremy P. Tarcher, New York, US.

Jahn, R. G., & Dunne, B. J. (2001). A modular model of mind/matter manifestations (M5). Journal of Scientific Exploration, 15, 299–329.

Jahn, R. G., & Dunne, B. J. (2005). The PEAR proposition. Journal of Scientific Exploration, 19(2), 195–245.

Jahn, R., Dunne, B., Bradish, G., Dobyns, Y., Lettieri, A., Nelson, R., Mischo, J., Boller, E., Bösch, H., Vaitl, D., Houtkooper, J., & Walter, B. (2000). Mind/machine interaction consortium: PortREG replication experiments. Journal of Scientific Exploration, 14(4), 499–555.

James, W. (1983). The Principles of Psychology. Cambridge, MA: Harvard University Press. (Original work published 1890).

Keen, M., Ellison, A, & Fontana, D. (1999). The Scole report: An account of an investigation into the genuineness of a range of physical phenomena associated with a mediumistic group in Norfolk, England. Proceedings of the Society for Psychical Research, 58 (Pt. 220), 149–392.

Lévy-Leblond, J.-M. (1988). Neither waves, nor particles, but quantons. Nature, 334, 19–20.

Kempf, A. (2008). Applied Mathematics 872: Quantum Field Theory for Cosmology: Lecture Notes. University of Waterloo, Waterloo, Canada.

Kochen, S. & Specker, E. P. (1967). The problem of hidden variables in quantum mechanics. Journal of Mathematics and Mechanics, 17(1), 59–87.

McTaggart, L. (2007). The Intention Experiment: Using your Thoughts to Change Your Life and the World. Free Press: New York, US.

Merrell-Wolff, F. (1994). Franklin Merrell-Wolff's Experience and Philosophy: A Personal Record of Transformation and a Discussion of Transcendental Consciousness. State University of New York Press, Albany, US.

Merrell-Wolff, F. (1995). Transformations in Consciousness: The Metaphysics and Epistemology. State University of New York Press, Albany, US.

Mishlove, J. (2000). The PK Man: A True Story of Mind over Matter. Hampton Roads Publishing Company, Charlottesville, US.

Mukhanov, V. F. & Winitzki, S. (2007). Introduction to Quantum Effects in Gravity. Cambridge University Press, Cambridge, UK.

Ng, Y. J. (2003). Selected topics in Planck-scale physics. Modern Physics Letters A, 18, 1073–1097.

Pfeiffer, T. & Mack, J. E. (Eds.). (2007). Mind Before Matter: Visions of a New Science of Consciousness. O Books, Winchester, UK.

Radin, D. I. (1997). The Conscious Universe: The Scientific Truth of Psychic Phenomena. HarperEdge, New York, US.

Sheldrake, R. (1988). The Presence of the Past: Morphic Resonance and the Habits of Nature. Times Books, New York, US.

Stapp, H. P. (2004). Mind, Matter and Quantum Mechanics (second edition). Springer, Berlin, Germany.

Stapp, H. P. (2007). The Mindful Universe. Springer, Berlin, Germany.

Stapp, H.P. (2009). Quantum Reality and Mind. Journal of Cosmology, 3, 570-579.

Sudbery, A. (1986). Quantum Mechanics and the Particles of Nature: An Outline for Mathematicians. Cambridge University Press, Cambridge, US.

Walker, E.H. (1970). The nature of consciousness. Mathematical Biosciences 7, 131–178.

Walker, E.H. (1977). Quantum mechanical tunneling in synaptic and ephaptic transmission. International Journal of Quantum Chemistry, 11, 103–127.

Walker, E.H. (2000). The Physics of Consciousness: Quantum Minds and the Meaning of Life. Perseus, Cambridge, US.

Wren-Lewis, J. (1988). The darkness of God: A personal report on consciousness transformation through an encounter with death. Journal of Humanistic Psychology, 28, 105–122.

Consciousness and Quantum Measurement: New Empirical Data

York H. Dobyns, Ph.D.

Department of Electrical Engineering, Engineering Quadrangle, Princeton University, Princeton, New Jersey 08544

Abstract

The quantum measurement problem remains mysterious, with multiple interpretations of the formalism making different assumptions about its nature. The various interpretations also make very different assumptions about the role of consciousness in this transition from superposed probabilities to definite observed events. Some regard it as completely irrelevant, some regard consciousness as essential to complete the transition, and at least one speculative model identifies this transition as the key physical substrate of consciousness itself. Because of this problematic status for consciousness in the physical theory of quantum mechanics, it seems noteworthy that recently published experimental work reports that a specific state of human consciousness has been observed to disrupt remotely the spatial superposition of photon states in a Michelson interferometer, detectably reducing the level of interference between the two beam paths. This suggests that, at the very least, the instrument is serving as a remote detector for the brain state corresponding to the experimentally induced state of consciousness. Moreover, further experimental work in this genre may shed important light on the physical properties of human consciousness and their relation to quantum measurement.

KEY WORDS: Consciousness; Conscious States; Quantum Measurement; Quantum Observation; Interferometry

1. Basics of The Quantum Measurement Problem

It is presumably well-known that the process by which the probability densities computed from quantum theory are converted into definite observational facts remains profoundly mysterious. The conceptual model of this process depends entirely on the interpretation of quantum mechanics favored by the analysts. The role and relevance of consciousness in this process varies enormously among interpretations. Some would regard the process as essentially irrelevant to consciousness except to the extent that it is part of the physical world in which humans and their minds exist. One example of such a view is seen in the "many worlds" or "many views of one world" interpretation (Everett, 1957; Squires, 1987). In this model, both an experiment and its conscious observer continue a deterministic evolution according to the equations of quantum mechanics and there is no probabilistic transition to definite outcomes; the appearance of such a transition to observers is essentially an illusion arising from the fact that the observing instrument correlates each state of the quantum system with a state of the observer that corresponds to having observed the particular quantum state in question, rather than the entire superposition. Other theories argue that so-called wave function collapse is an actual physical process proceeding independently of observation or measurement as such; classical objects composed of huge numbers of quantum particles spontaneously maintain themselves in classical states regardless of anyone's observations (Ghirardi et al. 1986; Joos et al. 2003). In contrast, the view championed by Wigner and various others holds that conscious observation is the fundamental cause of the transition from probabilities to definite outcomes (Von Neumann, 1955; Wigner, 1963, 1964; Stapp, 2001). In general, those holding this view contend that no observation has actually been made until some conscious being has become aware of the results. It is interesting to note that a fundamental relationship between consciousness and quantum measurement is also required by a view almost diametrically opposed to the Wignerian approach. In the speculative model of Penrose, quantum measurement or "wave function collapse" is viewed as a strictly physical process, but this process is fundamental to the existence of consciousness, and only systems that can maintain certain kinds of quantum superposition and collapse them in particular ways are capable of being conscious (Penrose, 1989, 1994).

One of the most commonly used experimental tools for examining quantum superposition and its breakdown is some form of the Mach-Zehnder interferometer, in which a light beam is split into separate paths and then reunited at another beam splitter. By suitably chosen geometry it is possible to arrange that the reunited beam interferes with itself. Such interference can take place only if the individual quanta of the split beam are free to propagate in a superposed state along both paths between the initial and final beam splitters. If a "which-way" measurement intervenes to establish which branch of the apparatus contains a particular photon, the interference at the final beam splitter is lost, a fact that can be established by the detection of a change in the normal interference pattern. An important point is that interference is destroyed by the mere existence of apparatus capable of performing a which-way measurement, whether or not it actually measures anything. As dramatized by the "Elitzur-Vaidman bomb test" thought experiment, the presence of a photon detector in one branch of the interferometer destroys interference even if it fails to detect anything because the photon traveled through the other branch (Elitzur and Vaidman, 1993). This can, of course, be viewed as a simple instance of the general principle that experiments on quantum objects examine only the properties they are designed to examine. An interferometer with a photon detector embedded in one branch of the light path is, by construction, an instrument for establishing which way the initial beam splitter directed the incident photon, and naturally cannot generate interference effects downstream of the detector. The general properties of the Mach-Zehnder interferometer and its sensitivity to which-way measurements are central to the following discussion.

2. Empirical Data Involving Consciousness

When considering the role of consciousness in the physical universe, physicists are somewhat handicapped by the fact that their traditional experimental techniques do not involve human beings as part of the apparatus, or even as subjects of inquiry. Such tests are generally considered to be part of other fields of science. Moreover, specific inquiries regarding consciousness are seldom useful or informative from a physical-science perspective because of the techniques necessarily used in the so-called "soft" sciences such as psychology, although in recent years there has been considerable input to such studies from allied fields such as neurophysiology.

It is therefore unsurprising that experiments in relatively remote and unfamiliar fields gather little notice in the physics literature even on those occasions when they do have significant implications for physics. Nevertheless, these investigations sometimes produce data that are relevant to fundamental physical theories. Since theoretical predictions must be checked against observational data, it seems inappropriate to ignore such data even when they come from unexpected sources.

The particular data in question come from experiments using a Michelson interferometer, which can be considered as a Mach-Zehnder interferometer in which the light paths are overlaid by reflection so that the same beam splitter can be used both to separate and to reunite the beams. It was found that human subjects were apparently able to perform a limited which-way measurement despite the absence of conventional detection apparatus in the light path (Radin 2008). This experiment was a refinement and extension of earlier experimental work by other researchers that had shown mixed and inconclusive results (Jeffers and Sloan, 1992; Ibison and Jeffers, 1998). It is a noteworthy feature of all these investigations that no attempt was made to evaluate the human subjects' success in actually acquiring which-way information; the existence of a which-way measurement was inferred from its physical effects on an interference pattern. While it might seem peculiar to design an interferometry experiment around a human subject's cognitive state, the primary hypothesis was derived from speculations about human capabilities which, while controversial, are supported by an extensive technical literature (Pratt et al. 1940; Rhine, 1971; Targ and Puthoff, 1974; Parker, 1975; Honorton, 1977; Tart et al. 1979; Bem and Honorton 1994; May, 1996; Brown, 2005). For consideration of the physical nature of consciousness the most interesting thing about this experiment is not the history leading to the adoption of its design, but the fact that it seems to have shown detectable physical consequences of a human subject's mental state in a physically separated, isolated, and shielded experimental system.

A brief overview of the Radin (2008) experimental report is necessary before discussion of its theoretical implications can proceed. The primary empirical finding is that a particular state of consciousness induced by human subjects had the effect of performing a which-way measurement, albeit one with fairly low quantum efficiency, on a nearby Michelson interferometer, which was shielded against electromagnetic interference and vibration. (The report's methodology section refers to a "double-steel-walled, electrically and acoustically shielded room" resting on a vibration isolation mat and with further layers of vibration isolation between the room's interior floor and the experimental apparatus. The implication of a separate floor suggests that the experimental space might more appropriately have been called a steel-walled box rather than a steel-walled room.) The refinements to earlier experiments (Jeffers and Sloan, 1992; Ibison and Jeffers, 1998) consisted largely in this superior isolation, and the change from a simple double-slit interference apparatus to the Michelson interferometer, allowing significant spatial separation of the beam paths. The method for measuring the extent of interference in the apparatus was to measure total light intensity in portions of the interference pattern that showed strong differences between the two-path pattern with interference and a one-path pattern without mutual interference.

Unfortunately, the report does not give actual light intensities for these measurements, instead presenting them either in arbitrary units or in statistical figures of merit. In these statistical terms, then, one can say that subjects skilled in maintaining a state of focused attention produced a change of the measured intensity amounting to 4.28 times the measurement uncertainty. Unskilled subjects produced an apparent change of only 0.29 times the measurement uncertainty, while control runs with no subjects, performed immediately after the sessions with skilled subjects, produced an apparent change of 0.46 times the measurement uncertainty. The changes referred to are the changes between the measured light intensity when the subject was, or was not, maintaining a state of focused attentiveness directed at the location of one branch of the interferometer. The classification of "skilled" or "unskilled" subjects is relevant due to the difficulty most untrained people experience in maintaining such focused mental states over significant intervals of time, as discussed in the report.

What makes these empirical findings of particular theoretical interest is the absence of any conventional measuring device in the interferometer beam path. It was noted above that the presence of apparatus capable of conducting a which-way measurement is sufficient to destroy the ability of the two light paths to interfere with each other. In this case, however, there are two conditions, one with full interference and one with reduced interference, in which from a conventional viewpoint no additional measuring apparatus has been introduced. This seems to force the conclusion that the which-way apparatus in this case consists of the specific cognitive state of the human subjects during the periods when they were instructed to maintain focused attention on the apparatus. This conclusion is less peculiar than it might seem at first inspection. On the presumption that a cognitive state must equate to a particular physical configuration of the subject's brain activity, there is a clearly identifiable physical difference between the two experimental conditions. Runs showing evidence of which-way measurement activity correspond to one condition, and the runs lacking such evidence correspond to the other.

It is, of course, somewhat unexpected that whatever physical changes the subjects are inducing in their brains by entering a state of focused attention should have an effect on instrumentation several meters away and heavily shielded. While a detailed physical mechanism is obscure, there is no shortage of roughly analogous situations in known experiments. Two examples seem particularly apropos. In the Aharonov-Bohm solenoid effect, electron beams propagating through a space free of electric and magnetic fields show changes in relative phase from the presence of a magnetic field completely confined within a solenoid in a region of space isolated from the beam paths (Aharonov and Bohm, 1959, 1961). So-called quantum eraser experiments actively rely upon the fact that an interference pattern can be altered or eliminated by remote manipulations of entangled partners of the photons actually participating in the interference (Kim et al. 2000). There is, of course, no reason to expect that Radin's subjects are actually acting as sources of a field-free potential, or have access to particles entangled with the interferometer's photon stream. These specific examples are presented not as plausible mechanisms for the observed effect, but simply as illustrations of the fact that known physical effects are entirely capable of circumventing methods of isolation, separation, or shielding which naïve physical intuition might expect to be adequate to protect an experimental system from outside influences.

3. Conclusions

It is premature to draw overly strong conclusions from a single experiment, not yet replicated by other researchers. (Although the experiment is itself a conceptual replication, the earlier experiments showed conflicting results and must be considered inconclusive.) Nevertheless, if these preliminary findings are confirmed, it would follow that at the very least we now know how to build an instrument to detect remotely the presence of one particular cognitive state in a human being, and that the physical mechanism mediating this detection is not yet understood. The observed phenomenon involves the resolution of a quantum superposition into distinct spatial states with definite locations, apparently in response to a purely cognitive and internal effort by a human subject. This fact suggests that further and more thorough investigations using this experimental paradigm might be able to throw considerable light on the relationship between human consciousness and the process that remains one of the fundamental mysteries of quantum mechanics.

Acknowledgments The author is indebted to Dean Radin for a number of informal presentations and communications without which this work would have remained unknown to him.

References

Aharonov, Y., Bohm, D. (1959). Significance of Electromagnetic Potentials in the Quantum Theory. Phys. Rev., 115, 485–491.

Aharonov, Y., Bohm, D. (1961). Further Considerations on Electromagnetic Potentials in the Quantum Theory. Phys. Rev., 123, 1511–1524.

Bem, D. J., Honorton, C. (1994). Does psi exist? Replicable evidence for an anomalous process of information transfer. Psychological Bulletin, 115, 4–18.

Brown, C. (2005). Remote Viewing: The Science and Theory of Nonphysical Perception. Farsight Press, Atlanta, GA, US.

Elitzur, A. C., Vaidman, L. (1993). Quantum mechanical interaction-free measurements. Found. Phys., 23, 987–997.

Everett, H. (1957). "Relative State" Formulation of Quantum Mechanics. Rev. Mod. Phys., 29, 454–462.

Ghirardi, G. C., Rimini, A., Weber, T. (1986). Unified dynamics for microscopic and macroscopic systems. Phys. Rev. D., 34, 470–491.

Honorton, C. (1977). Psi and internal attention states. In: Wolman, B. B. (Ed.), Handbook of Parapsychology, Van Nostrand Reinhold, New York, pp. 435–472.

Ibison, M., Jeffers, S. (1998). A double-slit diffraction experiment to investigate claims of consciousness-related anomalies. J. Sci. Explor., 12, 543–550.

Jeffers, S., Sloan, J. (1992). A low light level diffraction experiment for anomalies research. J. Sci. Explor., 6, 333–352.

Joos, E., Zeh, H. D., Kiefer, C., Giulini, D., Kupsch, J., Stamatescu, I.-O. (2003). Decoherence and the Appearance of a Classical World in Quantum Theory. Springer, New York, US.

Kim, Y. H., Yu, R., Kulik, S. P., Shih, Y. (2000). Delayed "Choice" Quantum Eraser. Phys. Rev. Lett., 84, 1–5.

May, E. C. (1996). The American Institutes for Research Review of the Department of Defense's STAR GATE Program: A Commentary. J. Sci. Explor, 10, 89–107.

Parker, A. (1975). States of Mind: ESP and Altered States of Consciousness. Taplinger, New York, US.

Penrose, R. (1989). The Emperor's New Mind. Oxford University Press, New York, US.

Penrose, R. (1994). Shadows of the Mind. Oxford University Press, New York, US.

Pratt, J. G., Rhine, J. B., Stuart, C. E., Smith, B. M. (1940). Extra-Sensory Perception After Sixty Years. Holt, New York, US.

Radin, D. (2008). Testing nonlocal observation as a source of intuitive knowledge. EXPLORE, 4, 25–35.

Rhine, J. B. (Ed.) (1971). Progress in Para-psychology. Parapsychology Press, Durham, NC, US.

Squires, E. J. (1987). Many views of one world — an interpretation of quantum theory. Eur. J. Phys., 8, 171–173.

Stapp, H. P. (2001). Quantum theory and the role of mind in nature. Found. Phys., 31, 1465–1499.

Targ, R., Puthoff, H. E. (1974). Information transmission under conditions of sensory shielding. Nature, 252, 602–607.

Tart, C. T., Puthoff, H. E., Targ, R. (Eds.) (1979). Mind at Large: IEEE Symposia on the Nature of Extrasensory Perception. Praeger Special Studies, New York, US.

Von Neumann, J. (1955). Mathematical Foundations of Quantum Mechanics. Princeton University Press, Princeton, US.

Wigner, E. P. (1963). The problem of measurement. Am J. Phys., 31, 6–15.

Wigner, E. P. (1964). Two kinds of reality. The Monist, 48, 248–264.

Consciousness and Quantum Physics:
A Deconstruction of the Topic
Gordon Globus, M.D.

Professor Emeritus of Psychiatry and Philosophy,
University of California Irvine , Irvine, CA

Abstract

The topic of "consciousness and quantum physics" is deconstructed. Consciousness is not only a vague concept with very many definitions but is entangled with unresolved controversies, notably the notorious measurement problem in quantum physics and the qualia problem in philosophy, so the problematic calls for redefinition. The key issue is that of primary "closure"--the nonphenomenality of quantum physical reality--and the action that brings "dis-closure." Dis-closure of the phenomenal world can be understood within the framework of dissipative quantum thermofield brain dynamics without any reference to consciousness. Some unsettling monadological consequences of this view are brought out in the discussion.

KEY WORDS: consciousness, quantum physics,dissipative quantum thermofield brain dynamics, measurement problem, between-two, monadology

1. Introduction

At present there is no agreed upon definition of consciousness--Vimal (2009) identified over forty!--so how could we discuss it in the same breath as the scientific field of quantum physics? A recent issue of The Journal of Consciousness Studies devoted ten articles to the topic of defining consciousness, the editor concluding that we should all try harder to both specify what we mean when referring to "consciousness" and pay more attention to the contexts within which that meaning applies. And we should embrace the resultant diversity … . (Nunn 2009, p.7) Might a science-based discussion of consciousness and quantum physics be barking up the wrong tree? And if so, how might discussion be redeployed away from consciousness without falling into the dullness of crass materialism?

Since "consciousness" is so ill-defined, we are at the mercy of tacit sub-textual meanings. Yet clues might be found in the term's etymology, which gains us a certain detachment. The very term "consciousness" already carries profound biases. It derives from the Latin con-scieri, which is to know-together, and accordingly cognitive-social. Conscientia--conscience--is an internalization of social knowing, viz. a self-knowing and judging. But today consciousness has a much broader meaning than this historical cognitive emphasis. "Consciousness" in present usage is not just a socialized knowing but is also perceptual. We say that we are conscious of the phenomenal world. The supplement to knowing found in the contemporary meaning of "consciousness" encompasses "qualia" too--the conscious experience of colors, sounds, odors, etc. --but this is precisely where there is hot debate. Despite enormous discussion (e.g. Kazniak 2001; Wright 2008) there is no philosophical consensus regarding the qualia problem. So the extension of the original cognitive meaning of "consciousness" to include qualitative experiences brings complications to any engagement with an unsuspecting physics, which ought to make us suspicious.

It should not be thought that substituting "awareness" or "experience" for "consciousness" improves the situation. "Aware" comes from an old English term meaning cautious (cf. "wary"), which is a cognitive activity. "Experience" (cf. "experiment") comes from the Latin experio, to try out, which is cognitive-behavioral. It is noteworthy that the term 'consciousness' does not even appear until the 17th century. If this is something so fundamental as to be related to quantum physics, why should it take so long to be distinguished in philosophical discourse? Were the philosophers of ancient Greece so un-wise?

As if the ambiguity and subtext of "consciousness" were not enough, con-sciousness is already party to a long-standing and still highly contentious problem within quantum physics itself: the "measurement problem," which is typified by Schrödinger's notorious cat. Consistent with the principles of quantum physics Schrödinger's cat seems to be in a superposition state of being dead and being alive, until a conscious observation is made.

Even if it is supposed that consciousness has nothing to do with the outcome--supposed that the wave function readily collapses on its own (Gihradi 2007; Hameroff and Penrose 1996)--the result is not a phenomenal cat, dead or alive as the case may be. Wave function collapse is to near-certainty of location, not to a phenomenal cat. The wave function is a wave of probability and its collapse is still expressed in probabilistic terms ("exceedingly near

1.0" at some point). Any phenomenality depends on the observer's consciousness, and so the measurement problem drags in some meta-physics. Since the tradition of metaphysics runs back through Kant and Descartes to Plato--a tradition that uncommonsensical quantum physics otherwise challenges at every turn--the very topic of consciousness and quantum physics cries for deconstruction.

There is no place for the phenomenal cat in quantum physics itself--that cat right there in the box, dead or alive, after you open it. Quantum field theory is well capable of describing macroscopic objects with sharp boundary structures (Umezawa 1993, Chapter 6). Scale is not an issue for quantum field theory. (There is no need to get to the macroscopic by the fiat of letting Planck's constant go to zero.) But a macroscopic quantum object is not of the same kind as a cat-in-a-box: that would be a colossal category mistake to equate them. Might quantum brain theory ride to the rescue? Many theories have been proposed for how quantum brain mechanisms might generate consciousness and thereby rescue from metaphysics the principle of the causal closure of the physical domain. (Quantum physicists in general have been slow to recognize the importance of quantum brain theory to their endeavor.) But these attempts run into the wasps nest already emphasized: the definability problem for consciousness, the qualia problem, and unyielding controversy over the measurement problem. A fresh start is tried here and the brutal consequences are faced.

2. Dis-Closure

The world presences, "is," exists, has Being, appears … . Instead of saying that we are "conscious of the world" it is less prejudicial to say that we always find ourselves already amidst one, waking and dreaming both. Being is no easy replacement for consciousness, to be sure … and the term "Being" may sound more problematic than "consciousness" to the physics ear. For reasons to be brought out, I shall use instead the term "dis-closure."

To speak of the quantum "world," as is sometimes loosely done, is self-contradictory. As already emphasized above, the quantum realm lacks phenomenality, has no appearance, is closed. What is needed is an account of the appearance of Being, presence, or since the fundamental property is closedness, what is called for is dis-closedness.

Dis-closure entails an action--an action on closure--a dis-closure in which Being--a cat in a box--appears. What is called for by the above deconstruction of consciousness in quantum physics is an account of dis-closure. Thermofield brain dynamics provides an explanation of dis-closure that may get free from the problematical consciousness.

3. Thermofield Brain Dynamics

The origins of thermofield brain dynamics go back to the quantum brain dynamics of Umezawa and coworkers in the late sixties (Umezawa 1995). It was recognized that symmetry-breaking in the ground state of the brain--the vacuum state of a water electric dipole field--offers a mechanism for memory. Sensory inputs fall into the ground after dissipating their energy and break the dipole symmetry. The broken symmetry is preserved by boson condensation (Nambu-Goldstone condensates). When the sensory input is repeated, the condensate-trace is excited from the vacuum state and becomes conscious. Jibu and Yasue (1995, 2004) worked this idea into a full-fledged quantum brain dynamics of consciousness.

Vitiello (1995, 2001, 2004) greatly extended quantum brain dynamics to a thermofield brain dynamics by bringing in dissipation. Now the brain is a dissipative system and its vacuum state has two modes: a system mode and an environment mode. The system mode contains the boson memory traces and the environment mode expresses ongoing input. ("Input" should be understood here as both sensory signals and signals the brain generates on its own, that is, other-generated signals and self-generated signals.) Neither mode exists without the other. The vacuum state is "between-two," between other-generated and self-generated signals on the one hand and memory traces on the other. Vitiello proposed that consciousness is not the quantum brain dynamics model of excitation of memory traces from the vacuum but is the state of match between dual modes. Consciousness for Vitiello is between-two.

Notable in the Vitiello model is a new version of ontological duality. The traditional dualities are the two substances of Descartes or the two aspects of a "neutral reality" proposed by Spinoza. Mitigated dualisms include Sperry's (1969) emergent level which is more than the sum of its interacting parts and Huxley's (1898) epiphenomenalism in which the mental is a nomological dangler without causal influence. The between-two is a new idea. The two are indissolubly coupled--no one without the other--and unlike ontological substances or aspects of a neutral substance, what is primary is their between.

Since Vitiello wedded thermofield brain dynamics to consciousness, the same difficulties already detailed arise. But we may alternatively reinterpret thermofield brain dynamics as a theory of dis-closure (Globus 2003, 2009). Dis-closure is between-two.

Phenomenal world appears when the dual modes belong-together, in the sense that a complex number "belongs-to" its complex conjugate. The match between such dual modes is real. Phenomenal world is a function of the brain's quantum vacuum state, dis-closed in the match between other-action, self-action and memory traces.

4. Paying the Dues for Giving-Up Consciousness

We should not expect to get off so easily after jettisoning consciousness for action-cum-disclosure. Something dear to our hearts is exploded: the world-in-common that faithful observers might by and large agree on. Not only do we lose our consciousness but we lose the world too. Now every quantum thermofield brain is dis-closing worlds in parallel. There is no world-in-common that we each represent (re-present) in our own way, nor do we each pick up a common world's sensory offerings according to our individual predilection (Gibson 1979; Neisser 1976), not even a common world that is selected by sensory input from the possibilities we variously bring to it (Edelman 1987). For the present proposal there is no physical reality of an external world, only unworldly macroscopic and microscopic quantum objects. All worlds are between-two.

So Being, which is to replace consciousness, can be precisely specified. Ontologically primary is distinctionless abground, and Being is secondarily dis-closed--appears--in virtue of an action on the abground, an action that unfolds. That is, the primary ontological condition is closure and Being requires its undoing: dis-closure. The deconstructed topic of "consciousness and quantum physics" is succeeded by the topic of "Being and quantum physics."

This view should not be confused with multiple worlds theory (Greene 2011), which just compounds the difficulties surrounding consciousness already discussed. In multiple worlds theory every possible result of wave function collapse is realized. In one world the Schrödinger cat is found alive by a consciousness and in another world found dead by a different consciousness. For the present account, in contrast, different observers perceive the same result. The worlds dis-closed are multiple yet in agreement. There is consensus to the extent that other-action, self-action and memory are comparable across brains.

The present view might be called "monadological" but in a distinct sense from that of Leibniz. Leibniz did not doubt that there is in fact a transcendent world bestowed through God's love. "God produces substances from nothing," Leibniz (1952, sect. 395) states in the Theodicy. The worlds in parallel of monads are in "pre-established harmony" with the transcendent world God thinks into being. But there is no transcendent world according to the view developed here. There is closure--a distinctionless "abground" (Heidegger 1999) or even "holomovement" (Bohm 1980; Bohm and Hiley 1993)--and multiple parallel phenomenal world disclosures. This is a rather scary thought, to lose the quotidian world-in-common, when you really think about it ...

Other macroscopic quantum objects besides brains also have a matching state of their between-two but the disclosures of, say, an old cabbage, barely change from moment to moment. To use the Kantian phrase, such a macroscopic quantum object "is in itself" but its Being doesn"t amount to much. The brain's genius is that the between-two comes under exquisite control by three influences: other-action, self-action and memory. Complex dis-closures flowingly evolve in waking life.

Three distinct types of brain state bring out some implications of the model. In the case of well-formed slow wave sleep, the between-two disclosure is closer to that of the cabbage. During active REM sleep, however, the between-two revives, though with the participation of other-action (sensory input) strongly inhibited. The between-two becomes a function of only residual self-actions (mainly from the preceding day, Freudian "day residues") and retraces (typically of emotional significance): the dream life is dis-closed. (See Globus (2010) for a detailed illustration of how this works.) Monadological disclosure accordingly varies dramatically in content across waking, dreaming and sleeping but in no case can be transcended. We are windowless monads in parallel and best get on with it! Such a counter-intuitive conclusion is founded in a relentless deconstruction of the role of consciousness in quantum physics. The successor concept to consciousness is "world-thrownness" in virtue of between-two dis-closure.

References

Bohm, D. (1980). Wholeness and the implicate order. Routledge & Kegan Paul, London.

Bohm, D. and Hiley, B. (1993). The Undivided Universe. Routledge & Kegan Paul, London.

Edelman, G. (1987). Neural Darwinism. Basic Books, New York.

Ghiradi, G. (2007). Collapse theories. In Stanford Encyclopedia of Philosophy. http://Plato.Stanford.edu/entries/qm-collapse/

Gibson, J. (1979). The ecological approach to visual perception. Houghton- Mifflin, Boston.

Globus, G. (2003). Quantum Closures and Disclosures: Thinking together Postphenomenology and Quantum Brain Dynamics. John Benjamins, Amsterdam.

Globus, G. (2009). The transparent becoming of world: A crossing between process thought and quantum neurophilosophy. John Benjamins, Amsterdam.

Green, B. (2010). The Hidden Reality. Knopf, New York.

Hameroff, S. Penrose, R. (1996). Conscious events as orchestrated space-time selections. Journal of consciousness studies 3, 36-53.

Heidegger, M. (1999). Contributions to philosophy (from Enowning). P. Emad & K. Maly, trans. Indiana University Press, Bloomington, Indiana.

Huxley, D.H. (1898). Methods and results: Essays by Thomas H. Huxley. D. Appleton, New York.

Jibu, M., Yasue, K. (1995). Quantum brain dynamics and consciousness. John Benjamins, Amsterdam.

Jibu, M., Yasue, K. (2004). Quantum brain dynamics and quantum field theory. In: Brain and being. Globus, G., Pribram, K., Vitello, G. eds. John Benjamins, Amsterdam.

Kaszniak, A. (ed.) (2001). Emotions, qualia and consciousness. World Scientific: Singapore.

Leibniz, G.W. (1952). Theodicy: Essays on the Goodness of God, the Freedom of Man, and the Origin of Evil. A. Farrer, ed., E. M. Huggard, trans. Yale University Press, New Haven.

Neisser, U. (1976). Cognition and Reality. W.H. Freeman, San Francisco.

Nunn, C. (2009). Editors introduction: Defining consciousness. J. of consciousness studies 16, 5-8.

Sperry, R. (1969). A modified concept of consciousness. Psychological review 77, 585- 590.

Umezawa, H. (1993). Advanced Field Theory: Micro, Macro, and Thermal Physics, American Institute of Physics, New York.

Umezawa, H. (1995). Development in concepts in quantum field theory in half century. Mathematica Japonica, 41, 109-124.

Vimal, R.L.P. (2009) Meanings attributed to the term "Consciousness". J. of consciousness studies, 16: 9-27.

Vitiello G. (1995). Dissipation and memory capacity in the quantum brain model. Int J of Modern Physics B 9, 973-989.

Vitiello, G. (2001). My Double Unveiled. John Benjamins, Amsterdam.

Vitiello, G. (2004). The dissipative brain. In: G. Globus, K. Pribram & G. Vitiello, eds. Brain and being. Amsterdam: John Benjamins.

Wright, E. (ed.) (2008). The case for qualia. MIT Press, Cambridge.

Logic of Quantum Mechanics and Phenomenon of Consciousness
Michael B. Mensky

P.N. Lebedev Physical Institute, Russian Academy of Sciences, Leninsky prosp. 53, 119991 Moscow,

Abstract

The phenomenon of consciousness, including its mystical features, is explained on the basis of quantum mechanics in the Everett's form. Everett's interpretation (EI) of quantum mechanics is in fact the only one that correctly describes quantum reality: any state of the quantum world is objectively a superposition of its classical counterparts, or "classical projections". They are "classically incompatible", but are considered to be equally real, or coexisting. We shall call them alternative classical realities or simply classical alternatives. According to the Everett's interpretation, quantum reality is presented by the whole set of alternative classical realities (alternatives). However, these alternatives are perceived by humans separately, independently from each other, resulting in the subjective illusion that only a single classical alternative exists. The ability to separate the classical alternatives is the main feature of what is called consciousness. According to the author's Extended Everett's Concept (EEC), this feature is taken to be a definition of consciousness (more precisely, consciousness as such, not as the complex of processes in the conscious state of mind). It immediately follows from this definition that turning the consciousness off (in sleeping, trance or meditation) allows one to acquire access to all alternatives. The resulting information gives rise to unexpected insights including scientific insights.

KEY WORDS: Quantum mechanics; quantum reality; Everett's interpretation; consciousness; unconscious; insights; miracles; probability

1 INTRODUCTION

Strange as this may seem, we do not know what is the nature of consciousness, especially of the very strange features of consciousness which resemble mystical phenomena. The most familiar examples of these mysterious phenomena are scientific insights (of course, we mean only "great insights" experienced by great scientists). Some people supposed that the mystery of consciousness may be puzzled out on the basis of quantum mechanics, the science which is mysterious itself.

This viewpoint has been suggested, as early as in 20th years of 20th century, by the great physicist Wolfgang Pauli in collaboration with the great psychologist Carl Gustav Jung. They supposed particularly that quantum mechanics may help to explain strange psychic phenomena observed by Jung and called "synchronisms". Jung told of a synchronism if a series of the events happened such that these events were conceptually close but their simultaneous (synchronous) emergence could not be justified causally. For example he observed causally unjustified, seemingly accidental, appearance of the image of fish six times during a single day. The work of Pauli and Jung on this topic was not properly published and was later completely forgotten, but it became popular in last decades (see about this in Enz, 2009).

The idea of connecting consciousness with quantum mechanics was suggested by some other authors, mostly without referring Pauli and Jung. In the last three decades this idea was supported by Roger Penrose (Penrose, 1991), (Penrose, 1994). He particularly remarked that people manage to solve such problems which in principle cannot be solved with the help of computers because no algorithms exist for their solving. Penrose suggested that quantum phenomena should be essential for explaining the work of brain and consciousness.

Usually attempts to explain consciousness on the base of quantum mechanics follow the line of consideration that is natural for physicists. Everything must be explained by natural sciences, may be with accounting quantum laws. Therefore, in order to explain consciousness, one has to apply quantum mechanics for analysis of the work of brain. For example, the work of brain may be explained as the work of quantum computer instead of classical one. Thus, it is usually assumed, explicitly or implicitly, that consciousness must be derived from the analysis of the processes in brain.

The approach proposed by the author in 2000 does not include this assumption. This approach is based on the analysis of the logical structure of quantum mechanics, and the phenomenon of consciousness is derived from this purely logical analysis rater than from the processes in brain. The actual origin of the concept of consciousness is, according to this approach, specific features of the concept of reality accepted in quantum mechanics (contrary to classical physics) and often called quantum reality.

Quantum reality has its adequate presentation in the so-called Everett's interpretation (EI) of quantum mechanics known also under name of many-worlds interpretation (Everett III, 1957). The approach of the author is based on the Everett's form of quantum mechanics and called Extended Everett's Concept (EEC).

Some physicists, having in mind purely classical concept of reality, consider the Everett's interpretation of quantum mechanics too complicated and "exotic". However, it is now experimentally proved that reality in our world is quantum, and the conclusions based on classical concept of reality, are not reliable. The comprehension of the concept of quantum reality was achieved after long intellectual efforts of genius scientists. Unfortunately, the ideas of Pauli and Jung were not properly estimated and timely used. The first whose thoughts about quantum reality became widely know was Einstein who, in the work with his coauthors, suggested so-called Einstein-Podolski-Rosen paradox (Einstein et al., 1935). Much later John Bell formulated now widely known Bell's theorem (Bell, 1964), (Bell, 1987) which provided an adequate tool for direct quantum-mechanical verification of the concept of quantum reality, the Bell's inequality. Less than in 20 years the group of Aspect experimentally proved (Aspect et al., 1981) that the Bell's inequality is violated in some quantum processes, and therefore reality in our world is quantum.

Most simple and convenient formulation of quantum reality was given even earlier that the Bell's works, in 1957, by the Everett's interpretation of quantum mechanics. It was enthusiastically accepted by the great physicists John Archibald Wheeler and Brice Dewitt, but was not recognized by the wide physical community until last decades of 20th century, when the corresponding intellectual base was already prepared. From this time the number of adepts of the Everett's interpretation grows permanently. Results of this difficult but very important process of conceptual clarification of quantum mechanics justify the appreciation of the Everett's interpretation as the only correct form of quantum mechanics. It is exciting that, as an additional prize, the Everett's interpretation explains the mysterious phenomenon of consciousness.

Quantum mechanics in the Everett's form implies coexisting "parallel worlds", or parallel classical realities. This clearly expresses the difference of quantum reality from the common classical reality. According to the author's Extended Everett's Concept (Menskii, 2000), consciousness is the ability to perceive the Everett's parallel worlds separately, independently from each other. An immediate consequence of this assumption is that the state of being unconscious makes all parallel realities available without the separation. This leads to irrational insights and other "mystical" phenomena. This is the central point of the theory making it plausible. Indeed, it is well known (from all spiritual schools and from deep psychological researches) that the strange abilities of consciousness arise just in the states of mind that are close to be-ing unconsciousness (sleeping, trance or meditation).

2 PARALLEL WORLDS

According to the Everett's "many-worlds" interpretation of quantum mechanics, quantum mechanics implies coexistence of "parallel classical worlds", or alternative classical realities. This follows from the arguments (see details below) including the following points:
  • The very important specific feature of quantum systems is that their states are vectors. This means that a state of any quantum system may be a sum (called also superposition) of other states of the same system. All the states which are the counterparts of this sum, are equally real, i.e. they may be said to coexist. This is experimentally proved for the states of microscopic systems (such as elementary particles or atoms).
  • However, this should be valid also for macroscopic systems (consisting of many atoms). It follows from the logical analysis of the measurements of microscopic systems. Indeed, let a microscopic system S be measured with the help of a macroscopic measuring device M. If the state of S is a sum of a series of states, then, after the measurement, the state of the combined sys-tem (S and M) is also a sum (each its term consisting of a state of S and the corresponding state of M).
  • Different states of the measuring device, by the very definition of a mea-suring device, have to be macroscopically distinct. Therefore, a macroscopic system may be in the state which is a sum (superposition) consisting of the states which are incompatible (alternative to each other) from the point of view of classical physics. However, quantum mechanics requires them to "coexist" (in the form of a sum, or superposition).
  • Therefore, classically incompatible states of our world (alternative clas-sical realities) must coexist as a sort of "parallel worlds" which are called Everett's worlds.

Let us now give some details of these arguments. What does it mean that the states of a quantum system are vectors? If vpi are states of some quantum system, then $\psi = \psi_1 + \psi_2 + \cdots$ is also a state of the same system, called a superposition of the states ψ_i (counterparts of the superposition).

This feature is experimentally proved for microscopic systems (such as elementary particles or atoms), but it has to be valid also for macroscopic systems. This follows from the analysis of measurements with microscopic measured systems and macroscopic measuring devices.

The conclusion following from this analysis is that, even for a macroscop-ic system, its state ψ may be a superposition of other states of this system, which have evident classical interpretation (are close to some classical states of the system) while the state ψ has no such an interpretation:

$$\psi = \psi_1 + \psi_2 + ... + \psi_n ... (1)$$

It is important that the states ψ here may be macroscopically distinct, therefore, from classical point of view incompatible, alternative to each other, presenting alternative classical realities. Nevertheless, it follows from quantum theory that even such macroscopically distinct states ψ_i may be in superposition, i.e. may coexist. Let us formulate the above situation a little bit more precisely. The quantum system is in the state denoted by the state vector and only this state objectively exists (however, taken as a whole, has no classical interpretation). The counterparts $\wedge$ of the superposition are in fact classical projections of the objectively existing quantum state ψ. These classical projections describe images of the quantum system which arise in consciousness of an observer (therefore, they concern the subjective aspect of quantum reality). This status of the classical projections will be made more transparent below.

In the following we shall use ψ for the state of our (quantum) world as a whole. The components ψi of the superposition will be alternative classical states of this world (more precisely, quasiclassical, i.e. the states as close to classical as is possible for the quantum world).

In the Everett's interpretation of quantum mechanics the states ψ are called Everett's worlds. We shall use also the terms "parallel worlds", "alternative classical realities", "classical alternatives" or simply "alternatives". In case if such alternatives are superposed (as in Eq. (1)), we shall say that they "coexist". Of course this word is nothing else than a convenient slang, meaning in fact "to form a superposition" or "to be in superposition". The status of the "coexistence" is connected with the consciousness and subjective perception of the world, which will be explained below.

3 EXTENDED EVERETT'S CONCEPT (EEC)

We see that the alternative classical realities in our quantum world may coexist (as components of a superposition presenting the state of the quantum world). Subjectively however each observer perceives only a single "classical alternative". These two assertions seem to contradict to each other. Are they in fact compatible? We shall show how this seeming contradiction is resolved in the Everett's interpretation (EI) and how it may be taken as a basis for the theory of consciousness and the unconscious if the EI is properly extended.

3.1 Everett's "Many-Worlds" Interpretation One may naively think that the picture of the world arising in his consciousness (the picture of a single classical alternative) is just what objectively exists. However, EI of quantum mechanics (unavoidably following from the logics of quantum mechanics applied to the phenomenon of quantum measurements) claims that it is only the superposition of all alternatives (as in Eq. (1)) that objectively exists.

The seemingly strange and counter-intuitive presentation of objective reality (in the Everett's form of quantum mechanics) as the set of many objectively coexisting classical realities adequately expresses quantum character of reality in our (quantum) world.

The single alternatives (components of the superposition) present various subjective perceptions of this quantum reality in an observer's consciousness. The natural question arises how the multiplicity of the "classical pictures" that may arise in our consciousness may be compatible with the subjective sensory evidence of only a single such picture.

This is the most difficult point of the EI and the reason why this interpretation has not been readily accepted by the physicists. This point may be made more transparent if it is presented in the terms of "Everett's worlds" as it has been suggested by Brice DeWitt.

Thus, all of the separate components of the superposition (classical alternatives, or Everett's worlds) are declared by Everett to be "equally real". No single alternative may be considered to be the only real, while the others being potentially possible but not actualized variants of reality (this might be accepted in classical physics, but not in quantum mechanics, because of the special character of quantum reality).

To make understanding of the EI easier, Brice DeWitt proposed (De-Witt & Graham, 1973) to think that each observer is present in each of the Everett's worlds. To make this even more transparent, one may think that a sort of twins ("clones") of each observer are present in all Everett's worlds. Subjective perception is the perception of a single twin. Objectively the twins of the given observer exist in all Everett's worlds, each of them perceiving corresponding alternative pictures.

Each of us subjectively perceives around him a single classical reality. However, objectively the twins, or clones, of each of us perceive all the rest realities. It is important that all twins of the given observer are equally real. It is incorrect to say that there is "I" and there are my twins, which are not "I". All twins embody me as an observer, each of them can be called "I".

Thus, the concept of "Everett's world" allows to make the Everett's presentation of quantum reality more transparent. We prefer to verbalize the same situation in another way (Menskii, 2000). We shall say that all alternative classical projections of the quantum world's state objectively exist, but these projections are separated in consciousness. Subjective perception of the quantum world by human's consciousness embraces all these classical pictures, but each picture is perceived independently of the rest.

Regardless of the way of wording, the Everett's assumption of objectively coexisting classical alternatives implies that all these alternatives may be accessible for an observer in some way or another. Yet it is not clear how the access to "other alternatives" (different from one subjectively perceived) may be achieved for the given observer. It is usually claimed that the EI does not allow observing "other alternatives". This makes the interpretation non-falsifiable and thus decreases its value.

It turns out however that the EI may be improved in such a way that that the question "How one can access to other alternatives?" is answered in a very simple and natural way. This improvement is realized in the author's Extended Everett's Concept. The (improved) EI becomes then falsifiable, although in a special sense of the word (see below Sect. 3.2).

3.2 Extension of the Everett's Interpretation Starting with the above mentioned formulation (that classical alternatives are separated in consciousness), the present author proposed (Menskii, 2000) to accept a stronger statement: consciousness is nothing else than separation of the alternatives.

This seemingly very small step resulted in important consequences. Finally the so-called Extended Everett's Concept (EEC) has been developed (Menskii, 2005), (Menskii, 2007), (Mensky, 2007), (Mensky, 2005), (Mensky, 2010).

The first advantage of EEC is that the logical structure of the quantum theory is simplified as compared with the EI.

The point is that the formulation "alternatives are separated in consciousness" (accepted in one of the possible formulations of EI) includes two primary (not definable) concepts, "consciousness" and "alternative separation". These concepts have no good definitions. One may object that many different definitions have been proposed for the notion "consciousness". This is right, but all these definitions concern in fact mental and sensual processes in brain rather than "consciousness as such", while the latter (more fundamental) notion has no good definition.

After the notions "consciousness" (more precisely, "consciousness as such") and "separation of alternatives" are identified (as it is suggested in EEC), only one of these concepts remains in the theory. Therefore, EEC includes only one primary concept instead of two such concepts in the EI. The logical structure of the theory is simplified after its extension.

Much more important is that EEC gives a transparent indication as to how an observer may obtain access to "other alternatives" (different from the alternative subjectively perceived by him). This very important question remains unanswered (or answered negatively) in the original form of the EI. This is seen from the following argument.

If consciousness = separation (of the alternatives from each other), then absence of consciousness = absence of separation.

Therefore, turning off consciousness (in sleeping, trance or meditation) opens access to all classical alternatives put together, without separation between them. Of course, the access is realized then not in the form of visual, acoustic or other conscious images or thoughts. Nothing at all can be said about the form of this access. However, if we accept EEC, then we may definitely conclude that the access is possible in the unconscious state of mind.

This of course has very important consequences. The access to the enormous "data base" consisting of all alternative classical realities enables one to acquire valuable information, or rather knowledge. This information is unique in the sense that it is unavailable in the conscious state when only a single alternative is subjectively accessible. One may suppose that a part of this unique information may be kept on returning to the usual conscious state of mind and recognized in the form of usual conscious images and thoughts.

Thus, when going over to the unconscious state, one obtains the information, or knowledge, which is in principle unavailable in the usual conscious state.

This information is unique first of all because it is taken from "other" classical alternatives (different from one subjectively observed). There is however something more that makes this information unique and highly valuable. All alternatives together form a representation of the quantum state of the world (vector $\wedge$ in Eq. (1)). Time evolution of this state vector, according to quantum laws, is reversible. This means that, given at some time moment, this vector is known also at all other times. Therefore, information about "all alternatives together" (i.e. about the state vector of the world) includes information from any time moments in future and past. This information may be thought of as being obtained with the help of a "virtual time machine".

Evidently, this makes "irrational" inspirations (including scientific insights) possible. Here is a simple example. Let a scientist be confronted with a scientific problem and consider a number of hypotheses for solving this problem. Going, by means of the above mentioned virtual time machine, into future and backward, the scientist may find out what of these hypotheses will be confirmed by future experiments or proved with the help of the future theories. Then, on returning to the conscious state, he will unexpectedly and without any rational grounds get certain about which of these hypotheses has to be chosen.

Remark that it is not necessary, for making use of such a virtual time machine, to turn off consciousness completely (although it is known that some important discoveries were made in sleeping, or rather after awakening). It is enough to disconnect it from the problem under consideration. This is why solutions of hard problems are sometimes found not during the work on these problems but rather during relaxation.

Preliminary "rational" work on the problem is however necessary. The deep investigation of all data concerning the problem enables the consciousness to form a sort of query (clear formulation of the problem and its connections with all relevant areas of knowledge). Then the query will be worked out in the unconscious state (during relaxation) and will result in an unexpected insight.

It is clear that not only scientific problems can be solved in this way, but also problems of general character. Quite probable that, besides ordinary intuitive guesses, we meet in our experience examples of super-intuitive insights of the type described above. Anybody knows that many efficient solutions come in the morning just after awakening. This fact may be an indirect confirmation of the ability of super-intuition.

4 PROBABILISTIC MIRACLES

Thus, Extended Everett's Concept (EEC) leads to the conclusion that unconscious state of mind allows one to take information "from other alternatives" that reveals itself as unexpected insights, or direct vision of truth.

Another consequence is feasibility of even more weird phenomenon looking as arbitrary choice of reality. Let us describe this ability in a special case of what can be called "probabilistic miracles".

Consider an observer who subjectively perceives one of the alternative classical realities at the present time moment t_0. Let in a certain future moment $t > t_0$ some event E may happen, but with a very small probability p. Call it the objective probability of the event E and suppose that this probability is small.

According to the Everett's interpretation of quantum mechanics, at time t two classes of alternative classical realities will exist so that the event E happens in each alternative of the first class and does not happen in the alternatives of the second class. The twins of our observer will be objectively present in each of the alternatives (this is the feature of Everett's worlds, see Sect. 3.1). However, subjectively our observer will feel to be in one of them. With some probability p it will turn out to be the alternative of the first class. The probability p may be called subjective probability of the event E for the given observer.

It is accepted in the Everett's interpretation that subjective and objective probabilities coincide, p = p. However, in the context of EEC we may assume that they may differ and, moreover, the observer may influence the value of subjective probability p'. Let us assume that the observer prefers the event E to happen. Then he can enlarge the subjective probability of this event, i.e. the probability to find himself subjectively at time t just in that classical reality in which this rare event actually happens.

Thus, besides the objective probability of any event, there is a subjective probability of this event for the given observer, and the observer may in principle influence the subjective probability. In the above mentioned situation, an event under consideration can happen according to usual laws of the natural sciences, but with small probability. This means that the objective probability of this event is small, it may seem even negligible. It is important that the objective probability is non-zero. One may say that among all alternatives at the moment t few of the alternatives correspond to the pictures of the world in which the event happens, and much more alternatives correspond to the pictures of the world where the event does not happen.

However, according to EEC, an observer can, simply by the force of his consciousness, make the subjective probability of this event close to unity. Then very likely he will find himself at the moment t in one of those classical realities where the event does happen.

The subjective experience of such an observer will evidence that the objectively improbable event may be realized by the effort of his will. This looks like a miracle. However, this is a miracle of a special type, which may be called "probabilistic miracle".

Probabilistic miracles essentially differ from "absolute" miracles that happen in fairy tales. The difference is that the event realized as a probabilistic miracle (i.e. "by the force of consciousness") may in principle happen in a quite natural way, although with a very small probability. This small but nonzero probability is very important. Particularly, because of fundamental character of probabilistic predictions in quantum mechanics, it is in principle impossible to prove or disprove the unnatural (miraculous) character of the happening.

Indeed, if the objectively rare event happens, the person who has strongly desired for it to happen is inclined to consider the happening as a result of his will. Yet any skeptic may insist in this situation that the event occurred in a quite natural way: what happened, was only a rare coincidence. The secret is in the nature of the concept of probability: if the probability of some stochastic event is equal p, then in a long series consisting of N tests the event will happen pN times (very rarely for small p). But it is in principle impossible to predict in which of these tests the event will happen. Particularly, it may happen even in the very first test from the long series of them.

The latter is a very interesting and general feature of the phenomena "in the area of consciousness" as they are treated in EEC. These phenomena in principle cannot be unambiguously assigned to the sphere of natural events (obeying the laws of natural sciences) or to the sphere of spiritual or psychic phenomena (which are treated by the humanities and spiritual doctrines). Impossibility to do this may be called relativity of objectiveness.

Synchronisms studied by Jung may be considered to be probabilistic miracles. One who observes a subject or event which somehow attracts his special attention, involuntarily thinks about it (often even not clearly fixing his thoughts). According to the above said, he may increase the subjective probability of immediately observing something similar or logically connected.

Some Biblical miracles can also be explained as probabilistic miracles. An example is the miracle at the Sea of Galilee where Jesus calmed the raging storm (Matthew 8:23-27). This was completely natural event. Wonderful was only the fact that the storm ceased precisely at that moment when this was necessary for Jesus and his disciples. The probability of "timely" occurring this natural event was of course very small. The miracle was probabilistic.

5 CONCLUDING REMARKS

We shortly followed in this paper the main ideas of Extended Everett's Concept (EEC) about nature of consciousness. Let us briefly comment on the further development of this theory.

All that has been discussed above, makes sense for humans (possessing consciousness) and may be partly for higher animals. However, the theory may be generalized to give the quantum concept of life in a more general aspect. Thus modified theory is meaningful not only for humans, but for all living beings (belonging to the type of life characteristic for Earth). The idea of the generalization is follows (see (Mensky, 2010) for details).

The main point of EEC is the identification of the "separation of classical alternatives" with the human's consciousness. Now we have to identify this quantum concept with the ability of the living beings to "perceive the quantum world classically". This is an evident generalization of consciousness but for all living beings. Instead of "consciousness" in EEC we have now "classical perceiving of quantum reality" which means that the alternative classical realities (forming the state of the quantum world) are perceived separately from each other.

Similarly to what we told about consciousness (in case of humans), this ability of living beings to "classically perceive the quantum world" is necessary for the very phenomenon of life (of local type). The reason is the same: elaborating efficient strategy of surviving is possible only in a classical world which is "locally predictable". Existing objectively in the quantum world, any creature is living in each of the classical realities separately from all the rest classical realities. Life is developing parallely in the Everett's parallel worlds.

Remark by the way that from this point of view "existing" and "living" are different concepts. Important difference is that existing (evolution in time) of the inanimate matter is determined by reasons while living of the living beings is partly determined also by goals (first of all the goal of survival). Let us make some other remarks concerning philosophical or rather meta-scientific aspects of EEC.

This theory shows that a conceptual bridge between the material (described by natural sciences) and the ideal (treated by the humanities and spiritual doctrines) does exist.

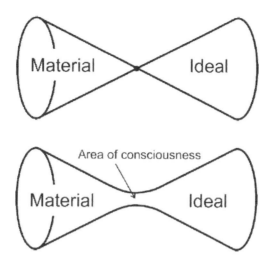

Fig 1: Carl Jung illustrated the relation between sphere of the material and sphere of the ideal as two cones with common vertex (above). In EEC the "area of consciousness" is common for both spheres (below). Some of the phenomena in the area of consciousness cannot be unambiguously assigned to exclusively one of the spheres: objectiveness is relative.

This bridge is determined in EEC in a concrete way, but the idea of such a bridge is not novel (see Fig. 1). The creators of quantum mechanics from the very beginning needed the notion of the "observer's consciousness" to analyze conceptual problems of this theory (the "problem of measurement"). In fact, the difficulties in solving these problems were caused by the insistent desire to construct quantum mechanics as a purely objective theory. Nowadays it becomes clear that there is no purely objective quantum theory. Objectiveness is relative (see Sect. 4).

There is a very interesting technical point in relations between the material and the ideal. We see from the preceding consideration that the description of the ideal, or psychic (consciousness and the unconscious), arises in the interior of quantum mechanics when we consider the whole world as a quantum system. This provides the absolute quantum coherence which is necessary for the conclusions that are derived from EEC. Usually only restricted systems are considered in quantum mechanics. The resulting theory is purely material. Ideal (psychic) elements arise as the specific aspects of the whole world. The unrestricted character of the world as a quantum system is essential for this (cf. the notion of microcosm).

All these issues demonstrate the specific features of the present stage of quantum theory. Including theory of consciousness (and the unconscious) in the realm of quantum mechanics (starting by Pauli and Jung and now close to being accomplished) marks a qualitatively new level of understanding quantum mechanics itself. The present stage of this theory can be estimated as the second quantum revolution. When being completed, it will accomplish the intellectual and philosophical revolution that accompanied creating quantum mechanics in the first third of 20th century.

References

Aspect, A., Grangier, P., Roger, G. (1981). Phys. Rev. Lett., 47, 460.

Bell, J. S. (1964). Physics, 1, 195. Reprinted in (Bell, 1987).

Bell, J. S. (1987). Speakable and Unspeakable in Quantum Mechanics. Cambridge Univ. Press, Cambridge.

DeWitt, B. S., Graham, N. (Eds.) (1973). The Many-Worlds Interpretation of Quantum Mechanics. Princeton Univ. Press, Princeton, NJ.

Einstein, A., Podolsky, B., Rosen, N. (1935). Phys. Rev., 47, 777.

Enz, C. P. (2009). Of Matter and Spirit. World Scientific Publishing Co., New Jersey etc. Everett III, H. (1957). Rev. Mod. Phys., 29, 454. Reprinted in (Wheeler & Zurek, 1983).

Menskii, M. B. (2000). Quantum mechanics: New experiments, new applications and new formulations of old questions. Physics- Uspekhi, 43, 585-600.

Menskii, M. B. (2005). Concept of consciousness in the context of quantum mechanics. Physics-Uspekhi, 48, 389-409.

Menskii, M. B. (2007). Quantum measurements, the phenomenon of life, and time arrow: Three great problems of physics (in Ginzburg's terminology). Physics-Uspekhi, 50, 397-407.

Mensky, M. (2007). Postcorrection and mathematical model of life in Extended Everett's Concept. NeuroQuantology, 5, 363-376. www.neuroquantology.com, arxiv:physics.gen-ph/0712.3609.

Mensky, M. (2010). Consciousness and Quantum Mechanics: Life in Parallel Worlds (Miracles of Consciousness from Quantum Mechanics). World Scientific Publishing Co., Singapore.

Mensky, M. B. (2005). Human and Quantum World (Weirdness of the Quantum World and the Miracle of Consciousness). Vek-2 publishers, Fryazino. In Russian.

Penrose, R. (1991). The Emperor's New Mind: Concepting Computers, Minds, and the Laws of Physics. Penguin Books, New York.

Penrose, R. (1994). Shadows of the Mind: a Search for the Missing Science of Consciousness. Oxford Univ. Press, Oxford.

A Quantum Physical Effect of Consciousness

Shan Gao

Unit for HPS & Centre for Time, SOPHI,
University of Sydney, Sydney, NSW 2006, Australia

Abstract

It is shown that a conscious being can distinguish definite perceptions and their quantum superpositions, while a physical measuring system without consciousness cannot distinguish such nonorthogonal quantum states. This result may have some important implications for quantum theory and the science of consciousness. In particular, it implies that consciousness is not emergent but a fundamental feature of the universe.

KEY WORDS: consciousness, quantum superposition, quantum-to-classical transition, panpsychism

1. Introduction

The relationship between quantum measurement and consciousness has been studied since the founding of quantum mechanics (von Neumann 1932/1955; London and Bauer 1939; Wigner 1967; Stapp 1993, 2007; Penrose 1989, 1994; Hameroff and Penrose 1996; Hameroff 1998, 2007; Gao 2004, 2006b, 2008b). Quantum measurement problem is generally acknowledged as one of the hardest problems in modern physics, and the transition from quantum to classical is still a deep mystery. On the other hand, consciousness remains another deep mystery for both philosophy and science, and it is still unknown whether consciousness is emergent or fundamental. It has been conjectured that these two mysteries may have some intimate connections, and finding them may help to solve both problems (Chalmers 1996).

There are two main viewpoints claiming that quantum measurement and consciousness are intimately connected. The first one holds that the consciousness of an observer causes the collapse of the wave function and helps to complete the quantum measurement or quantum-to-classical transition in general (von Neumann 1932/1955; London and Bauer 1939; Wigner 1967; Stapp 1993, 2007). This view seems understandable. Though what physics commonly studies are insensible objects, the consciousness of observer must take part in the last phase of measurement. The observer is introspectively aware of his perception of the measurement results, and consciousness is used to end the infinite chains of measurement here. The second view holds that consciousness arises from objective wavefunction collapse (Penrose 1989, 1994; Hameroff and Penrose 1996; Hameroff 1998, 2007). One argument is that consciousness is a process that cannot be described algorithmically, and the gravitation-induced wavefunction collapse seems non-computable as a fundamental physical process, and thus the elementary acts of consciousness must be realized as objective wavefunction collapse, e.g., collapse of coherent superposition states in brain microtubules. Though these two views are obviously contrary, they both insist that a conscious perception is always definite and classical, and there are no quantum superpositions of definite conscious perceptions.

Different from these seemingly extreme views, it is widely thought that the quantum-to-classical transition and consciousness are essentially independent with each other (see, e.g. Nauenberg (2007) for a recent review). At first sight, this common-sense view seems too plain to be intriguing. However, it has been argued that, by permitting the existence of quantum superpositions of different conscious perceptions, this view will lead to an unexpected new result, a quantum physical effect of consciousness (Gao 2004, 2006b, 2008b). In this article, we will introduce this interesting result and discuss its possible implications.

2. The Effect

Quantum mechanics is the most fundamental theory of the physical world. Yet as to the measurement process or quantum-to-classical transition process, the standard quantum mechanics provides by no means a complete description, and the collapse postulate is just a makeshift (Bell 1987). Dynamical collapse theories (Ghirardi 2008), many-worlds theory (Everett 1957) and de Broglie-Bohm theory (Bohm 1952) are the main alternatives to a complete quantum theory. The latter two replace the collapse postulate with some new structures, such as branching worlds and Bohmian trajectories, while the former integrate the collapse postulate with the normal Schrödinger evolution into a unified dynamics. It has been recently shown that the dynamical collapse theories are probably in the right direction by admitting wavefunction collapse (Gao 2011). Here we will mainly discuss the possible quantum effects of consciousness in the framework of dynamical collapse theories, though the conclusion also applies to the other alternatives. Our analysis only relies on one common character of the theories, i.e., that the collapse of the wave function (or the quantum-to-classical transition in general) is one kind of objective dynamical process, essentially independent of the consciousness of observer, and it takes a finite time to finish.

It is a well-known result that nonorthogonal quantum states cannot be distinguished (by physical measuring device) in both standard quantum mechanics and dynamical collapse theories (see, e.g. Wootters and Zurek 1982; Ghirardi et al 1993; Nielsen and Chuang 2000). However, it has been argued that a conscious being can distinguish his definite perception states and the quantum superpositions of these states, and thus when the physical measuring device is replaced by a conscious observer, the nonorthogonal states can be distinguished in principle in dynamical collapse theories (Gao 2004, 2006b, 2008b). The distinguishability of nonorthogonal states will reveal a distinct quantum physical effect of consciousness, which is lacking for physical measuring systems without consciousness. In the following, we will give a full exposition of this result.

Let $v1$ and $v2$ be two definite perception states of a conscious being, and $v1 + v2$ is the quantum superposition of these two definite perception states. For example, $v1$ and $v2$ are triggered respectively by a small number of photons with a certain frequency entering into the eyes of the conscious being from two directions, and $v1 + v2$ is triggered by the superposition of these two input states. Assume that the conscious being satisfies the following slow collapse condition, i.e., that the collapse time of the superposition state $v1 + v2$, denoted by tc, is longer than the normal conscious time tp of the conscious being for definite states, and the time difference is large enough for him to identify. This condition ensures that consciousness can take part in the process of wavefunction collapse; otherwise consciousness can only appear after the collapse and will surely have no influence upon the collapse process. Now we will explain why the conscious being can distinguish the definite perception states $v1$ or $v2$ and the superposition state $v1 + v2$.

First, we assume that a definite perception can appear only after the collapse of the superposition state $v1 + v2$. This assumption seems plausible. Then the conscious being can have a definite perception after the conscious time tp for the states $v1$ and $v2$, but only after the collapse time tc can the conscious being have a definite perception for the superposition state $v1 + v2$. Since the conscious being satisfies the slow collapse condition and can distinguish the times tp and tc, he can distinguish the definite perception state $v1$ or $v2$ and the superposition state $v1 + v2$. Note that a similar argument was first given by Squires (1992).

Next, we assume that the above assumption is not true, i.e., that the conscious being in a superposition state can have a definite perception before the collapse has completed. We will show that the conscious being can also distinguish the states v1 + v2 and v1 or v2 with non-zero probability.

(1). If the definite perception of the conscious being in the superposed state v1 + v2 is neither v1 nor v2 (e.g. the perception is some sort of mixture of the perceptions v1 and v2), then obviously the conscious being can directly distinguish the states v1 + v2 and v1 or v2.

(2). If the definite perception of the conscious being in the superposed state v1+v2 is always v1, then the conscious being can directly distinguish the states v1+v2 and v2. Besides, the conscious being can also distinguish the states v1 + v2 and v1 with probability 1/2. The superposition state v1 + v2 will become v2 with probability 1/2 after the collapse, and the definite perception of the conscious being will change from v1 to v2 accordingly. But for the state v1, the perception of the conscious being has no such change.

(3). If the definite perception of the conscious being in the superposed state v1 + v2 is always v2, the proof is similar to (2).

(4). If the definite perception of the conscious being in the superposed state v1 + v2 is random, i.e., that one time it is v1, and another time it is v2, then the conscious being can still distinguish the states v1 + v2 and v1 or v2 with non-zero probability. For the definite perception states v1 or v2, the perception of the conscious being does not change. For the superposition state v1 + v2, the perception of the conscious being will change from v1 to v2 or from v2 to v1 with non-zero probability during the collapse process.

In fact, we can also give a compact proof by reduction to absurdity. Assume that a conscious being cannot distinguish the definite perception states v1 or v2 and the superposition state v1 + v2. This requires that for the superposition state v1 + v2 the conscious being must have the perception v1 or v2 immediately after the conscious time tp, and moreover, the perception must be exactly the same as his perception after the collapse of the superposition state v1 + v2. Otherwise he will be able to distinguish the superposition state v1 + v2 from the definite state v1 or v2. Since the conscious time tp is shorter than the collapse time tc, the requirement means that the conscious being knows the collapse result beforehand. This is impossible due to the essential randomness of the collapse process. Note that even if this is possible, the conscious being also has a distinct quantum physical effect, i.e., that he can know the random collapse result beforehand.

To sum up, we have shown that if a conscious being satisfies the slow collapse condition, he can readily distinguish the nonorthogonal states v1 + v2 (or v1 - v2) and v1 or v2, which is an impossible task for a physical measuring system without consciousness.

3. The Condition

The above quantum physical effect of consciousness depends on the slow collapse condition, namely that for a conscious being the collapse time of a superposition of his conscious perceptions is longer than his normal conscious time. Whether this condition is available for human brains depends on concrete models of consciousness and wavefunction collapse. For example, if a definite conscious perception involves less neurons such as several thousand neurons, then the collapse time of the superposition of such perceptions will be readily in the same level as the normal conscious time (several hundred milliseconds) according to some dynamical collapse models (Gao 2006a, 2006b, 2008a, 2008b). This result is also supported by the Penrose-Hameroff orchestrated objective reduction model (Hameroff and Penrose 1996; Hagan, Hameroff and Tuszynski 2002). In the model, if a conscious perception involves about 109 participating tubulin, then the collapse time will be several hundred milliseconds and in the order of normal conscious time. When assuming that 10% of the tubulin contained becomes involved, the conscious perception also involves about one thousand neurons (there are roughly 107 tubulin per neuron). In addition, even though the slow collapse condition is unavailable for human brains, it cannot be in principle excluded that there exist some small brain creatures in the universe who satisfy the slow collapse condition (see also Squires 1992).

A more important point needs to be stressed here. The collapse time estimated above is only the average collapse time for an ensemble composed of identical superposition states. The collapse time of a single superposition state is an essentially stochastic variable, which value can range between zero and infinity. As a result, the slow collapse condition can always be satisfied for some collapse events with a certain probability. For these random collapse processes, the collapse time of the single superposition state is much longer than the average collapse time and the normal conscious time, and thus the conscious being can distinguish the nonorthogonal states and have the distinct quantum physical effect. As we will see, this ultimate possibility will have important implications for the nature of consciousness.

Lastly, we note that the slow collapse condition is also available in the many-worlds theory and de Broglie-Bohm theory (Gao 2004). For these two theories, the collapse time will be replaced by the decoherence time. First, since a conscious being is able to be conscious of its own state, he can always be taken as a closed self-measuring system in theory. In both many-worlds theory and de Broglie-Bohm theory, the state of a closed system satisfies the linear Schrödinger equation, and thus no apparent collapse happens or the decoherence time is infinite for the superposition state of a closed conscious system. Therefore, the slow collapse condition can be more readily satisfied in these theories when a conscious system has only a very weak interaction with environment. By comparison, in most dynamical collapse theories, the superposition state of a closed system also collapses by itself. Secondly, a conscious system (e.g. a human brain or neuron groups in the brain) often has a very strong interaction with environment in practical situations. As a result, the decoherence time is usually much shorter than the collapse time, and the slow collapse condition will be less readily satisfied in many-worlds theory and de Broglie-Bohm theory than in the dynamical collapse theories. This difference can be used to test these different quantum theories.

4. Implications

Consciousness is the most familiar phenomenon. Yet it is also the hardest to explain. The relationship between objective physical process and subjective conscious experience presents a well-known hard problem for science (Chalmers 1996). It retriggers the recent debate about the long-standing dilemma of panpsychism versus emergentism (Strawson et al 2006; Seager and Allen-Hermanson 2010). Though emergentism is currently the most popular solution to the hard problem of consciousness, many doubt that it can bridge the explanation gap ultimately. By comparison, panpsychism may provide an attractive and promising way to solve the hard problem, though it also encounters some serious problems (Seager and Allen-Hermanson 2010). It is widely believed that the physical world is causally closed, i.e., that there is a purely physical explanation for the occurrence of every physical event and the explanation does not refer to any consciousness property (see, e.g. McGinn 1999). But if panpsychism is true, the fundamental consciousness property should take part in the causal chains of the physical world and should present itself in our investigation of the physical world. Then does consciousness have any causal efficacy in the physical world?

As we have argued above, a conscious observer can distinguish two non-orthogonal states, while the physical measuring system without consciousness cannot. Accordingly, consciousness does have a causal efficacy in the physical world when considering the fundamental quantum processes. This will provide a strong support for panpsychism. In fact, we can argue that if consciousness has a distinct quantum physical effect, then it cannot be emergent but be a fundamental property of substance. Here is the argument.

If consciousness is emergent, then the conscious beings should also follow the fundamental physical principles such as the principle of energy conservation etc, though they may have some distinct high-level functions. According to the principles of quantum mechanics, two nonorthogonal states cannot be distinguished. However, a conscious being can distinguish the nonorthogonal states in principle. This clearly indicates that consciousness violates the quantum principles, which are the most fundamental physical principles. Therefore, the consciousness property cannot be reducible or emergent but be a fundamental property of substance. It should be not only possessed by the conscious beings, but also possessed by atoms as well as physical measuring devices. The difference only lies in the conscious content. The conscious content of a human being can be very complex, while the conscious content of a physical measuring device is probably very simple. In order to distinguish two nonorthogonal states, the conscious content of a measuring system must at least contain the perceptions of the nonorthogonal states. It might be also possible that the conscious content of a physical measuring device can be complex enough to distinguish two nonorthogonal states, but the effect is too weak to be detected by present experiments.

On the other hand, if consciousness is a fundamental property of substance, then it is quite natural that it violates the existing fundamental physical principles, which do not include it at all. It is expected that a complete theory of nature must describe all properties of substance, thus consciousness, the new fundamental property, must enter the theory from the start. Since the distinguishability of nonorthogonal states violates the linear superposition principle, consciousness will introduce a nonlinear element to the complete evolution equation of the wave function. The nonlinearity is not stochastic but definite. It has been argued that the nonlinear quantum evolution introduced by consciousness has no usual problems of nonlinear quantum mechanics (Gao 2006b).

Lastly, it should be noted that the above argument for panpsychism depends on the assumption that the wavefunction collapse or the quantum-to-classical transition in general is an objective physical process. However, the conclusion is actually independent of the origin of the wavefunction collapse. If the wavefunction collapse results from the consciousness of observer, then consciousness will also have the distinct quantum effect of collapsing the wave function, and thus consciousness should be a fundamental property of substance too. In addition, we stress that this conclusion is also independent of the interpretations of quantum mechanics. It only depends on two firm facts: one is the existence of indefinite quantum superpositions, and the other is the existence of definite conscious perceptions.

5. Conclusions

It is widely thought that the quantum-to-classical transition and consciousness are two essentially independent processes. But this does not mean that the result of their combination must be plain. In this article, we have shown that a conscious being can have a distinct quantum physical effect during the quantum-to-classical transition. A conscious system can measure whether he is in a definite perception state or in a quantum superposition of definite perception states, while a system without consciousness cannot distinguish such nonorthogonal states. This new result may have some important implications for quantum theory and the science of consciousness. In particular, it may provide a quantum basis for panpsychism.

References

Bell, J. S. (1987). Speakable and Unspeakable In Quantum Mechanics. Cambridge: Cambridge University Press.

Bohm, D. (1952). A suggested interpretation of quantum theory in terms of "hidden" variables, I and II. Phys. Rev. 85, 166-193.

Chalmers, D. (1996). The Conscious Mind. Oxford: University of Oxford Press.

Everett, H. (1957). "Relative state" formulation of quantum mechanics, Rev. Mod. Phys. 29, 454-462.

Gao, S. (2004). Quantum collapse, consciousness and superluminal communication, Found. Phys. Lett, 17(2), 167-182.

Gao, S. (2006a). A model of wavefunction collapse in discrete space-time, Int. J. Theo. Phys. 45 (10), 1943-1957.

Gao, S. (2006b). Quantum Motion: Unveiling the Mysterious Quantum World. Bury St Edmunds: Arima Publishing.

Gao, S. (2008a). God Does Play Dice with the Universe. Bury St Edmunds: Arima Publishing.

Gao, S. (2008b). A quantum theory of consciousness. Minds and Machines 18 (1), 39-52.

Gao, S. (2011). Meaning of the wave function, Int. J. Quant. Chem. Article first published online: http://onlinelibrary.wiley.com/doi/10.1002/qua.22972/abstract.

Ghirardi, G. C., Grassi, R., Butterfield, J., and

Fleming, G. N. (1993). Parameter dependence and outcome dependence in dynamic models for state-vector reduction, Found. Phys., 23, 341.

Ghirardi, G. (2008). Collapse Theories, The Stanford Encyclopedia of Philosophy (Fall 2008 Edition), Edward N. Zalta (ed.), http://plato.stanford.edu/archives/fall2008/entries/qm-collapse/.

Hagan, S., Hameroff, S. R., and Tuszynski, J. A. (2002). Quantum computation in brain microtubules: decoherence and biological feasibility, Phys. Rev. E 65, 061901.

Hameroff, S. R. (1998). Funda-Mentality: Is the conscious mind subtly linked to a basic level of the universe? Trends in Cognitive Sciences 2(4):119-127.

Hameroff, S. R. (2007). Consciousness, neurobiology and quantum mechanics: The case for a connection, In: The Emerging Physics of Consciousness, edited by Jack Tuszynski, New York: Springer-Verlag.

Hameroff, S. R. and Penrose, R. (1996), Conscious events as orchestrated space-time selections, Journal of Consciousness Studies, 3 (1), 36-53.

London, F., and Bauer, E. (1939). La théorie de l'observation en mécanique quantique. Hermann, Paris. English translation: The theory of observation in quantum mechanics. In Quantum Theory and Measurement, ed. by J.A. Wheeler and W.H. Zurek, Princeton University Press, Princeton, 1983, pp. 217-259.

McGinn, C. (1999). The Mysterious Flame: Conscious Minds in a Material World. New York: Basic Books.

Nauenberg, M. (2007). Critique of "Quantum enigma: Physics encounters consciousness". Foundations of Physics 37 (11), 1612–1627.

Nielsen, M. A. and Chuang, I. L. (2000). Quantum Computation and Quantum Information. Cambridge: Cambridge University Press. Section 1.6.

Penrose, R. (1989). The Emperor's New Mind. Oxford: Oxford University Press.

Penrose, R. (1994). Shadows of the Mind. Oxford: Oxford University Press.

Seager, W. and Allen-Hermanson, S. (2010). Panpsychism, The Stanford Encyclopedia of Philosophy (Fall 2010 Edition), Edward N. Zalta (ed.), http://plato.stanford.edu/archives/fall2010/ entries/panpsychism/.

Squires, E. (1992). Explicit collapse and superluminal signaling, Phys. Lett. A 163, 356-358.

Stapp, H. P. (1993). Mind, Matter, and Quantum Mechanics. New York: Springer-Verlag.

Stapp, H. P. (2007). Mindful Universe: Quantum Mechanics and the Participating Observer. New York: Springer-Verlag.

Strawson, G. et al. (2006). Consciousness and its Place in Nature: Does Physicalism entail Panpsychism? (ed. A. Freeman). Exeter, UK: Imprint Academic.

von Neumann, J. (1932/1955). Mathematical Foundations of Quantum Mechanics. Princeton: Princeton University Press. German original Die mathematischenGrundlagen der Quantenmechanik. Berlin: Springer-Verlag, 1932.

Wigner, E. P. (1967). Symmetries and Reflections. Bloomington and London: Indiana University Press, 171-184.

Wootters, W. K. and Zurek, W. H. (1982). A single quantum cannot be cloned. Nature 299, 802-803.

The Conscious Observer in the Quantum Experiment

Fred Kuttner and Bruce Rosenblum

Physics Department, University of California, Santa Cruz,
1156 High Street, Santa Cruz, CA 95064

Abstract

A quantum-theory-neutral version of the two-slit experiment displays the intrusion of the conscious observer into physics. In addition to the undisputed experimental results, only the inescapable assumption of the free choice of the experimenter is required. In discussing the experiment in terms of the quantum theory, other aspects of the quantum measurement problem also appear.

KEY WORDS: Consciousness, quantum, experiment, free-will, John Bell

1. INTRODUCTION

The intrusion of the observer into physics appeared at the inception of quantum theory eight decades ago. With this "quantum measurement problem," the physics discipline encountered something apparently beyond "physics" (Greenstein & Zajonc 1997).

Photons and electrons manifested "wave-particle duality": They exhibited wave properties or particle properties depending on the experimental technique used to observe them. Wave properties imply a spread-out entity, while particle properties imply a not spread-out entity. The contradiction was perhaps acceptable for these not-quite-real objects seen only as effects on macroscopic measuring apparatus (Heisenberg 1971).

Today, quantum weirdness is demonstrated in increasingly large systems (Haroche & Raimond 2006), and interpretations of "what it all means" proliferate (Elitzur et. al. 2006). Essentially every interpretation ultimately requires the intrusion of the conscious observer to account for the classical-like world of our experience (Squires 1994, Penrose, R. 2005).

The quantum measurement problem is often considered a problem of the quantum theory: How to explain the collapse of the multiple possibilities of the wavefunction to a single observed actuality. This is indeed unresolved (Squires, 1993). However, the measurement problem also arises directly from the quantum-theory-neutral experiment, and depends crucially on the assumption of free will of the experimenter. We present a version of the archetypal quantum experiment illustrating the intrusion of the conscious observer into the experiment.

2. THE ARCHETYPAL QUANTUM EXPERIMENT

According to Richard Feynman, "[The two-slit experiment] contains the only mystery. We cannot make the mystery go away by "explaining" how it works. . . In telling you how it works we will have told you about the basic peculiarities of all quantum mechanics" (Feynman, et. al. 2006).

In the two-slit experiment one can choose to demonstrate either of two contradictory things: that each object was a compact entity coming through a single slit or that each was a spread out entity coming through both. Similar experiments have been done with photons, electrons, atoms, large molecules, and are being attempted with yet larger objects such as live viruses (Clauser 2010). We will just refer to "objects."

We present an equivalent version of the two-slit experiment in which one can choose to show that an object was wholly in a single box (Rosenblum & Kuttner 2002). But one could have chosen to show that that same object was not wholly in a single box. By telling the story with objects captured in boxes, one can decide at leisure which of the two contradictory situations to demonstrate for each isolated object. This displays the quantum challenge to our intuition that an observer-independent physical reality exists "out there." We describe quantum-theory-neutral experiments, by telling only what could be directly observed.

The experimenter is presented with a set of box pairs, say twenty pairs of boxes. Each pair of boxes contains a single object. How the box pairs were prepared is irrelevant for these quantum-theory-neutral experiments. Since it's easiest to describe the preparation in quantum language, we do that in the next section.

The "Which Box" Experiment The experimenter is instructed to determine, for this set of box pairs, which box of each pair contains the object. He does this by placing each box pair in turn in the same position in front of a screen that an object would mark on impact. He then cuts a narrow slit first in one box of the pair, and then the other. For some box pairs, an impact occurs only on opening the first box, and then not on opening the second box. For others, the impact occurs only on the second opening. In this "which box" experiment, the experimenter thus determines which box of each pair contained the object, and which box was empty. The experimenter establishes that for this set of box pairs, each object had been wholly in a single box of its pair.

Repeating this with box pairs placed in the same position in front of the screen, the experimenter notes a more or less random spread of marks on the screen.

The "Interference" Experiment The experimenter is presented with second set of box pairs. This time he is instructed to cut slits in both boxes of each pair at about the same time. He does so, positioning each box pair in the same position in front of the screen. (It's an interference experiment, and we so name it. But we make no reference to waves.)

This time the objects do not impact randomly. There are regions where many objects land, and regions where none land. Each object followed a rule specifying the regions in which it was allowed to land.

To investigate the nature of this rule, the experimenter repeats the experiment with different spacings of the boxes of a pair from each other. He finds that the rule each object follows depends on the spacing of its box pair. Each object "knows" the spacing of its box pair. Something of each object therefore had to have been in each box of its pair. The experimenter establishes that—unlike the previous set, for which objects were each wholly in a single box—for this set of box pairs, objects were not wholly in a single box.

The Free Choice Of Experiment The experimenter is reminded that he established that the objects in the first set of box pairs were wholly in a single box, while the objects in the second set of box pairs were not wholly in a single box. Now presented with a third set of box pairs, he is asked to establish whether the objects in this set of box pairs are, or are not, wholly in a single box.

The experimenter arbitrarily chooses to do the "which box" experiment, and thus establishes that this box-pair set had contained objects wholly in a single box. Given another set of box pairs and similar instructions, he chooses the "interference" experiment, and establishes that the objects in this set were not wholly in a single box.

Offered further sets of box pairs, the experimenter finds that each time he chooses to do a "which box" experiment, objects were wholly in a single box. Each time he chooses an "interference" experiment, he establishes a contradictory physical situation, that objects were not wholly in a single box. His free choice of experiment seemed to create the prior history of what had been in the boxes. He's baffled.

If the experimenter's choice of experiment were predetermined to match what was actually in each box pair set, he would see no problem. He recognizes this, but he is certain his choices were freely made. His conscious certainty of his free will causes him to experience a measurement problem with the archetypal quantum experiment. In fact, the free choice of the observation set is generally recognized as an essential aspect of any inductive science.

No experiment in classical physics raised the issue of free will. In classical physics, questions of free will arose only out of an ignorable aspect of the deterministic theory.

We emphasize that in describing the intrusion of the observer into the archetypal quantum experiment we never referred to quantum theory, wavefunctions, or waves of any kind. Even were quantum theory never invented, one could do these experiments, and the results would present an inexplicable enigma (Greenstein & Zajonc 1997).

3. THE BOX-PAIR EXPERIMENT IN QUANTUM THEORY

The Preparation Of The Box Pairs Objects are sent one at a time, at a known speed, toward a "mirror" that equally transmits and reflects their wavefunction. In Figure 1, a wavefunction is shown at three successive times. The reflected part is subsequently reflected so that each part is directed into one of a pair of boxes. The doors of the boxes are closed at a time when the wavefunction is within the boxes.

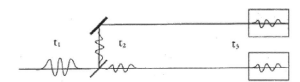

Figure 1. Schematic diagram of the preparation of the box pairs. The object's wavefunction is shown at three successive times.

Dividing a wavefunction into well-separated regions is part of every interference experiment. Holding an object in a box pair without disturbing its wavefunction would be tricky, but doable in principle. Capturing an object in physical boxes is not actually required for our demonstration. A sufficiently extended path length would be enough. The box pair is a conceptual device to emphasize that a conscious choice can be made while an object exists as an isolated entity.

Observation In the box-pairs version of the two-slit experiment, the wavefunction spreads widely from the small slit in a box. In the "which box" experiment, it emerges from each single box and impinges rather uniformly on the detection screen. In the "interference" experiment, parts of the wavefunction emerge simultaneously from both boxes and combine to form regions of maxima and minima on the detection screen.

The Born postulate has the absolute square of the wavefunction in a region giving the probability of an object being "observed" there. In the Copenhagen interpretation of quantum mechanics, observation takes place, for all practical purposes, as soon as the microscopic quantum object encounters the macroscopic screen (Griffiths 1995, Stapp 1972). Macroscopic objects are then assumed to be classical-physics objects viewed by the experimenter. Other interpretations of quantum mechanics, attempting to go beyond practical purposes, consider observation to be more involved with the actual conscious experience of the experimental result.

History Creation Finding an object in a single box means the whole object came to that box on a particular single path after its earlier encounter with the semi-transparent mirror. Choosing an interference experiment would establish a different history: that aspects of the object came on two paths to both boxes after its earlier encounter with the semi-transparent mirror. (As noted above, the question of history creation also arose in the quantum-theory-neutral experiment.) Quantum cosmologist John Wheeler (1980) suggested that quantum theory's history creation be tested. He would have the choice of which experiment to do delayed until after the object made its "decision" whether to come on a single path or whether to come on both at the semi-transparent mirror. The experiment was done with photons and a mirror arrangement much like our Figure 1. Getting the same results as in the usual quantum experiment would imply that the relevant history was indeed created by the later choice of experiment.

For a human to make a conscious choice of which experiment to do takes perhaps a second, in which a photon travels 186,000 miles. Therefore the actual "choice" of experiment was made by a fast electronic switch making random choices. The most rigorous version of the experiment was done in 2007 (Jacques et al., 2007), when reliable single-photon pulses could be generated, and fast enough electronics were available. The result (of course?) confirmed quantum theory's predictions. Observation created the relevant history.

Non-locality and Connectedness When an object is observed to be in a particular location, its probability of being elsewhere becomes zero. Its wavefunction elsewhere "collapses" to zero, and to unity (a certainty) in the location in which the object was found. If an object is found to be in one box of its pair, its wavefunction in the other box instantaneously becomes zero–no matter how far apart the boxes are.

In its usual interpretation, quantum theory does not include an object in addition to the wavefunction of the object. The wavefunction is, in this sense, the physical entity itself. Thus the wavefunction being affected by observation everyplace at once is problematic in the light of special relativity, which prohibits any matter, or any message, to travel faster than the speed of light. The non-local, instantaneous collapse of the wavefunction on observation poses the quantum measurement problem as viewed from quantum theory.

The instantaneous, non-local collapse of the wavefunction provoked Einstein to challenge the completeness of quantum theory with the famous EPR paper (Einstein, et al. 1935). To avoid what Einstein later derided as "spooky action at a distance," EPR held that there must be properties at the microscopic level that quantum theory did not include. However, since EPR provided no experimental challenge to quantum theory, it was largely ignored by physicists for three decades as merely arguing a philosophical issue.

John Bell (1964) proved a theorem allowing experimental tests establishing the existence of an instantaneous connectedness, Einstein's "spooky action." The experiments (Freedman & Clauser, 1972; Aspect et al. 1984) showed that if objects had interacted, what an observer chose to observe about one of them would instantaneously influence the result that an arbitrarily remote observer chose to observe for the other object.

The Bell results included the assumption of the free will of the observers, that their choices of what to observe were independent of each other and independent of all prior physical events. Denying that assumption would be "more mind boggling" than the connectedness the denial attempts to avoid. Such denial would imply, Bell wrote: "Apparently separate parts of the world would be conspiratorially entangled, and our apparent free will would be entangled with them" (Bell 1981).

4. THE ROBOT FALLACY

The most common argument that consciousness is not involved in the quantum experiment is that a not-conscious robot could do the experiment. However, for any experiment to be meaningful, a human must eventually evaluate it. A programmed robot sees no enigma. Consider the human evaluation of the robot's experiment:

The robot presents a printout to the human experimenter. It shows that with some sets of box pairs the robot chose a which-box experiment, establishing that the objects were wholly in a single box. With other sets of box pairs, choosing the interference experiment, it established that the objects were not wholly in a single box.

On the basis of this data, the human experimenter could conclude that certain box-pair sets actually contained objects wholly in a single box, while others contained objects not wholly in a single box. However, a question arises in the mind of the experimenter: How did the robot choose the appropriate experiment with each box-pair set? What if, for example, the robot chose a which-box experiment with objects not wholly in a single box? A partial object was never reported.

Without free will, the not-conscious robot must use some "mechanical" choice procedure. Investigating, the experimenter finds, for example, that it flips a coin. Heads, a which-box experiment; tails interference. The experimenter is troubled by the mysterious correlation between the landing of the coin and what was presumably actually in a particular box-pair set.

To avoid that inexplicable correlation, the experimenter replaces the robot's coin flipping with the one choice method she is most sure is not correlated with the contents of a box-pair set: her own free choice. Pushing a button telling the robot which experiment to do, she establishes what she would by doing the experiment directly, that by her conscious free choice she can establish either of two contradictory physical situations. In the end, the robot argument establishes nothing.

5. CONCLUSION

Extending the implications of quantum mechanics beyond the microscopic realm admittedly leads to ridiculous-seeming conclusions. Nevertheless, the experimental results are undisputed, and quantum theory is the most basic and most battle-tested theory in all of science.

The embarrassing intrusion of the conscious observer into physics can be mitigated by focusing on observation in quantum theory, the collapse (or decoherence) of the wavefunction. However, the inescapable assumption of free choice by the experimenter displays the intrusion of the observer in the quantum-theory-neutral quantum experiment, logically prior to the quantum theory.

The intrusion was less disturbing when confined to never-directly-observed microscopic objects. However, the vast no-man's-land that once separated the microscopic and the macroscopic realms, allowing a tacit acceptance of this view, has been invaded by technology.

Bell's theorem, and the experiments it stimulated, seems to rule out a resolution of the quantum measurement problem by the existence of an underlying structure, somehow involving only properties localized in quantum objects. An overarching structure, somehow involving conscious free will, seems required (Squires 1991).

Acknowledgments: Parts of this article have been taken from the second edition of our book, Quantum Enigma: Physics Encounters Consciousness, with the permission of Oxford University Press.

References

Aspect A., Dalibard J., Roger G. (1982). Experimental Test Of Bell Inequalities Using Time-Varying Analyzers. Physical Review Letters 49, 1804-1807.

Bell, J.S. (1964). On the Problem of Hidden Variables in Quantum Mechanics. Physics 1, 195.

Bell, J. S. 1981. Bertlmann's Socks and the Nature of Reality. Journal de physique 42, 41.

Clauser, J.F. (2010). deBroglie Wave Interference of Small Rocks and Live Viruses. In: Cohen, R.S., Horne, M., Stachel, J. (Eds.), Experimental Metaphysics: Quantum Mechanical Studies for Abner Shimony, Volume One. Kluwer Academic, Dordrecht, The Netherlands, pp. 1-12.

Einstein, A., Podolsky, B., Rosen, N. (1935). Can quantum-mechanical description of physical reality be considered complete? Physical Review 47, 777-780.

Elitzur, A. Dolev, S., Kolenda, A. (Eds), (2006). Quo Vadis Quantum Mechanics. Springer, Berlin.

Feynman, R.P., Leighton, R.B., Sands, M. (2006). The Feynman Lectures on Physics, Vol. III. Addison-Wesley, Reading, MA.

Freedman, S.J., Clauser, J. F. (1972). Experimental Test Of Local Hidden-Variable Theories. Physical Review Letters 28, 938-941.

Greenstein, G., Zajonc, A.G. (1997). The Quantum Challenge: Modern Research on the Foundations of Quantum Mechanics. Jones and Bartlett, Sudbury, MA.

Griffiths, D.J. (1995). Introduction to Quantum Mechanics. Prentice Hall, Englewood Cliffs, NJ.

Haroche, S., Raimond, J-M. (2006). Exploring the Quantum: Atoms, Cavities, and Photons. Oxford University Press, Oxford.

Heisenberg, W. (1971) Physics and Beyond: Encounters and Conversations. Harper & Row, New York.

Jacques, V., Wu, E., Grosshans, F., Treussart, F., Grangier, P., Aspect, A., Roch, J-F. (2007). Experimental realization of Wheeler's delayed-choice gedanken experiment. Science 315, 966-968.

Penrose, R. (2006). Foreword. In: Elitzur, A. Dolev, S., Kolenda, A. (Eds), Quo Vadis Quantum Mechanics. Springer, Berlin, pp. v-viii.

Rosenblum, B., Kuttner, F. (2002) The Observer in the Quantum Experiment. Foundations of Physics 32, 1273-1293.

Squires, E.J. (1991). One Mind Or Many - A Note On The Everett Interpretation Of Quantum-Theory. Synthese, 89, 283-286.

Squires, E.J. (1993). Quantum-Theory And The Relation Between The Conscious Mind And The Physical World. Synthese, 97, 109-123.

Squires, E.J. (1994). Quantum Theory And The Need For Consciousness. Journal of Consciousness Studies 1, 201-204.

Stapp, H.P. (1972). The Copenhagen Interpretation. American Journal of Physics 40, 1098-1115.

Wheeler (1980). Delayed Choice Experiments and the Bohr-Einstein Dialog. In: The American Philosophical Society and the Royal Society: Papers Read at a Meeting June 5, 1980. American Philosophical Society, Philadelphia, PA.

Does Quantum Mechanics Require A Conscious Observer?

Michael Nauenberg

Physics Dept. University of California Santa Cruz, CA, USA

Abstract

The view that the implementation of the principles of quantum mechanics requires a conscious observer is based on misconceptions that are described in this article.

KEY WORDS: Quantum Physics, Wave function, Observer, Consciousness

The notion that the interpretation of quantum mechanics requires a conscious observer is rooted, I believe, in a basic misunderstanding of the meaning of a) the quantum wavefunction ψ, and b) the quantum measurement process. This misunderstanding originated with the work of John von Neumann (1932) on the foundations of quantum mechanics, and afterwards it was spread by some prominent physicists like Eugene Wigner (1984); by now it has acquired a life of its own, giving rise to endless discussions on this subject, as shown by the articles in the Journal of Cosmology (see volumes 3 and 14).

Quantum mechanics is a statistical theory that determines the probabilities for the outcome of a physical process when its initial state has been determined. A fundamental quantity in this theory is the wavefunction ψ which is a complex function that depends on the variables of the system under consideration. The absolute square of this function, ψ^2, gives the probability to find the system in one of its possible quantum states. Early pioneers in the development of quantum mechanics like Niels Bohr (1958) assumed, however, that the measurement devices behave according to the laws of classical mechanics, but von Neumann pointed out, quite correctly, that such devices also must satisfy the principles of quantum mechanics. Hence, the wavefunction describing this device becomes entangled with the wavefunction of the object that is being measured, and the superposition of these entangled wavefunctions continues to evolve in accordance with the equations of quantum mechanics. This analysis leads to the notorious von Neumann chain, where the measuring devices are left forever in an indefinite superposition of quantum states. It is postulated that this chain can be broken, ultimately, only by the mind of a conscious observer.

Forty five years ago I wrote an article on this subject with John Bell who became, after von Neumann, the foremost contributor to the foundations of quantum mechanics, where we presented, tongue in cheek, the von Neumann paradox as a dilemma:

> The experiment may be said to start with the printed proposal and to end with the issue of the report. The laboratory, the experimenter, the administration, and the editorial staff of the Physical Review are all just part of the instrumentation. The incorporation of (presumably) conscious experimenters and editors into the equipment raises a very intriguing question... If the interference is destroyed, then the Schrodinger equation is incorrect for systems containing consciousness. If the interference is not destroyed, the quantum mechanical description is revealed as not wrong but certainly incomplete (Bell and Nauenberg, 1966).

We added the remark that "we emphasize not only that our view is that of a minority, but also that current interest in such questions is small. The typical physicist feels that they have been long answered, and that he will fully understand just how, if ever he can spare twenty minutes to think about it." Now the situation has changed dramatically, and interest in a possible role of consciousness in quantum mechanics has become widespread. But Bell, who died in 1990 , believed in the second alternative to the von Neumann dilemma, remarking that :

> I think the experimental facts which are usually offered to show that we must bring the observer into quantum theory do not compel us to adopt that conclusion (Davies and Brown, 1986).

Actually, by now it is understood by most physicists that von Neumann's dilemma arises because he had simplified the measuring device to a system with only a few degrees of freedom, e.g. a pointer with only two states (see Appendix). Instead, a measuring device must have an exponentially large number of degrees of freedom in order to record, more or less permanently, the outcome of a measurement. This recording takes place by a time irreversible process. The occurrence of such processes in Nature already mystified 19th century scientists, who argued that this feature implied a failure in the basic laws of classical physics, because these laws are time reversible. Ludwig Boltzmann resolved this paradox by taking into account the large number of degrees of freedom of a macroscopic system, which implied that to a very high degree of probability such a system evolved with a unique direction in time. Such an irreversibility property is also valid for quantum systems, and it constitutes the physical basis for the second law of thermodynamics, where the arrow of time is related to the increase of entropy of the system.

Another misconception is the assumption that the wavefunction ψ describing the state of a system in quantum mechanics behaves like a physical object. For example, the authors of a recent book discussing quantum mechanics and consciousness claim that

> In quantum theory there is no atom in addition to the wavefunction of the atom. This is so crucial that we say it again in other words. The atom's wave-functions and the atom are the same thing; "the wave function of the atom" is a synonym for "the atom". Since the wavefunction ψ is synonymous with the atom itself, the atom is simultaneously in both boxes. The point of that last paragraph is hard to accept. That is why we keep repeating it (Rosenblum and Kuttner, 2006).

If the wavefunction ψ is a physical object like an atom, then the proponents of this flawed concept must require the existence of a mechanism that lies outside the principles governing the time evolution of the wavefunction ψ in order to account for the so-called "collapse" of the wavefunction after a measurement has been performed. But the wavefunction ψ is not a physical object like, for example, an atom which has an observable mass, charge and spin as well as internal degrees of freedom. Instead, ψ is an abstract mathematical function that contains all the statistical information that an observer can obtain from measurements of a given system. In this case there isn't any mystery that its mathematical form must change abruptly after a measurement has been performed. For further details on this subject, see (Nauenberg, 2007) and (van Kampen, 2008). The surprising fact that mathematical abstractions can explain and predict real physical phenomena has been emphazised by Wigner (Wigner 1960), who wrote:

> The miracle of appropriateness of the language of mathematics for the formulation of the laws of physics is a wonderful gift which we neither undestand nor deserve.

I conclude with a few quotations, that are relevant to the topic addressed here, by some of the most prominent physicists in the second half of the 20th century.

Richard P. Feynman (Nobel Prize, 1965):

> Nature does not know what you are looking at, and she behaves the way she is going to behave whether you bother to take down the data or not (Feynman et al., 1965).

Murray Gellmann (Nobel Prize, 1969):

> The universe presumably couldn't care less whether human beings evolved on some obscure planet to study its history; it goes on obeying the quantum mechanical laws of physics irrespective of observation by

physicists (Rosenblum and Kuttner 2006, 156).

Anthony J. Leggett (Nobel Prize 2003):

It may be somewhat dangerous to explain something one does not understand very well [the quantum measurement process] by invoking something [consciousness] one does not understand at all! (Leggett, 1991).

John A. Wheeler:

Caution: "Consciousness" has nothing whatsover to do with the quantum process. We are dealing with an event that makes itself known by an irreversible act of amplification, by an indelible record, an act of registration. Does that record subsequently enter into the "consciousness" of some person, some animal or some computer? Is that the first step into translating the measurement into "meaning" meaning regarded as "the joint product of all the evidence that is available to those who communicate." Then that is a separate part of the story, important but not to be confused with "quantum phenomena." (Wheeler, 1983).

John S. Bell:

From some popular presentations the general public could get the impression that the very existence of the cosmos depends on our being here to observe the observables. I do not know that this is wrong. I am inclined to hope that we are indeed that important. But I see no evidence that it is so in the success of contemporary quantum theory.

So I think that it is not right to tell the public that a central role for conscious mind is integrated into modern atomic physics. Or that `information' is the real stuff of physical theory. It seems to me irresponsible to suggest that technical features of contemporary theory were anticipated by the saints of ancient religions... by introspection.

The only 'observer' which is essential in orthodox practical quantum theory is the inanimate apparatus which amplifies the microscopic events to macroscopic consequences. Of course this apparatus, in laboratory experiments, is chosen and adjusted by the experiments. In this sense the outcomes of experiments are indeed dependent on the mental process of the experimenters! But once the apparatus is in place, and functioning untouched, it is a matter of complete indifference - according to ordinary quantum mechanics - whether the experimenters stay around to watch, or delegate such 'observing' to computers, (Bell, 1984).

Nico van Kampem:

Whoever endows ψ with more meaning than is needed for computing observable phenomena is responsible for the consequences. (van Kampen, 1988).

Appendix. Schrodinger's Cat: This cat story is notorious. It requires one to accept the notion that a cat, which can be in innumerable different biological states, can be represented by a two component wavefunction ψ, a bit of nonsense that Erwin Schrodinger, one of the original inventors of quantum mechanics, himself originated. One of the two components represents a live cat, and the other a dead cat. The cat is enclosed in a box containing a bottle filled with cyanide that opens when a radioactive nucleus in the box decays. Thus, this fictitious cat is a measuring device that is supposed to determine whether the nucleus has decayed or not when the box is opened. But according to the principles of quantum mechanics formulated by von Neumann, such a cat ought to be in a superposition of life and dead cat states, yet nobody has ever observed such a cat. Instead, it is expected that a movie camera - a real measuring device - that is also installed in the box containing the cat, would record a cat that is alive until the unpredictable moment that the radioactive nucleus decays, opening the bottle containing the cyanide that kills the cat. For obvious reasons such a gruesome experiment has never been performed. It is claimed that Schrodinger never accepted the statistical significance of his celebrated wavefunction.

References

Bohr, N. (1958). Quantum Physics and Philosophy, Causality and Complementarity in Essays 1958/1962 on Atomic Physics and Human Knowledge. Vintage Books

Bell, J. S., Nauenberg, M. (1966). The moral aspects of quantum me- chanics, in Preludes in Theoretical Physics, edited by A. De Shalit, Herman Feschbach, and Leon van Hove (North Holland, Amsterdam), pp. 279-286. Reprinted in J.S. Bell Speakable and Unspeakable in Quantum Mechanics (Cambridge Univ. Press 1987) p. 22

Bell, J. S. (1987). Introductory remarks at Naples-Amal meeting, May 7, 1984. In: Bell, J.S. Speakable and Unspeakable in Quantum Mechanics. Cambridge Univ. Press, p.170,

Davies, P.C.W., Brown, J.T. (1986). Ghost in the Atom. Cambridge Univ. Press, Interview with J. Bell, pp. 47-48

Feynman, R.P., Leighton, R.B., Sands,M. (1965). The Feynman lectures on Physics vol. 3 (Addison Wesley, Reading) 3-7

Leggett, A. (1991) Reflections on the Quantum Paradox, In: Quantum Implications, Routledge, London, p. 94

Nauenberg, M. (2007). Critique of Quantum Enigma: Physics encounters Consciousness, Foundations of Physics 37, 1612-162

Rosenblum, B and Kuttner, F. (2006). Quantum Enigma, Physics Encounters Consciousness . Oxford Univ. Press, p. 106

van Kampen, N. G. (1988). Ten theorems about quantum mechanical measurements Physica A 153, 97 .

van Kampen, N.G. (2008) The Scandal in Quantum Mechanics, American Journal of Physics 76, 989

von Neumann, J. (1932) Measurement and Reversibility, Chapters V and VI of Mathematische Grundlagen der Quantemmechanik, translated into English by R.T. Mayer, Mathematical Foundations of Quantum Mechanics, Princeton Univ. Press, Princeton (1955) pp. 347-445

Wigner, E. (1984). Review of the Quantum-Mechanical Measurement Problem, Science, Computers and the Information Onslaught, eds. D.M. Kerr et al.. Academic Press, New York, pp. 63-82 Reprinted in "The Collected Works of Eugene Paul Wigner", Part B, vol. 6, Springer-Verlag, Berlin, p. 240

Wheeler, J. A. (1983). Law without law. In: Quantum Theory and Measurement, edited by Wheeler, J.A. and Zurek, W.H., Princeton Univ. Press, Princeton, p. 196.

Wigner, E. (1960) The Unreasonable Effectiveness of Mathematics, Communications in Pure and Applied Mathematics 13, 1-14.

Consciousness Vectors
Steven Bodovitz

Principal, BioPerspectives,
1624 Fell Street, San Francisco, CA 94117 USA

Abstract

One of the defining characteristics, if not the defining characteristic of consciousness is the experience of continuity. One thought or sensation appears to transition immediately into the next, but this is likely an illusion. I propose that consciousness is broken up into discrete cycles of cognition and that the sense of continuity is the result of determining the magnitude and direction of changes between cycles. These putative consciousness vectors are analogous to motion vectors that enable us to perceive continuous motion even when watching a progression of static images. Detailed characterization of consciousness vectors, assuming they exist, would be a significant advance in the characterization of consciousness.

KEY WORDS: brainstorming, consciousness, conscious vector, consciousness vector, continuity, creativity, delay, DLPFC, dorsolateral prefrontal cortex, motion vector, philosophical zombie, sports psychology

Time is the substance I am made of. Time is a river which sweeps me along, but I am the river; it is a tiger which destroys me, but I am the tiger; it is a fire which consumes me, but I am the fire. - Jorge Luis Borges (1946).

1. Introduction

To paraphrase the eloquence of Borges, we are made of time and consumed by time. The continuity of experience is one of the defining features, if not the defining feature of consciousness. To be more specific, as first explained by Karl Lashley, each thought or sensation is stable, but each is immediately present after the other, fully formed, with no experience of the underlying processing that led each to become conscious (Lashley, 1956).

Another way to think about the continuity is through a thought experiment of the inverse condition. Start by imagining a lower state of continuity, in which each individual thought is stable, but gaps are apparent. Each. Word. For. Example. In. This. Sentence. Is. Separated. The extra breaks affect your experience of reading the sentence, because you have to think about the flow of the words to get the meaning. Now jump to a complete loss of continuity. Each. Word. Is. Completely. Frozen. In. Time. For. A. Moment. Each. Pops. Into. Cognition. And. Is. Replaced. By. Another. Without temporal integrity, we are repeatedly frozen in time. Frozen memories can inform us where we've been, but not where we are going. We become biological computers without sentience.

The concept of separating information processing from sentience has been proposed in a much more colorful manner by David Chalmers, who describes a philosophical zombie that roughly appears to be human, but otherwise has no awareness (Chalmers, 1996). This is not as abstract as it sounds, because one aspect of this concept has been demonstrated by Hakwan Lau and Richard Passingham (Lau & Passingham, 2006). These researchers used a variant of the well-known paradigm of masking. In a simple version, subjects are briefly shown an image, known as the target, followed quickly by a second brief image, known as the mask, and if the timing falls into well-defined parameters, the target is eliminated from conscious awareness (Koch, 2004a). Lau and Passingham used a more complex version known as a type II metacontrast masking, but the underlying principle is the same, and they tested the accuracy of identifying the target, in this case a square or a diamond, followed by asking the subjects to press keys to indicate whether they actually saw the identity of the target or simply guessed what it was. By using different lengths of time between the presentation of the target and the mask, the researchers were able to identify two conditions in which the accuracy of identifying the target was statistically the same, but the subjective assessments of awareness were significantly different (Lau & Passingham, 2006). Cognition (defined as high-level biological computation) and awareness can be separated, although presumably only under certain circumstances and for brief periods of time.

Taken together, the thought experiment and the actual experiment suggest that the output of cognitive processing is transferred into consciousness in a continuous or seemingly continuous process. The normal limit for information transfer is the speed of light, which is clearly faster than human perception, but not instantaneous. True continuity would presumably require a mechanism based on quantum mechanics. The possibility that microtubules mediate coherent quantum states across large populations of neurons was proposed by Stuart Hameroff and Roger Penrose (1996). This hypothesis has received indirect support in recent years. Physicists at the University of Geneva, for example, demonstrated quantum entanglement by observing two-photon interferences well above the Bell inequality threshold (Salart et al.

2008), but this was with isolated pairs of photons. Moreover, physicists at the University of California at Santa Barbara were able to coax a mechanical resonator into two states at once, which showed for the first time that quantum events could be observed in complex objects, but this required cooling to near absolute zero (Cho, 2010; O'Connell et al. 2010). Notwithstanding this recent progress, whether microtubules, which undergo constant remodeling, can be islands of quantum events in the biochemical and electrical cauldron of the human brain at 37 degrees Celsius remains to be observed. I propose an alternative hypothesis that, rather than true continuity, consciousness is broken up into discrete cycles of cognition and that the sense of continuity is the result of determining the magnitude and direction of changes between cycles.

2. Consciousness Is Likely Discontinuous

Even though the experience of continuity is a defining characteristic of consciousness, it is likely an illusion. The experimental evidence for the discontinuity is largely based on the delay between sensory perception and conscious awareness. Briefly, the pioneering work on the delay was performed by Benjamin Libet, in which he and his colleagues showed an undetectable stimulus could become conscious after approximately 500 msec (Libet et al. 1964; Libet et al. 1967; Libet et al. 1991), but it is not clear whether the delay was due to the processing time to reach consciousness or the time for summation of the stimulus to reach threshold, and others have criticized Libet's conclusions (for example, see Gomes, 1998; Pockett, 2002). A better study was designed by Marc Jeannerod and colleagues, in which subjects were trained to grasp one of three dowels following the appropriate signal and performed the task with a reaction time of 120 msec. When the subjects were asked to verbalize when they first became aware of the signal, the response time was 420 msec, or 300 msec longer (Castiello et al. 1991). Even allowing 50 msec for the required muscle contraction for verbalization, the delay is still a quarter of a second (Koch, 2004b). Thus, according to this experiment, the frequency of cycles of cognition is roughly 4 per second. A larger and arguably more compelling body of evidence for the delay comes from the well-established phenomena of masking, as described above, in which a mask eliminates and replaces the awareness of a target. The elimination is not the result of interfering with the sensory input because if a second mask is presented, the first mask can be eliminated and the awareness of the target can be restored (Dember & Purcell, 1967). The elimination is only possible with a delay between sensory perception and consciousness. The delay, in turn, indicates that consciousness is discontinuous (Koch, 2004c; Libet, 1999).

3. Continuity and Consciousness Vectors

If consciousness is discontinuous, but appears to be continuous, then the problem of understanding consciousness becomes better posed: what creates the continuity? I propose that the sense of continuity is the result of determining the magnitude and direction of changes between cycles (Bodovitz, 2008). These putative consciousness vectors, however, are largely undefined. They presumably track the magnitudes and directions of multiple changes in parallel and/or in aggregate. Moreover, they presumably track changes in inherently qualitative information, such as words and concepts. While these open questions leave the key tenet of this hypothesis unsubstantiated, they create opportunities for breakthroughs by experts in advanced mathematics, physics and/or computer science. At the very least, efforts to model consciousness vectors may provide insights into the value of using the flow of information as feedback for better organizing complex and dynamic data.

The most significant substantiation of consciousness vectors is through analogy to motion vectors, which add motion to a series of otherwise discrete images. The standard speed for movies based on film is 24 frames per second, but rather than strobing, we perceive smooth motion. This is because motion vectors are calculated by the visual system, most likely in visual area V5, also known as visual area MT (middle temporal). Without motion vectors, vision becomes a series of still images, a condition known as akinetopsia or visual motion blindness (Shipp et al. 1994; Zihl et al. 1983; Zihl et al. 1991). The strobe effect makes otherwise simple tasks, such as crossing a street, extremely difficult. The cars are a safe distance away, then bearing down, without any sense of the transition. Even though there is memory of where the cars were, there is no sense of where they are going. Likewise, without consciousness vectors, simple cognitive tasks involving even a limited series of steps would be extremely difficult.

Motion vectors, like consciousness vectors, appear relatively simple at first approximation. In fact, the retina is arguably even a two-dimensional, Euclidian array of detectors, and most objects in motion follow standard trajectories. Yet, the exact neural computations to generate motion vectors have been difficult to determine and are the subject of decades of debate (for review, see Born & Bradley, 2005), although there is consensus that they involve the mapping of retinal activity onto higher-order visual processors such as those in V1 and V5. Thus identifying the calculations for motion vectors may provide the ideal model system for identifying the calculations for the more complex consciousness vectors.

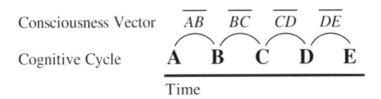

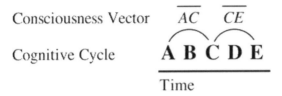

4. Continuity and the Awareness of Change

If consciousness vectors and a sense of continuity are necessary for consciousness, then the corollary is that changes in cognition are necessary for awareness. This corollary is supported by the fact that we only see changes in our visual field. Even though an image may be static, our eyes never are, even during fixation. Our eyes are in constant motion with tremors, drifts and microsaccades. If these fixational eye movements are eliminated, then visual perception fades to a homogenous field (Ditchburn & Ginsborg, 1952; Riggs & Ratliff, 1952; Yarbus, 1967). The significance of these fixational movements for visual processing has long been debated, and no clear consensus has emerged (for review, see Martinez-Conde et al. 2004). The best correlation of neuronal responses to fixational eye movements are specific clusters of long, tight bursts, which might enhance spatial and temporal summation (Martinez-Conde et al. 2004); in addition, a more recent study showed that fixational eye movements improve discrimination of high spatial frequency stimuli (Rucci et al. 2007). But a lack of enhancement or improved discrimination does not explain the complete loss of visual perception. A better explanation is that changes in cognition are necessary for awareness.

5. Discussion

If cognition is broken up into discrete cycles and consciousness vectors create the illusion of continuity, then conscious feedback has pitfalls. It is slow, such that any action that occurs in less than approximately 250 msec will be over before reaching consciousness. Moreover, if events are happening too quickly and/or you are thinking too fast, your conscious feedback will miss changes in cognition, and, to make matters worse, you will have no immediate awareness of any deficiencies and will only be able to deduce the errors afterwards (see figure 1).

In addition, according to this theory, conscious feedback is inherently subtractive. The feedback tracks the magnitude and direction of what has already happened, thereby constraining the introduction of new ideas. All things otherwise being equal, turning down the feedback should inspire more creativity by allocating more energy to new information. Of course, all things otherwise being equal, without feedback, thoughts will be much more disorganized.

Ideally, these practical benefits are only the beginning. If consciousness vectors are real, and if we can begin to understand how they are calculated, we will have a much deeper knowledge of the highest functions of the human brain and possibly be able to apply our insights to artificial intelligence. Unlocking consciousness vectors may unlock human consciousness.

Acknowledgment: I would like to thank Aubrey Gilbert for her insights and careful review. Some of the material in this review was previously published in Bodovitz, 2008. Whereas the previous review included an argument about the possible localization of the brain region responsible for calculating consciousness vectors, this review is focused more on the significance of continuity and the role of putative consciousness vectors.

References

Bodovitz, S. (2008). The neural correlate of consciousness. Journal of Theoretical Biology, 254(3), 594-598.

Borges, J.L. (1946). A New Refutation of Time.

Born, R.T., Bradley, D.C. (2005). Structure and Function of Visual Area MT. Annual Review of Neuroscience, 28, 157-189.

Castiello, U., Paulignan, Y., Jeannerod, M. (1991). Temporal dissociation of motor responses and subjective awareness. A study in normal subjects. Brain, 6, 2639-2655.

Chalmers, D.J. (1996). The conscious mind: in search of a fundamental theory. Oxford University Press, New York, US.

Cho, A. (2010). The first quantum machine. Science, 330(6011), 1604

Dember, W.N., Purcell, D.G. (1967). Recovery of masked visual targets by inhibition of the masking stimulus. Science, 157, 1335-1336.

Ditchburn, R.W., Ginsborg, B.L. (1952). Vision with a stabilized retinal image. Nature, 170, 36-37.

Gomes, G. (1998). The timing of conscious experience: a critical review and reinterpretation of Libet's research. Conscious and Cognition, 7(4), 559-595.

Hameroff, S.R., Penrose, R. (1996). Orchestrated reduction of quantum coherence in brain microtubules: a model for consciousness. In: Hameroff, S.R., Kaszniak, A.W., Scott, A. C. (Eds.) Toward a Science of Consciousness. MIT Press, Cambridge, MA, pp. 507- 540.

Koch, C. (2003). Lecture 15: On Time and Consciousness. In: California Institute of Technology course CNS/Bi 120. http://www.klab.caltech.edu/cns120/videos.php

Koch, C. (2004a). The quest for consciousness: a neurobiological approach. Roberts & Company, Englewood, Colorado, US, pp. 257-259.

Koch, C. (2004b). The quest for consciousness: a neurobiological approach. Roberts & Company, Englewood, Colorado, US, p. 214.

Koch, C. (2004c). The quest for consciousness: a neurobiological approach. Roberts & Company, Englewood, Colorado, pp. 249-268.

Lashley, K. (1956) Cerebral Organization and Behavior. In: Cobb, S. & Penfield, W. (Eds.) The Brain and Human Behavior. Williams and Wilkins Press, Baltimore, Maryland.

Lau, H.C., Passingham, R.E. (2006). Relative blindsight in normal observers and the neural correlate of visual consciousness. Proceedings of the National Academy of Sciences, 103(49), 18763-18768.

Libet, B. (1999). How does conscious experience arise? The neural time factor. Brain Research Bulletin, 50(5/6), 339-340.

Libet, B., Alberts, W.W., Wright, E.W., Jr., Feinstein, B. (1967). Responses of human somatosensory cortex to stimuli below threshold for conscious sensation. Science, 158, 2597-1600.

Libet, B., Alberts, W.W., Wright, E.W., Jr., Delattre, L.D., Levin, G., Feinstein, B. (1964). Production of threshold levels of conscious sensation by electrical stimulation of human somatosensory cortex. Journal of Neurophysiology, 27, 546-578.

Libet, B., Pearl, D.K., Morledge, D.A., Gleason, C.A., Hosobuchi, Y., Barbaro, N.M. (1991). Control of the transition from sensory detection to sensory awareness in man by the duration of a thalamic stimulus: the cerebral 'time-on' factor. Brain, 114, 1731-1757.

Martinez-Conde, S., Macknik, S.L. Hubel, D.H. (2004). The role of fixational eye movements in visual perception. Nat Rev Neurosci. 5(3), 229-240.

O'Connell, A.D., Hofheinz, M., Ansmann, M., Bialczak, R.C., Lenander, M., Lucero, E., Neeley, M., Sank, D., Wang, H., Weides, M., Wenner, J., Martinis, J.M., Cleland, A.N. (2010). Quantum ground state and single-phonon control of a mechanical resonator. Nature, 464, 697-703.

Pockett, S. (2002). On subjective back-referral and how long it takes to become conscious of a stimulus: a reinterpretation of Libet's data. Conscious and Cognition, 11(2), 144-161.

Riggs, L.A., Ratliff, F. (1952). The effects of counteracting the normal movements of the eye. J. Opt. Soc. Am. 42, 872-873.

Rucci, M., Iovin, R., Poletti, M., Santini, F. (2007). Miniature eye movements enhance fine spatial detail. Nature, 447, 851-854.

Salart, D., Baas, A., Branciard, C., Gisin, N., Zbinden, H. (2008). Testing the speed of 'spooky action at a distance'. Nature, 454, 861–864.

Shipp, S., de Jong, B.M., Zihl, J., Frackowiak, R.S., Zeki, S. (1994). The brain activity related to residual motion vision in a patient with bilateral lesions of V5. Brain, 117(5), 1023-38.

Yarbus, A.L. (1967). Eye Movements and Vision. New York: Plenum.

Zihl, J., von Cramon D., Mai, N., Schmid, C. (1991). Disturbance of movement vision after bilateral posterior brain damage. Further evidence and follow up observations. Brain, 114(5), 2235-2252.

Zihl, J., von Cramon, D., Mai, N. (1983). Selective disturbance of movement vision after bilateral brain damage. Brain, 106(2), 313-340.

Quantum Physics, Advanced Waves and Consciousness

Antonella Vannini Ph.D, and Ulisse Di Corpo

[1]Lungotevere degli Artigiani 32 – 00153 ROME - ITALY

Abstract

An essential component of the Copenhagen Interpretation of quantum mechanics is Schrödinger's wave equation. According to this interpretation, consciousness, through the exercise of observation, forces the wave function to collapse into a particle. Schrödinger's wave equation is not relativistically invariant and when the relativistically invariant wave equation (Klein-Gordon's equation) is taken into account, there is no collapse of the wave function and no justification for consciousness as a prerequisite to reality. Klein-Gordon's wave equation depends on a square root and yields two solutions: retarded waves which move forwards in time and advanced waves which move backwards in time. Advanced waves were considered to be unacceptable since they contradict the law of causality, according to which causes always precede effects. However, while studying the mathematical properties of Klein-Gordon's equation, the mathematician Luigi Fantappiè noted that retarded waves are governed by the law of entropy (from Greek en=diverge, tropos=tendency), whereas advanced waves are governed by a law opposite to entropy which leads to concentration of energy, differentiation, complexity, order and growth of structures. Fantappiè named this law syntropy (syn=converge, tropos=tendency) and noted that its properties coincide with the qualities of living systems, arriving in this way at the conclusion that life and consciousness are a consequence of advanced waves (Fantappiè, 1942).

KEY WORDS: Consciousness, Advanced waves, Syntropy, Feeling of Life, Free Will, Quantum Physics

1. Introduction

The Copenhagen Interpretation of quantum mechanics was formulated by Niels Bohr and Werner Heisenberg in 1927 during a joint work in Copenhagen, and explains the dual nature of matter (wave/particle) in the following way:

- Electrons leave the electronic cannon as particles.

- They dissolve into waves of superposed probabilities, in a superposition of states.

- The waves go through both slits, in the double slit experiment, and interfere, creating a new state of superposition.

- The observation screen, performing a measurement, forces the waves to collapse into particles, in a well defined point of the screen.

- Electrons start again to dissolve into waves, just after the measurement.

An essential component of the Copenhagen Interpretation is Schrödinger's wave equation, reinterpreted as the probability that the electron (or any other quantum mechanical entity) is found in a specific place. According to the Copenhagen Interpretation, consciousness, through the exercise of observation, forces the wave function to collapse into a particle. This interpretation states that the existence of the electron in one of the two slits, independently from observation, does not have any real meaning. Electrons seem to exist only when they are observed. Reality is therefore created, at least in part, by the observer.

In the paper Quantum Models of Consciousness it is argued that quantum models of consciousness can be divided in three main categories (Vannini, 2008):

1. models which assume that consciousness creates reality and that consciousness is a prerequisite of reality;

2. models which link consciousness to the probabilistic properties of quantum mechanics;

3. models which attribute consciousness to a principle of order of quantum mechanics.

Considering the criteria of scientific falsification and of biological compatibility Vannini (2008) notes that:

- Quantum models of consciousness which belong to the first category show a tendency towards mysticism. All these models start from the Copenhagen Interpretation of quantum mechanics and assume that consciousness itself determines reality. These models try to describe reality as a consequence of panpsychism, and assume that consciousness is an immanent property which precedes the formation of reality. The concept of panpsychism is explicitly used by most of the authors of this category. These assumptions cannot be falsified.

- Quantum models of consciousness which belong to the second category consider consciousness to be linked to a realm, for example that of the Planck's constant, which cannot be observed by modern science and which is impossible to falsify or test using experiments.

- Quantum models of consciousness which belong to the third group attribute consciousness to principles of order which have been already discovered and used for physical applications (laser, superconductors, etc.). The order principles on which most of these models are based require extreme physical conditions such as, for example, absolute zero temperatures (-273 C°). These models do not meet the criteria of biological compatibility.

Vannini concludes that only the models which originate from the Klein-Gordon equation, which unites Schrödinger's wave equation (quantum mechanics) with special relativity and are not pure quantum mechanical models, survive the selection of scientific falsification and biological compatibility.

2. Klein-Gordon's Equation

In 1925 the physicists Oskar Klein and Walter Gordon formulated a probability equation which could be used in quantum mechanics and was relativistically invariant. In 1926 Schrödinger simplified Klein-Gordon's equation in his famous wave equation (ψ) in which only the positive solution of Klein-Gordon's equation was considered, and which treats time in an essentially classical way with a well defined before and after the collapse of the wave function. In 1927 Klein and Gordon formulated again their equation (2) as a combination of Schrödinger's wave equation (quantum mechanics) and the energy/momentum/mass equation of special relativity (1).

$$E^2 = c^2 p^2 + m^2 c^4 \qquad \qquad 1)$$

Energy/momentum/mass equation

Where E is the Energy of the object, m the mass, p the momentum and c the constant of the speed of light. This equation simplifies in the famous $E=mc^2$ when the momentum is equal to zero (p=0).

$$E\psi = \sqrt{p^2 + m^2}\psi \qquad \qquad 2)$$

Klein-Gordon's wave equation

Klein-Gordon's wave equation depends on a square root and yields two solutions: the positive solution describes waves which diverge from the past to the future (retarded waves); the negative solution describes waves which diverge from the future to the past (advanced waves). The negative solution introduces in science final causes and teleological tendencies. Consequently, it was considered to be unacceptable.

In 1928 Paul Dirac tried to get rid of the unwanted negative solution by applying the energy/momentum/mass equation to the study of electrons, turning them into relativistic objects. But, also in this case, the dual solution emerged in the form of electrons (e^-) and antiparticles (e^+). The antiparticle of the electron, initially named neg-electron, was experimentally observed in 1932 by Carl Anderson in cosmic rays and named positron. Anderson became the first person who proved empirically the existence of the negative energy solution; the negative solution was no longer an impossible mathematical absurdity, but it was an empirical evidence. Dirac's equation predicts a universe made of matter which moves forwards in time and antimatter which moves backwards in time. The negative solution of Dirac's equation caused emotional distress among physicists. For example Heisenberg wrote to Pauli: "The saddest chapter of modern physics is and remains the Dirac theory" (Heisenberg, 1928); "I regard the Dirac theory … as learned trash which no one can take seriously" (Heisenberg, 1934). In order to solve this situation, Dirac used Pauli's principle, according to which two electrons cannot share the same state, to suggest that all states of negative energy are occupied, thereby forbidding any interaction between positive and negative states of matter. This ocean of negative energy which occupies all positive states is called the Dirac sea.

It is important to note that it appears to be impossible to test the existence of advanced waves in a laboratory of physics:

- According to Fantappiè, advanced waves do not obey classical causation, therefore they cannot be studied with experiments which obey the classical experimental method (Fantappiè, 1942).

- According to Wheeler's and Feynman's electrodynamics, emitters coincide with retarded fields, which propagate into the future, while absorbers coincide with advanced fields, which propagate backward in time. This time-symmetric model leads to predictions identical with those of conventional electrodynamics. For this reason it is impossible to distinguish between timesymmetric results and conventional results (Wheeler & Feynman, 1949).

- In his Transactional Interpretations of Quantum Mechanics, Cramer states that "Nature, in a very subtle way, may be engaging in backwards-in-time handshaking. But the use of this mechanism is not available to experimental investigators even at the microscopic level. The completed transaction erases all advanced effects, so that no advanced wave signalling is possible. The future can affect the past only very indirectly, by offering possibilities for transactions" (Cramer, 1986).

3. The Law of syntropy

At the end of 1941, the mathematician Luigi Fantappiè was working on the equations of relativistic and quantum physics when he noted that the dual solution of the Klein-Gordon equation explains two symmetrical laws:

- +Eψ (retarded waves) describes waves diverging from causes located in the past, governed by the law of entropy;

- −Eψ (advanced waves) describes waves converging towards causes located in the future and governed by the law of syntropy.

According to Fantappiè the main properties of retarded and advanced waves are:

1. Retarded waves:
   a. Causality: diverging waves exist as a consequence of causes located in the past.
   b. Entropy: diverging waves tend towards the dissipation of energy (heat death).
2. Advanced waves:
   a. Retrocausality: converging waves exist as a consequence of causes located in the future.
   b. Syntropy:
      - converging waves concentrate matter and energy in smaller spaces (ie this principle is well described by the large quantities of energy accumulated by living systems of the past and now available in the form of coal, petrol and gases).
      - Entropy diminishes. Entropic phenomena are governed by the second law of thermodynamics according to which a system tends towards homogeneity and disorder. The inversion of the time arrow also inverts the second law of thermodynamics, so that a reduction in entropy and an increase in differentiation are observed.
      - Final causes, attractors, which absorb converging waves are observed. From these final causes syntropic systems originate.
      - Because syntropy leads to the concentration of matter and energy, and this concentration cannot be indefinite, entropic processes are needed to compensate syntropic concentration.

These processes take the form of the exchange of matter and energy with the environment. For example metabolism is divided into:

o   anabolism (syntropy) which includes all the processes which transform simple structures into complex structures, for example nutritive elements into bio-molecules, with the absorption of energy.

o   catabolism (entropy) which includes all the processes which transform higher level structures into lower level structures, with the release of energy.

Fantappiè noted that the properties of syntropy coincide with the qualities of living systems: finality, differentiation, order and organization.

Other authors suggested the existence of the law of syntropy associated to living systems. For example:

· Albert Szent-Gyorgyi (Nobel prize 1937 and discoverer of vitamin C) underlined that "One major difference between amoebas and humans is the increase in complexity, which presupposes the existence of a mechanism which is capable of contrasting the second law of thermodynamics. In other words a force must exist which is capable of contrasting the universal tendency of matter towards chaos, and of energy towards heat death. Life processes continuously show a decrease in entropy and an increase in inner complexity, and often also in the complexity of the environment, in direct opposition with the law of entropy." In the 1970s Szent-Gyorgyi concluded that in living systems there was wide evidence of the existence of the law of syntropy, even though he never managed to infer it from the laws of physics. While entropy is a universal law which leads towards the disintegration of all types of organization, syntropy is the opposite law which attracts living systems towards forms of organization which are always more complex and harmonic (Szent-Gyorgyi, 1977). The main problem, according to Szent-Gyorgyi, is that "a profound difference between organic and inorganic systems can be observed … as a man of science I cannot believe that the laws of physics lose their validity at the surface of our skin. The law of entropy does not govern living systems." Szent-Gyorgyi dedicated the last years of his life to the study of syntropy and its conflict with the law of entropy (Szent-Gyorgyi, 1977).

· Erwin Schrödinger talks about the concept of negative entropy. He was looking for the nutrient which is hidden in our food, and which defends us from heat death. Why do we need to eat biological food; why can we not feed directly on the chemical elements of matter? Schrödinger answers this question by saying that what we feed on is not matter but neg-entropy, which we absorb through the metabolic process (Schrödinger, 1944).

- Ilya Prigogine, winner in 1977 of the Nobel prize for chemistry, introduced in his book "The New Alliance", a new type of thermodynamics, the "thermodynamics of dissipative systems", typical of living systems. Prigogine stated that this new type of thermodynamics cannot be reduced to dynamics or thermodynamics (Prigogine, 1979).

- Hermann Haken, one of the fathers of the laser, introduced a level that he named "ordinator", which he used to explain the principles of orders typical of living systems (Haken, 1983).

4. Experiments

According to the Copenhagen Interpretation no advance effects should be possible, since time flows from the past to the future. On the contrary Fantappiè's syntropy model suggests that life and consciousness are a consequence of advanced waves (Fantappiè, 1942) and should therefore show anticipatory reactions. Is it possible to devise experiments in order to test which of the two models is correct?

In 1981 Di Corpo extended Fantappiè's hypothesis suggesting that structures which support vital functions, such as the autonomic nervous system (ANS), should show anticipatory reactions since they need to acquire syntropy. Consequently, if the Advanced Waves Interpretation is correct the parameters of ANS, such as heart rate and skin conductance, should react before stimuli (Di Corpo, 1981, 2007; Vannini & Di Corpo, 2008, 2009, 2010), on the contrary if the Copenhagen Interpretation is correct no reactions before stimuli should be observed.

Since 1997, anticipatory pre-stimuli reactions in the parameters of the autonomic nervous system have been reported in several studies, for example:

1 The first experimental study was produced by Radin in 1997 and monitored heart rate, skin conductance and fingertip blood volume in subjects who were shown for five seconds a blank screen and for three seconds a randomly selected calm or emotional picture. Radin found significant differences, in these autonomic parameters, preceding the exposure to emotional versus calm pictures. In 1997 Bierman replicated Radin's results confirming the anticipatory reaction of skin conductance to emotional versus calm stimuli and in 2003 Spottiswoode and May, of the Cognitive Science Laboratory, replicated Bierman and Radin's experiments performing controls in order to exclude artifacts and alternative explanations. Results showed an increase in skin conductance 2-3 seconds before emotional stimuli are presented

(p=0.0005). Similar results have been obtained by other authors, using parameters of the autonomic nervous system (McDonough et al., 2002), (McCraty et al., 2004), (May Paulinyi & Vassy, 2005) and (Radin, 2005).

2. In the article "Heart Rate Differences between Targets and Nontargets in Intuitive Tasks", Tressoldi describes two experiments which show anticipatory heart rate reactions (Tressoldi et al., 2005). Trials were divided in 3 phases: in the presentation phase 4 pictures were shown and heart rate data was collected; in the choice phase pictures were presented simultaneously and the subject was asked to guess the picture which the computer would select; in the target phase the computer selected randomly one of the four pictures (target) and showed it on the monitor. In the first experiment a heart rate difference of 0.59 HR, measured in phase 1 during the presentation of target and non target pictures, was obtained (t = 2.42, p=0.015), in the second experiment the heart rate difference was 0.57 HR (t = 3.4, p=0.001).

3. Daryl Bem, psychology professor at the Cornell University, studies retrocausality using well known experimental designs in a "time-reverse" pattern. In his 2011 article "Feeling the Future: Experimental Evidence for Anomalous Retroactive Influence on Cognition and Affect" Bem describes 9 well-established psychological effects in which the usual sequence of events was reversed, so that the individual's responses were obtained before rather than after the stimulus events occurred. For example in a typical priming experiment the subject is asked to judge if the image is positive (pleasant) or negative (unpleasant), pressing a button as quickly as possible. The response time (RT) is registered. Just before the image a "positive" or "negative" word is briefly shown. This word is named "prime". Subjects tend to respond more quickly when the prime is congruent with the following image (both positive or negative), whereas the reaction times become longer when they are not congruent (one is positive and the other one is negative).

    In retro-priming experiments Bem used IAPS (International Affective Picture System) emotional pictures. Results show the classical priming effect with reaction times faster when the prime is congruent with the image. Considering all 9 experiments, conducted on a sample of more than 1,000 students, the retrocausal effect size is $p = 1.34 \times 10^{-11}$.

4. In the article "Collapse of the wave function?" Vannini and Di Corpo describe 4 experiments which gradually control different types of artefacts and show a statistical significance of prestimuli heart rate effects of $p=1/10^{27}$ (Vannini & Di Corpo, 2010).

5. How Can These Results Be Interpreted?

Anticipatory pre-stimuli reactions seem to be incompatible with the Copenhagen Interpretation, since Schrödinger's wave equation treats time in an essentially classical way and rejects the possibility of pre-stimuli reactions (effects before causes). Dick Bierman tried to overcome this limit of the Copenhagen Interpretation with his CIRTS model (Consciousness Induced Restoration of Time Symmetry), presented at the PA 2008 conference (Bierman, 2008). This model states that almost all formalisms in physics are time-symmetric. Nevertheless the Copenhagen Interpretation of quantum mechanics, which postulates the collapse of the wave function, introduces a break of time symmetry at the point of collapse. The assumption of CIRTS is that the brain, when it is sustained by consciousness, is such a special system that it partially restores time-symmetry and therefore allows advanced waves to occur. The time symmetry restoring condition is not the brain per se but the brain sustained by consciousness. The restoration of time symmetry is suggested to be proportional to the brain volume involved in consciousness. CIRTS considers consciousness to be a pre-requisite of reality with special properties which restore time-symmetry. However, in CIRTS the rationale behind consciousness is missing and its special properties seem to arise from nothing. Contrary to Bierman's model, Luigi Fantappiè's syntropy model and Chris King's quantumtransactions model describe consciousness as a consequence of the properties of advanced waves: — Fantappiè states that, according to the converging properties of advanced waves, living systems are energy and information absorbers and that the "feeling of life" can be described as a consequence of these converging and absorbing properties of advanced waves. On the contrary it would be difficult to justify the feeling of life as a consequence of diverging and emitting properties which characterize retarded waves. The equivalence "feeling of life = advanced waves" leads to the conclusion that systems based on the retarded solution, as for example machines and computers, would never show the "feeling of life" independently from their complexity, whereas systems based on the advanced solution, as for example life itself, should always have a "feeling of life", independently from their complexity.

According to King, the constant interaction between information coming from the past and information coming from the future would place life in front of bifurcations. This constant antagonism between past and future would force life into a state of free will and consciousness. Consequently consciousness would be a property of all living structures: each cell and biological process would be forced to choose between information coming from the past and information coming from the future (King, 1996). This constant state of choice would be common to all levels of life and would give form to chaotic behaviour on which the conscious brain would feed. King (1996) states that "The chaotic processes which are observed in the neuronal system can be the result of behaviour which is apparently random and probabilistic, since they are non local in space and time. This would allow neuronal networks to connect in a subquantum way with non local situations and explain why behaviour results in being non deterministic and non computational."

The followings are some of the fundamental differences between Bierman's CIRTS model and Fantappiè's syntropy model:

1. Fantappiè focused on the Klein-Gordon's equation and excluded other time-symmetric equations, such as the electromagnetic wave equation. The rational of this choice is that at the quantum level time would be unitary (past, present and future would coexist) whereas at the macro-level time flows forward and advanced waves would be impossible. This conclusion was reached considering the mathematical properties of retarded waves which obey classical causation and propagate from the past to the future, and of advanced waves which obey final causation and propagate from the future to the past. Fantappiè noted that in diverging systems, such as our expanding universe, entropy prevails forcing time to flow forwards and forbidding advanced solutions. On the contrary in converging systems, such as black holes, syntropy prevails, time flows backwards and retarded solutions would be impossible; whereas in systems balanced between diverging and converging forces, such as atoms, time would be unitary, past, present and future would coexist and both advanced and retarded waves would be possible. In the CIRTS model Bierman considers advanced solutions possible also at the macro level, without taking into account the restrictions posed by the law of entropy.

2. Fantappiè argued that, as a consequence of the fact that advanced waves exist at the quantum level, living systems need a way to "extract" advanced waves from the quantum level in order to sustain living functions and contrast the destructive effects of entropy. Fantappiè found this mechanism in water, in the hydrogen bridge, a bond among the hydrogen atom and two electrons, found by Maurice Huggins in 1920, which allows to explains the anomalous properties of water (Ball, 1999). The hydrogen bridge makes water totally different from other liquids, mainly by increasing its cohesive forces (syntropy) and this would be the reason why water is so essential to life, since it allows the flow of advanced waves from the micro to the macro level. Consequently, in the syntropy model advanced waves are not associated to the brain, but are considered a fundamental property of all living systems. On the contrary, CIRTS suggests that advanced waves are mediated by con-

sciousness and therefore should be a consequence of conscious brain activities. Bierman produces evidence in experiments conducted with meditators, but this evidence can be easily read as an increase of the role of the autonomic nervous system during meditation, and not as a consequence of consciousness. It is well known that, while meditating, subjects often experience a state of trance as a consequence of the fact that the aim is usually that of "turning off the mind".

3. In the CIRTS model consciousness is a pre-requisite of reality. In the syntropy model the feeling of life is a consequence of the cohesive and unitary properties of advanced waves. According to the syntropy model, any form of life has a feeling of life. Consequently we would have a feeling of life also when no brain activity is observed. This would explain why all forms of life, even the most simple ones, show anticipatory reactions (Rosen, 1985) and why, for example, patients during surgery in a state of anesthetic-induced unconsciousness tend to defend themselves and subjects with no brain activity react and defend themselves when their organs are removed for transplant. According to the syntropy model, the feeling of life does not reside in the brain; however, the brain provides memory which allows us to remember and reason regarding our conscious experiences.

4. CIRTS associates pre-stimuli reactions to coherence whereas the syntropy model associates pre-stimuli reactions to feelings and emotions. Coherence is a concept which is quite difficult to measure, whereas emotions can be easily measured using the parameters of the autonomic nervous system. Nevertheless Bierman introduces a formula in order to justify why pre-stimuli reactions are lower than post-stimuli reactions. In this formula the volume of the brain affected by coherence is divided by the total volume of the brain. The example reported by Bierman, relative to skin conductance, seems to support this formula. However, when using heart rate measurements pre-stimuli reactions and post-stimuli reactions tend to have the same size of effect. Even though effects vary greatly among subjects and generalization seems not to be appropriate, HR data contradicts Bierman's formula.

6. Conclusion

According to the syntropy model the dual manifestation of the quantum world in the form of waves and particles is not the consequence of the collapse of the wave equation, but the consequence of the dual causality at the quantum level: retarded waves, past causality, and advanced waves, future causality (Cramer, 1986). The advanced waves model does not need the collapse of the wave function and, consequently, does not need a time-symmetry restoration system. Advanced waves would explain not only the dual manifestation particle/waves, but also non-locality and entanglement (De Beauregard, 1977). On the contrary the CIRTS model finds its justification within the Copenhagen Interpretation of quantum mechanics and requires the collapse of the wave function.

The Copenhagen Interpretation was formulated in 1927 and can be considered the expression of the Zeitgeist, "the spirit of the time", since it reflects the idea of men as semi-Gods who, through the exercise of consciousness, can create reality. When Erwin Schrödinger discovered how Heisenberg and Bohr had used his wave equation, with ideological and mystical implications which provided powers of creation to consciousness, he commented: "I don't like it, and I am sorry I ever had anything to do with it" (Schrödinger, 1944).

References

Anderson C.D. (1932). The apparent existence of easily deflectable positives, Science, 76:238. Ball P. (1999). H$_2$O A Biography of Water, Weidenfeld & Nicolson, London.

Bem D.J. (2010). Feeling the Future: Experimental Evidence for Anomalous Retroactive Influence on Cognition and Affect. Journal of Personality and Social Psychology (in press), DOI: 10.1037/a0021524, http://dbem.ws/FeelingFuture.pdf

Bierman D.J., Radin D.I. (1998). Conscious and anomalous non-conscious emotional processes: A reversal of the arrow time? Toward a Science of Consciousness, Tucson III. MIT Press, 367-386.

Bierman D.J. (2008). Consciousness Induced Restoration of Time-Symmetry (CIRTS), a Psychophysical Theoretical Perspective, Proceedings of the PA Convention, Winchester, England, 13-17 August 2008.

Cramer J.G. (1986). The Transactional Interpretation of Quantum Mechanics, Reviews of Modern Physics, 58: 647-688.

De Beauregard C. (1977). Time Symmetry and the Einstein Paradox, Il Nuovo Cimento, 42(B).

Di Corpo U. (1981), Un nuovo approccio strutturale ai fondamenti della psicologia. Ipotesi teoriche ed esperimenti. Dissertation, University of Rome "La Sapienza".

Di Corpo U. (2007). The conflict between entropy and syntropy: the vital needs model. SSE Proceedings, Norway, 132-138.

Dirac P. (1928). The Quantum Theory of the Electron, Proc. Royal Society, London, 117: 610-624; 118: 351-361.

Fantappiè L. (1942). Sull'interpretazione dei potenziali anticipati della meccanica ondulatoria e su un principio di finalità che ne discende. Rend. Acc. D'Italia, 4(7).

Haken H. (1983). Synergetics, an Introduction: Nonequilibrium Phase Transition and Self- Organization in Physics, Chemistry, and Biology, Springer-Verlag.

Heisenberg W. (1928). Letter to W. Pauli, PC, May 3, 1: 443.

Heisenberg W. (1934). Letter to W. Pauli, PC, February 8, 2: 279.

King C.C. (1996). Quantum Mechanics, Chaos and the Conscious Brain. Journal of Mind and Behavior, 18: 155-170.

May E.C., Paulinyi T., Vassy Z. (2005). Anomalous Anticipatory Skin Conductance Response to Acoustic Stimuli: Experimental Results and Speculation about a Mechanism, The Journal of Alternative and Complementary Medicine, 11(4): 695-702.

McCratly R., Atkinson M., Bradely R.T. (2004). Electrophysiological Evidence of Intuition: Part 1, Journal of Alternative and Complementary Medicine, 10(1): 133-143.

McDonough B.E., Dons N.S., Warren C.A. (2002). Differential event-related potentials to targets and decoys in a guessing task, in Journal for Scientific Exploration, 16: 187-206.

Prigogine I. and Stengers I. (1979). La Nouvelle Alliance, Gallimard.

Radin D.I. (1997). Unconscious perception of future emotions: An experiment in presentiment. Journal of Scientific Exploration, 11(2): 163-180.

Radin D.I., Schlitz M. J. (2005). Gut feelings, intuition, and emotions: An exploratory study, Journal of Alternative and Complementary Medicine, 11(4): 85-91.

Rosen R. (1985). Anticipatory Systems, Pergamon Press, USA.

Schrödinger E. (1944). What is Life? The Physical Aspects of the Living Cell, Cambridge University Press.

Szent-Gyorgyi A. (1977). Drive in Living Matter to Perfect Itself, Synthesis, 1(1): 14-26.

Spottiswoode P., May E. (2003). Skin Conductance Prestimulus Response: Analyses, Artifacts and a Pilot Study, Journal of Scientific Exploration, 17(4): 617-641.

Tressoldi P. E., Martinelli M., Massaccesi S., Sartori L. (2005). Heart Rate Differences between Targets and Nontargets in Intuitive Tasks, Human Physiology, 31(6): 646–650.

Vannini A. (2005). Entropy and Syntropy. From Mechanical to Life Science, NeuroQuantology, 3(2): 88-110.

Vannini A. (2008). Quantum Models of Consciousness, Quantum Biosystems, 2: 165-184.

Vannini A. and Di Corpo U. (2008). Retrocausality and the Healing Power of Love, NeuroQuantology, 6(3): 291-296.

Vannini A. and Di Corpo U. (2009). A Retrocausal Model of Life, in Filters and Reflections. Perspective on Reality, ICRL Press, Princeton, NJ, USA, 231-244.

Vannini A. and Di Corpo U. (2010). Collapse of the wave function? Pre-stimuli heart rate reactions. NeuroQuantology, 8(4): 550-563.

Wheeler J.A. and Feynman R. (1949). Classical Electrodynamics in Terms of Direct Interparticle Action. Reviews of Modern Physics, 21: 425-433.

The Quantum Hologram
And the Nature of Consciousness

Edgar D. Mitchell, Sc.D.[1], and Robert Staretz, M.S.

[1]Apollo Astronaut, 6th Man to Walk on the Moon

Abstract

We present a new model of information processing in nature called the Quantum Hologram which we believe is supported by strong evidence. This evidence suggests that QH is also a model that describes the basis for consciousness. It explains how living organisms know and use whatever information they know and utilize. It elevates the role of information in nature to the same fundamental status as that of matter and energy. We speculate that QH seems to be nature's built-in vast information storage and retrieval mechanism and one that has been used since the beginning of time. This would promote QH as a theory which is a basis for explaining how the whole of creation learns, self-corrects and evolves as a self-organizing, interconnected holistic system.

KEY WORDS: Awareness, Consciousness, Entanglement, Information, Intention, Intuition, Mind, Non-Locality, Perception, Phase Conjugate Adaptive Resonance, Quantum Hologram, Resonance, Zero Point Field

1. Definition of Consciousness

One common dictionary definition of consciousness is "the ability to be aware of and to be able to perceive the relationship between oneself and one's environment". The most basic definition, however, is simply "awareness". Another definition suitable for more complex organizations of matter such as animals with a brain includes a description which contains some of the following ideas: "thoughts, sensations, perceptions, moods, emotions, dreams, and awareness of self". Just like life itself, consciousness is one of those things that is easy to recognize but very difficult to define. It has been debated by philosophers in the West since the time of ancient Greek civilization over twenty five hundred years ago.

Eastern traditions have been wrestling with the concept of consciousness for millennia and seem to have a much better handle on it although still not nearly complete. In the West, explanations of consciousness have been mostly ignored or left to our religious traditions. This is certainly true since the time of Descartes and the philosophy of Cartesian duality. It has only been in very recent times that a serious effort to understand mind or consciousness has been undertaken by the scientific community. Much of the effort now underway is based on the assumption of epiphenomenalism, that consciousness, or mind if you prefer, is a byproduct of the functioning of underlying physical structures of the brain and that mind is confined entirely within the brain's processes. However, there is a considerable amount of accumulating experimental and anecdotal evidence suggesting that this interpretation is not correct (Chalmers 1996; Penrose 1994).

At a basic level consciousness seems to be associated with a sense of separation and awareness of the surrounding environment from the conscious entity. It also seems to be associated with the ability to process, store and / or act on information gathered from that external environment. But is consciousness restricted to a functioning brain? Are microscopic organisms such as viruses, amoeba, and algae conscious in some primitive sense? Clearly they do not have brains let alone a nervous system or even neurons. And yet they demonstrate purposeful behavior and are aware of their environment. Amoeba, for example, search for food by moving on pseudo pods toward prey that they eventually surround, engulf and digest. Several types of algae are so versatile that they change the process how they obtain food based on available sunlight. When light is plentiful, they gravitate towards it, which they sense through a photoreceptor at one end of the cell. If the light is too bright, they will swim away toward more suitable lighting conditions.

At a more primitive level viruses are considered by many scientists as non-living because they do not meet all the criteria commonly used in the definition of life. They do, however exhibit some aspects of consciousness or at least some rudimentary form of an awareness of their surroundings. Unlike most organisms, viruses are not made of complete cells. They reproduce by invading and taking over the machinery of their target host cell. When a virus comes into contact with a potential host, it inserts itself into the genetic material of the host's cell. The infected cell is then instructed to produce more viral protein and genetic material instead of performing its normal functions. Is that purposeful behavior or intentionality by the invading virus?

It would seem that based on our first definition, even simple living entities are conscious to some degree, since they display a level of awareness and intentionality to, in some way, manipulate their environment. And, it's not just restricted to living entities. We find certain properties all the way down to the subatomic level, particles in some sense aware of their environment. How is this possible? At the molecular, atomic and subatomic levels it is through the quantum phenomenon of entanglement and non-locality that particles act and react to other particles with which they have become entangled.

2. The Roots of Consciousness

Could it be that at the most fundamental level consciousness begins with these ubiquitous quantum events? We believe that is, in fact, the case. Furthermore recent evidence suggests that certain quantum phenomena (Schempp 1998, 2007, 2008; Mitchell 1995, 2003, 2008) operate at the macro level as well as the micro level and are responsible for many phenomena that living entities experience that cannot be otherwise explained. This would explain how twins or mother and child seem to communicate telepathically when at least one of them is under extreme duress as we have seen is so often reported anecdotally in the literature. In fact, as we shall soon see, several of these so called quantum group effects including a whole class of so-called psychic phenomena have been documented throughout recorded history. As we shall show shortly, some of these phenomena have been either demonstrated or suggested in recent laboratory experiments.

Just like everything else in nature, moving up the evolutionary chain of increasing complexity in organisms is built upon the foundation of what has come before. For consciousness, we propose an evolutionary scaffolding as illustrated in Figure 1. At the lowest level resides the most basic aspects of undifferentiated awareness built upon the quantum principles of entanglement, non-locality and coherent emission / absorption of photons. These phenomena are ubiquitous throughout the world of matter. At this most elementary level all matter seems to be interconnected with all other matter and this interconnection even transcends space and time. We postulate that this is the basis for the most fundamental aspect of consciousness which we describe as undifferentiated awareness and this mechanism of basic perception extends up the entire evolutionary chain of increasing complexity of living organisms. The differences in consciousness being in degree and not in kind as one moves from left to right up the consciousness ladder.

Moving beyond the simplest level of the consciousness towards mentality (e.g. higher functions of consciousness / mind), the next level pertains to the consciousness of simple life composed primarily of single celled organisms.

Here we have the beginnings of a crude capability of awareness through the use of molecular structures that are sensitive to their environment utilizing either chemical and / or electro-magnetic means. In the latter case this is especially prevalent at those frequencies in the EM spectrum corresponding to visible light, infrared and ultra-violet waves. Sensing the external environment by these means have been considered the primary mechanisms of perception that have been the focus of classical science for quite some time now. For simple organisms, like plants, amoeba, viruses, etc. clearly there are no brain structures to facilitate perception. Marcer (1997) has applied a theory called the Quantum Hologram (see below) to propose that life at the most basic level, including such things as prokaryote cells and neurons in higher organisms, exchange information with their environment by utilizing the quantum property of non-locality. The implication here is that all organisms from the simplest to the most complex are interconnected at a very fundamental level using information obtained by nonlocal quantum coherence (Ho 1997). Furthermore they are even interconnected with their external environment by their coherent quantum emissions via the mechanism of the Quantum Hologram as we shall soon demonstrate (Marcer et al. 1997).

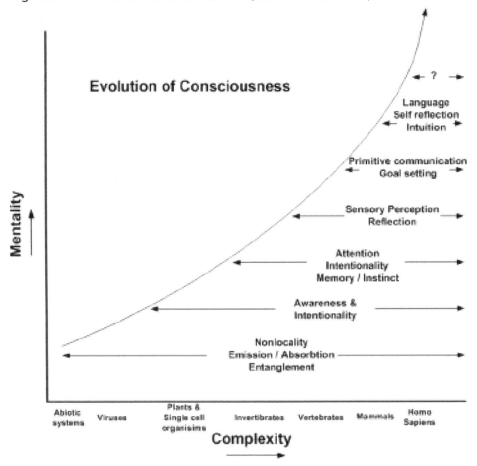

Figure 1 - Evolution of Consciousness

Nature always seems to evolve into mechanisms and structures that enhance an organism's survivability in its environment. Other higher levels of perception and awareness are necessary to locate objects in space-time in addition to including the non-local quantum simple awareness effects as we have just described. So, as we move further up the evolutionary ladder, we continue to enhance mentality as shown in Figure 1. At each level, the organism has access to the perceptual mechanisms of the levels below. Clearly, at each level the organism is utilizing information (e.g. patterns of energy and matter) obtained from its environment. This implies that there is a process (e.g. consciousness) that uses and assigns meaning to this information. Note that "meaning" is also information that places the perceived information into context for use by the organism.

Penrose and Hamereoff (1998) have proposed that microtubules in brain cells might be responsible for more fundamental forms of perception. They also postulate that these microtubules provide the foundation for the emergence of higher orders of consciousness in species with a brain. Microtubules are hollow cylindrical polymers of the protein tubulin which organize cellular activities. These protein lattices exist in the cell's cytoskeleton found within the brain's neurons. Penrose and Hamerehoff claim that tubulin states are governed by quantum mechanical effects within each tubulin interior and these effects function as a quantum computer using "quantum bits" that interact non-locally with other tubulins and with the Quantum Hologram. When enough tubulins are entangled long enough to reach a certain threshold a "conscious event" occurs. Each event results in a state which regulates classical neural activities such as triggering neural firings that ultimately affect perception, learning and / or memory.

At first glance, quantum states in biological systems seem difficult to maintain in brains because these quantum states generally require extreme cold (e.g. close to 0°K) to eliminate thermal noise produced by the environment. Some researchers argue that this is necessary to prevent decoherence of these quantum states. However Penrose and Hameroff claim that decoherence may be prevented by the hollow microtubules themselves which act as shields to the surrounding "noisy" environment.

3. Holographic Processing

It has been suggested that the brain processes and stores information holographically as a massively parallel processing and associative computer system. Pribram (1999) and others have studied this extensively and demonstrated it in both the laboratory with animals and in operating theaters on humans. In the latter case the brain has been exposed and stimulated with low voltage electrical signals while the patient was conscious to describe the resulting experience. These subjects have recalled extremely detailed and vivid memories as if they were actually reliving the experiences being recalled. Animals that have had portions of their brains damaged or removed have been able to recall memories (ex. optimum ways to run a maze) even when the damage has been extensive. These experiments and several others provide evidence that suggest that brains store information holographically (e.g. stored as images contained within interference patterns). Marcer has further extended this to postulate that not only information is stored in this manner but that information is processed holographically in the brain as well. He has also attributed this processing to, in effect, creating a detailed three dimensional movie generating the stream of consciousness that the mind experiences.

Holographic processing is accomplished with the brain acting as a phase conjugating device (e.g. a phase gate) which is type of logic circuit where the inputs are sensitive to the phase of the input signal. The result is a "virtual" signal which is a mirror image of the quantum emissions (e.g. photons of light) actually emitted from the object being perceived. The brain acts as an information receptor utilizing adaptive resonance with a specific range of EM frequencies (e.g. wavelengths) in its input path. The input signals received are a representation of the external object resonating with similar virtual signals generated (output) by the brain. This sets up a resonance condition which may be interpreted as a standing wave between the object and the brain. The input signal is really the quantum emission spectrum of the object being perceived.

Like all holographic processing, the associative pattern that is created facilitates retrieval of information in a resonant loop utilizing the overlapping reference signals of quantum emissions from the external object. It enables the perceiving organism's brain structures to perform pattern classification and recognition of the resonating signals. This resonance process is called phase conjugate adaptive resonance (PCAR). We believe that PCAR is the basis for the most fundamental level of perception in all living organisms in the evolutionary tree of life (Mitchell 2001). As an example think of bats, dolphins, whales that use sonar to send out signals and receive reflections back to locate targets. PCAR is the brain analog of that process.

One of the most important aspects of a laser hologram is that it exhibits the distributive property. This means that even a small part of an entire holographic record contains the entire record of the recorded image but with less resolution (e.g. definition) when reconstructed. Figure 2 is an actual quantum hologram or wave interference pattern of a patient's brain that would appear when exposed on a photographic plate. The left column labeled "A" represents the resulting interference pattern and the right column labeled "B" shows the corresponding 3 dimensional brain image. These images were produced by a typical Magnetic Resonance Imaging (MRI) machine similar to the ones used in medical diagnosis. In the left column (labeled "A") in the middle, and bottom row of pictures, the outside and inside respectively of the entire interference pattern shown in A (top row) have been removed to show the reduced resolution of B, compared to B (top) to illustrate A's holographic nature.

Quantum holography operates similarly in that quantum emissions from complex matter, for example, bio-matter, carry information about the entire organism. Stem cell research supports this concept. The fact that living cells in any organism evolve and grow from more simple stem cells, implies quantum entanglement throughout the organism and its composite parts, with an associated instantaneous exchange of information through PCAR. Thus some information about the entire organism is carried in the quantum emissions from its parts.

For those readers who are familiar with recent developments in ground based astronomical telescopes, a problem that has plagued astronomers since the invention of the telescope has been dealing with the aberrations in the telescopic images caused by the shimmering from the earth's fluid atmosphere. Recent developments in laser technology and high speed computing have allowed astronomers to eliminate these aberrations. A coherent laser beam is targeted to follow the same path that the telescope is focused on. As the laser beam is reflected off the shimmering atmosphere back to a receiver, the phase delay in the returning signal is processed and compared in real time against the reference beam transmitted. This comparison enables the computer to correct for aberrations with the telescope's optical imaging system caused by the atmospheric distortions. The result is that we are now able to receive clear images on earth based telescopes just like we can do with the Hubble Space Telescope which, of course, is outside the earth's atmosphere. This concept of self correcting optical imaging telescopes is not unlike the PCAR process described above.

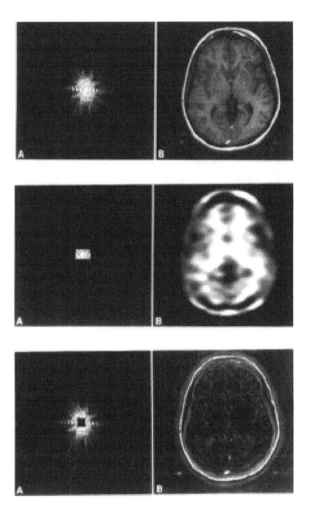

Figure 2. Quantum Hologram. Illustration retrieved from: http://
www.bcs.org.uk/siggroup/cyber/quantumholography.htm   with
permission

PCAR is necessary for the brain to perceive objects as they really exist in
three dimensional space. If the brain had to rely solely on the visible light
spectrum that was reflected off the external object and onto the retina of the
eyes, the object would appear two dimensional just as it would be if a picture
of the object was recorded photographically with a camera. Contrary to the
popular opinion that we see objects in three dimensions entirely because of
binocular vision, just close one eye and observe an external object with the
remaining open eye. The object appears "out there" and not as an image "in
the brain" because of PCAR. This clearly presents a survival advantage to an
organism allowing it to accurately see and locate objects (especially predators
and food) in three dimensional space.

Holographic processing is not restricted to processing sensory information in the visible light portion of the electromagnetic spectrum but it applies to enhancing all of the five normal senses. Consider snapping your fingers. The sound seems to originate from the location of the fingers in 3-D space and not at a point within the brain. As before, this experience results from the fact that the signal carrying the sound to the brain is resonating with the conjugate virtual signal created in the brain.

Figure 3 is an illustration describing the PCAR process. Emissions from the object of attention (e.g. the apple) are received (e.g. input) by the brain. The brain in turn creates phase conjugate (mirror image) "virtual" waves to identify the object. The standing wave that results allows the brain to locate and associate the object in space. The standing waves are created by interference of the two waves traveling in opposite directions. Recall that standing waves are waves that do not appear to propagate but are fixed in position and just move in the vertical direction about the zero point on the reference line. This standing wave creates the resonant condition that allows the brain to process the information so as to locate the object in 3 dimensional space.

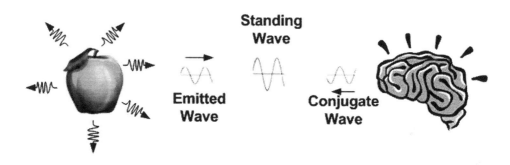

Figure 3. - The PCAR Process

Max Planck, considered by most as the founder of Quantum theory solved the problem of the so-called ultraviolet catastrophe in the late 1890's. He postulated a theory, now known as the Planck postulate, that electromagnetic energy could be emitted or absorbed only in discrete quanta which formed the basis of the description of black body radiation. This was ultimately extended and used to describe how all matter absorbs and reemits photons (quanta of energy) from and into the quantum foam of the zero point field (ZPF) that pervades all matter and even the vacuum of space (Haisch et al. 1997). Normally these emissions are random exchanges of energy between particles and the ZPF. However, the emissions from complex matter (e.g. living organisms) have been shown to exhibit quantum coherence and also carry information non-locally. Recall that the quantum phenomena of non-locality implies instantaneous transmission of information across space and time (Darling 2005).

4. Quantum Emissions and Non-Locality

As we shall demonstrate, non-locality also applies to macro scale objects and is referred to in this paper as a "group" phenomenon (Schempp 1998 and 2008). As a simple example, consider visiting a sacred place of worship such as the Notre Dame Cathedral in Paris. As one enters the cathedral, it is hard not to feel a sense of hush, awe and reverence. Over the centuries, countless people have entered this majestic cathedral with these very feelings. And these feelings were literally absorbed by the structure over the years through the process of quantum emission from the people and resonance with the very atoms and molecules of the cathedral structures. The longer the exposure to this resonance, the more coherence has been achieved with the molecules and atoms in the structure. This coherence re-manifests as emissions back into the environment which then resonate with the visiting people (via the cellular mechanism proposed above) entering the structure. The result is the subjective feelings of hush, awe and reverence which is exactly what a visitor experiences when entering the cathedral. This is another example of PCAR.

In Figure 3, we showed the emissions from the apple resonating with and being absorbed by the brain. However, the opposite is also true. The associated biomass of the entire body is also emitting coherent quantum fluctuations that are being absorbed by the apple and is therefore having some effect on the apple as well. Now add in everything else in the environment surrounding the apple and the human, which would lead one to conclude that every object, in some sense, has an effect on every other object. Like it or not, we appear to live in a participatory universe - there is no such thing as pure objective reality and we influence everything that we interact with. Perhaps this is the same mechanism why we "feel" positive energy from some people while others seem to emit negative energy?

Quantum Holography (QH), which we have alluded to several times above, is a recently discovered attribute of all physical matter and has been validated by experimental work with functional magnetic resonating imaging (fMRI). In his work with MRI tomography, Schempp (1999) used a mathematical formalism to expand quantum information theory. He validated his approach by significantly improving the definition and specificity of MRI and, in the process, discovered the inherent information content of the emitter-absorber model of quantum mechanics. This work provides a model to understand quantum level information processing of biological systems, specifically how the reception and processing of information leads to the functions of memory, awareness, attention and intention. We extend Schempp's work and postulate that all the cells of any biological entity and all its other organ systems, including the brain, have evolved as a massively parallel, learning, computing system. And the key ingredient of understanding this computing system and its processes is the quantum hologram which we will now describe.

As we have previously described, quantum emissions from any material entity carry information non-locally about the event history (e.g. an evolving record of everything that has happened) of the quantum states of the emitting matter. Recall that these quantum emissions are in the form of EM waves of many different wavelengths (or frequencies if you prefer) and that the information associated with these emissions is contained in both the amplitude and the phase relationships of the emitted waves as interference patterns. This is similar to the way that information is stored in the interference pattern on a holographic plate as described previously. These interference patterns can carry an incredible amount of information including the entire space-time history of living organisms.

5. The Quantum Hologram

Mounting evidence seems to indicate that every physical object (both living and nonliving) has its own unique resonant holographic memory and this holographic image is stored in the Zero Point Field (Marcer et al. 1997). Information in the ZPF is stored non-locally and cannot be attenuated. Furthermore this information can be picked up via the mechanism of resonance as we described above. This information, its storage and its access is collectively called the Quantum Hologram (QH).

We can think of an organism's QH as its nonlocal information store in the ZPF that is created from all the quantum emissions of every atom, molecule and cell in the organism. Every objective or physical experience, along with every subjective experience is stored in our own personal hologram and we are in constant resonance with it. Each of us has our own unique resonant frequencies or our unique QH which acts as a "fingerprint" to identify our non local information stored in the zero point field. Since the event history of all matter is continually broadcast non-locally and stored in the QH, the QH can be viewed as a three dimensional vista / movie evolving in time which fully describes everything about the states of the object that created it. Not only do we each have our own unique QH, but it is also possible for others to tap into parts of it through resonance. We shall develop this idea more fully later in this paper.

To illustrate how resonance with an object's or living organism's QH might work, consider the following example. Take two identical guitars, tune the corresponding strings on each guitar to the same frequencies and place them on the opposite sides of a room. Now pluck a string on one of the guitars and notice what happens to the corresponding string on the guitar at the other side of the room. It will begin to vibrate in resonance with the first guitar. This is not unlike the example with singer Ella Fitzgerald and the shattered champagne glass that has been popularized on TV commercials several years ago. It turns out that the vibrating strings on each guitar will produce a standing wave. The vibrations cause the wave to travel down the string (incident wave) to the point where the string is attached to the guitar. The wave will reflect off that point (producing a reflected wave) and travel back in the opposite direction as a mirror image of the incident wave. As the waves meet they will interfere with each other and produce our standing wave which is then propagated through the air.

Now add a third identical guitar with the corresponding strings also tuned to the identical frequencies as the other two. If the corresponding strings on each of any two of the guitars are plucked simultaneously at the same point on the string, the corresponding string on the third guitar will again begin to vibrate as before but with one slight difference. Since both plucked strings were struck at the same point and at the same time, the sound waves produced from each will constructively interfere and reinforce each other in the air resulting in sound waves of greater amplitude. So as before, the string on the third guitar will begin to resonate again but this time with greater amplitude. This assumes that the guitars are place at appropriate locations such that the sound waves from the other two guitars arrive so that the waves arrive in phase. The result will be that they will constructively interfere with each other. If the distances are such that the signals arrive out of phase and destructively interfere, they may cancel out at the third guitar.

Now, repeat this process adding a 4th guitar with the proper placement and so on. In each case the amplitude of the resonating standing wave will continue to increase (unless the responding guitar string should happen to break from the large amplitude of the wave it is receiving). This analogy of the strengthening of the resonating wave shall be of particular importance when accessing information stored in the ZPF. The simple reason is the larger the amplitude of the standing wave, the easier it is for another object to resonate with it.

The analogy of the guitars is similar to how information is stored in the Quantum Hologram with the ZPF. Since the brain operates as a massively parallel quantum computer. The brain does this by setting up a resonant condition with microtubules scatted throughout the brain tuned to the same frequency as the standing waves of the same frequency located in the ZPF. As we mentioned before every macro-scale physical object in nature has its own unique quantum hologram. It exists in 4D space time reality and is a non-local information structure that never attenuates. And, most importantly, it carries the entire event history of the physical object it was created from or, in the case of living organisms, the entire subjective and objective reality experienced by that organism. All this information about the entity is carried in the amplitude, frequencies (e.g. wavelengths) and in the phase relationships of those waves from the emitted entity. Perhaps, most important of all, is the fact that the information stored in the QH is recoverable through the process of resonance not only with the individual organism that created it but with other organisms as well if they are "tuned" to it. This seems to happen most commonly in humans when strong emotional connections exist between the two.

Note that we are not suggesting that we are all virtual beings living in a "literal" holographic reality as interference patterns on nature's holographic plate. We are all real beings living in a very real material existence consisting of matter, energy and information just as we experience it. Also the quantum hologram is not about the discovery of some new kind of subtle energies such as "élan vital", qi or prana suggested by many throughout history. Neither is it about multidimensional theories nor living in other planes of existence other than our normal 4 dimensional space time reality. But this does mean that we now have a mechanism to describe how mind can manipulate matter. We will have considerably more to say about this later in this paper.

The Quantum Hologram is a model of how reality works. Like all models it enables us to make predictions and create interpretations about how nature operates. We can test those predictions to validate and refine the model and perhaps someday even design, build and utilize technologies that implement various aspects of the model's predictions. But the map is not the territory and, like all models, it must be refined as more information becomes available and our understanding improves. And, most importantly, models are subject to interpretation based on our prior knowledge and experiences.

Our QH model seems to explain many effects including aspects of mind, memory, stream of consciousness, various factors affecting health, psychic events, Jung's collective unconscious, the Akashic record and other phenomena that arise out of the resonance with the QH residing in the zero point field. Before the discovery of quantum holography we had no mechanism to model or account for these phenomena let alone for information transfers between objects that these effects imply.

We believe that QH is supported by both experimental and anecdotal evidence suggesting it is also a model that describes the basis for consciousness. It explains how living organisms know and use whatever information they know and utilize. It elevates the role of information in nature to the same fundamental status as that of matter and energy. In fact the QH seems to be nature's built-in vast information storage and retrieval mechanism and one that has been used since the beginning of time. This would promote QH as a theory which is basis for explaining how the whole of creation learns, self-corrects and evolves as a self-organizing, interconnected holistic system. Since the laws of nature appear to be the same throughout the universe there is no reason that it should not also apply to extraterrestrial consciousness as well.

6. Applications & Implications of QH

We will now look at many previously unexplained phenomena and describe how they can all be explained with the quantum holographic model. Then we will attempt to describe some of the profound implications and ramifications to which this theory leads. We will discuss anecdotal evidence, actual experiments, their implications and potential further applications of the Quantum Holographic (QH) model. Before we begin, let us briefly summarize what was earlier in this paper. We described how QH describes a real phenomenon of nature that has been validated in the laboratory. We postulated that it is a description of reality that is based on a mathematical formalism (e.g. a theoretical model) of how nature implements and utilizes information, memory, perception, attention and intention. Furthermore we suggest that QH explains many phenomena in nature where no adequate mechanisms were previously known to describe them. This is particularly true in accounting for the transfer of information between material objects or between objects and their environment.

QH offers a hypothesis and convincing evidence that explains how living terrestrial organisms know and how they utilize information. In doing so, it elevates information to the same fundamental status throughout the universe as matter and energy. Furthermore when energy, matter and information are utilized in processes, QH leads us to the very basis of consciousness itself. So, perhaps the most profound implication of all is that the QH model provides a basis for explaining how the whole of creation learns, self corrects, evolves by being, in some sense, conscious of itself. In other words, QH describes the universe as a self-organizing inter-connected conscious holistic system.

We postulate that the storage mechanism for the Quantum Hologram resides in the zero point field (ZPF). This field is ubiquitous, nonlocal, cannot be attenuated, lasts indefinitely (e.g. never loses coherence), can store unlimited quantities of information and any portion of it encodes the whole just as a hologram does. It can be thought of not only as nature's information storage mechanism but also as nature's information transfer mechanism. QH information is contained in the amplitude, frequencies and the phase relationships of the underlying interference patterns from the emitted quanta. This information is emitted and absorbed by all objects and exists in four dimensional space / time reality. QH applies to all scale sizes from the smallest subatomic particle to the largest structures in the cosmos and takes place at all temperatures (even down to absolute zero). It exists simultaneously beneath the classical descriptions of how information is exchanged between non living objects and below the normal five senses for living organisms.

For living organisms QH applies to intra and inter communications between cells, organs and organ systems, and finally between organisms as well as with the larger environment as suggested by Lipton (2005), Sheldrake (1981) and several others. It applies to all living organisms on earth as well as to all biological entities that exist throughout the cosmos. Whether abiotic or biotic, the entire event history of all matter anywhere in the universe from the micro scale to the macro scale is being continuously broadcast nonlocally by coherent quantum emissions. This history is also reabsorbed by (e.g. received) and interacts with all other matter and the ZPF through the exchange of quantum information.

The mechanism of QH applies to all of the cells of the human body (approximately 50-100 trillion) and answers the question that is often posed dealing with how all these cells cooperate and work together to make the whole human. While they are actively cooperating, thousands of cells are dying continuously every second; so many, in fact, that over the course of one week the body will have billions of new cells and yet you remain you with the same memories and the same functionality and the same distinct features. How does that happen?

Every one of our cells contains the same genetic blueprint of DNA and clearly that DNA and environmental influences exert major influences over the development and functioning of our cells. But cells are not only subordinate to DNA; they also function and maintain homeostasis by communicating and cooperating simultaneously with many other cells of the body and by the information they receive from the environment. Much of this inter-cellular signaling is electrochemical in nature but biologists still struggle with some aspects of the mechanisms utilized in this information transfer. With up to 100 trillion cells it is hard to imagine how that many cells can remain in harmony by the slow process of electrochemical signaling especially under times of great distress when survival of the entire organism is at stake and / or requires extremely rapid and coordinated responses.

The primacy of DNA as the master blueprint for an organism has been the central dogma for biology for a long time. There is now very convincing evidence that all organisms on earth from plants to mammals acquire characteristics through the interaction with their environment and can then pass these characteristics on to their offspring (Lipton 2005). This process is called "epigenetic inheritance" and has spawned a new field in biology called epigenetics which is the study of the mechanisms by which the environment influences cells and their offspring without changing genetic codes. This is forcing scientists to rethink evolutionary theory and harks back to the days of Lamarckian evolution. Lamarck's theory, developed 50 years before Darwin, hypothesized that evolution was based on cooperative interaction between organisms and their environment. This interaction enabled these organisms to pass on adaptations necessary for survival as the environment changed.

Lipton states that "results from the Human Genome Project are forcing biologists to the recognition that they no longer can just use genetics to explain why humans are at the top of the evolutionary ladder on earth. From this effort, it turned out that there is not much difference in the total number of genes found in humans and those found in primitive organisms". So where does the information come from that defines who we are? Lipton further goes on to state that "cellular constituents are woven into a complex web of crosstalk, feedback and feedforward communication loops and that thousands of scientific studies over the years have consistently revealed that EM signaling affects every aspect of biological functioning".

How does this mechanism work? Could QH offer an explanation? In addition to DNA and environmental influences in all earth based living organisms, inter-cellular communication is especially critical in embryonic development. From a single fertilized egg, the embryo divides thousands of times and each time producing identical offspring cells called stem cells. Then at some critical point when the embryo has reached a certain size, something truly miraculous happens. Cells begin to differentiate and form groups of like cells that will eventually become all the highly specialized tissues and organs that make up the human body. Out of the entire mass of undifferentiated cells making up the embryo, how does a particular stem cell suddenly know that it is to transform into a heart cell, liver cell, neuron, etc? Clearly, some of the differentiation results from electrochemical signaling with the immediate surrounding cells. This exchange is certainly necessary and provides information about how a cell must change to express itself correctly to become the right type of cell at the right place and at the right time. But is it possible that this signaling, by itself is not sufficient to explain the full development of the embryo into a complete organism?

Sheldrake (1997) has studied this problem and has proposed a theory called the Hypothesis of Formative Causation. It describes an alternative explanation for how the structure and form (morphology) of an organism develops. In his model, developing organisms are shaped by fields which exist within and around them and these fields contain the form and shape of the organism. He proposes that each species has its own information field, and within each organism there are fields nested within fields. All of these fields contain information derived from previous expressions of the same kind of organisms. He further states:

> That a field's structure has a cumulative memory, based on what has happened to the species in the past. This idea applies not only to living organisms but also to protein molecules, crystals, even to atoms. In the realm of crystals, for example, the theory would say that the form a crystal takes depends on its characteristic morphic field. Further, the morphic field is a broader term which includes the fields of both form and behavior;

Sheldrake's view is that nature forms habits (e.g. memories) and over time these habits strengthen and influence following generations. Similarly, other habits atrophy over time from lack of continued use. In fact Sheldrake is not alone in proposing such a mechanism. The great psychologist Carl Jung has proposed "the collective unconscious" which represents a vast information store containing the entire religious, spiritual and mythological experiences of the human species. According to Jung, these archetypes have existed since ancient times and are inherited where they exist deep with the human psyche and heavily influence the thinking mind. In a similar manner, Teilhard de Chardin proposed the concept of the "noosphere" which represents the collective consciousness of the human species that emerges from the interaction of human minds. De Chardin asserted that as individuals and the global society evolve into more complex networks, the noosphere evolves along with it.

Finally there is the Akashic record which was developed in the Sanskrit and ancient Indian culture. It is described as an all pervasive foundation that contains not only all knowledge of the human experience but also the entire history of the universe. Our normal five senses cannot access this information but it can be accessed through spiritual practices such as meditation. In the last few years, Laszlo (2004) has also been promoting a theory he has named the A-field which contains many aspects that are also very similar to the concepts described in this paper. All these concepts imply a mechanism very similar to our description of QH.

7. Resonance and the Quantum Hologram

Whatever name this mechanism is called, we postulate that the primary means for accessing transcendent information is via the process of resonance. Remember, that since the laws of nature appear to operate the same everywhere in the universe these is no reason to conclude that QH would not also apply to biological entities anywhere in the universe. In higher organisms with brains, the massively parallel processing capabilities of the brain structures are capable of simultaneously resonating with QH information at an incredible range of frequencies. This is shown in Figure 4 where the effects resulting from varying degrees of resonance with the QH is depicted.

Spectrum of QH Resonance

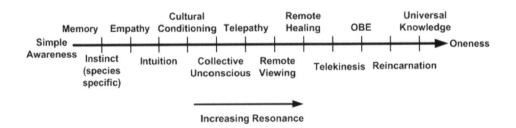

Figure 4. - RESONANCE SPECTRUM

The simplest form of resonance (e.g. entanglement) is shown on the left side of the graph. Moving to the right we show phenomena that manifests with increasing degrees of resonance and frequencies. We have included several phenomena on this graph such as Out-of-Body-Experiences (OBEs) and reincarnation but, as we shall soon see, our explanations of them are based on QH theory and require a different interpretation than those commonly found in popular literature. Finally, we shall describe how the degrees of resonance can occur along with techniques to facilitate them.

We have indicated earlier that information is nothing more than what is contained in patterns of matter or energy. The meaning that is derived from these patterns is developed in the mind of the percipient based on prior experience (e.g. knowledge and memory). In other words, all events are subject to interpretation and that in turn is based on the prior experiences and beliefs of the percipient. The more knowledge and experience we gain the more likely we will interpret an event closer to actual reality.

Changing beliefs especially when they are not based on knowledge but instead are based on faith, however, are another matter entirely. For example, in colonial America, most people attributed thunder and lightning to evil spirits. At that time the obvious solution to the problem was to ward off the evil spirits by ringing church bells. Needless to say that was not very effective. More than a few well intentioned souls were electrocuted while in the bell tower ringing those bells. We now know that the premise of evil spirits is totally incorrect and that thunder and lightning are merely the results of electrostatic discharges between the atmosphere and the ground. How did we get to this understanding? We evolved our understanding and beliefs by investigating and learning about how nature really works through trials, by observation and by experimentation (remember the Ben Franklin experiments with kites we learned about in grade school).

8. Experimental Evidence

We shall now describe some of the experiments testing the concept of non-locality and their findings. There is considerable experimental and anecdotal evidence, although some of it controversial, to suggest that simple organisms perceive and respond to nonlocal information. In the area of human experimentation, results have likewise been mixed for much of the last 75 years. However meta-analysis by Radin (1997) and independently by Utts (1991) across a large and appropriate spectrum of experiments demonstrates compelling statistics that the perception of non-local information exists and is real. Meta-analyses is a new tool which has become essential in many of the soft sciences including ecology, psychology, sociology and medicine. The essence of meta-analysis is that outcomes of collections of previous experiments are analyzed by statistical methods which combine results from different existing studies that address a set of related research hypotheses.

Perhaps if there were a larger body of experimental evidence for simple life forms, similar results of meta-analysis would emerge. Failure to replicate results in well constructed experiments does not, in the case of subtle consciousness phenomena, prove that the phenomenon is missing but rather that a hidden mechanism below the threshold of classical measurement may be operating. For example, the most telling experimental evidence to explain the sometimes inconsistent results relates to direct nonlocal and / or experimenter effects. These effects are unintentional biasing effects on the results of an experiment caused by the expectations, beliefs or preconceptions on the part of the experimenter.

Schmiedler (1972) isolated the "sheep / goat" ("sheep" is a label for believers and "goat" is a label for non-believers in psychic experiments) effect in human experiments decades ago. Experimenters and /or participants in human telepathy (or similar nonlocal) experiments exhibited results statistically above or below chance results depending on their subjective bias towards the experiment. In other words 100% wrong answers would be as statistically significant as 100% correct answers in such tests, and in addition would betray the mind set or intention of the subject whereas only chance results would be inconclusive. More recently, a series of experiments by Schlitz (1997) investigating intentionality clearly demonstrated that experimenter bias (intentionality) affected the outcome even in double blind experiments. Thus, in the subtle realms of mind and consciousness studies, bias, belief and intention clearly have an effect.

The lack of an existing theoretical structure in classical science to support any type of perception of non-local information, much less to support bias, belief or intention as having a nonlocal effect, is quite sufficient to account for anomalous results in many scientific experiments. The prevailing dogma of classical science against any type of non-local action at the level of macro scale reality has not prevented experiments from successfully being conducted. It has sometimes caused positive results to be dismissed as anomalous, of faulty design or outright fraud when in most of these cases the results were defensible had proper nonlocal theory been available.

Radin (2006) describes a series of experiments conducted in the latter half of the 20th century on a whole range of psychic phenomena that suggests that experimenters are obtaining far more correlations than can be expected by chance. This was done by performing meta-analyses for random number generators (RNG) studies subjected to psycho-kinesis (PK) intention which resulted with the odds against chance of 35 trillion to one over the entire database. This analysis followed a decade long series of experiments by Dunne and Jahn (1988) at Princeton University provided overwhelming evidence that human subjects could produce statistically skewed results in mechanical processes normally considered to be driven by random processes. A similar study with Ganzfeld meta-analysis by Radin demonstrated results with odds against chance of 29×10^{18} to one (e.g. one chance in 29,000,000,000,000,000,000). Radin goes on to describe several other studies showing similar results.

Radin has also discovered that audiences watching stage performances would skew the output of random number generators during periods of high emotional content in the performance. In a wide-ranging audience participation experiment, he recorded the output of computer random number generators during the television broadcasts of the O.J. Simpson murder trial. Most television news programs covered this event live for weeks on end with millions of viewers. Again, the results of random number generators set up to monitor this event were skewed corresponding to emotional peaks during the trial drama and corresponding to the number of people watching. A similar effect was noted on 9/11/2001 at the time of the World Trade Center disaster in New York City.

The thesis in the Princeton experiments was that participant intentionality created non random effects to bias the skewed distribution. In the Radin experiments, the results were not the result of intentionality because the participants were unaware of the experiment, but his hypothesis was that rapt attention drove the system away from randomness and toward greater order. These results suggest that attention and intention provide closely correlated outcomes and further, that randomness may not be a property of nature but what may be perceived as random noise in a system may just be awareness that is not in resonance at that moment with the particular perceptual system.

Many types of mind-to-mind or mind-to-object experiments have been rigorously and routinely conducted for decades with statistical significance but they are often dismissed or ignored by mainstream science because the implications of non-local action are so foreign to the mainstream view of objectivism and the possibility of mind-matter interactions. However, if we consider the condition of resonance is necessary (specifically PCAR as described earlier), then we must also consider the perceived object (e.g. the target) and the percipient's perceptual system as entrained in a phase locked resonant feedback loop. The incoming wave from the target carrying the emitted information may be labeled as "perception" from the view point of the percipient, and the return path may be labeled as attention (or intention) depending on what the percipient is trying to achieve. Note however that this is a two way street, the act of perceiving also affects the target object being perceived! Therefore we do live in a participatory universe. There is no such things as pure objectivity.

In the case of non-local effects at a distance, outside the body, simple correlation of entangled particles is the most basic form of perception. And these correlations between entangled particles are reciprocal. Action on one particle creates an effect on other entangled particles instantaneously and even across large distances. This phenomenon is no less important for macro scale objects.

Sheldrake (1999) has conducted experiments with dogs whereby the animals correctly anticipated their owner's departure from a remote location to return home. He has also conducted other successful experiments on previously unexplained behaviors of animals. In one example rats that were learning to traverse a new maze benefited non-locally from the experience of others that had previously learned the maze in the total absence of classical space time information. Other examples include distant (e.g. nonlocal) awareness of deaths and accidents, animals that heal humans and those sensitive to forebodings of natural disasters.

It is not surprising then, that humans exhibit an even wider range of reactions to non-local information. The evidence suggests that humans can perceive, recognize and give meaning to nonlocal information across a broad range of complexity, from inanimate objects, simple organisms, animals and other humans (refer to Figure 4). The existence of QH provides an adequate informational structure to permit a theory for the observed results. This is a classical example, where results are repeatedly observed over time that fall outside the prevailing paradigm, and must await new developments in science before the phenomenon can be adequately explained. Perhaps this explains psychic abilities.

In humans, it is a well established meditation principle that prolonged focused attention on an object of meditation causes the percipient and the target object to appear to merge so that a much deeper level of understanding about the object is obtained. This includes information such as its history or internal functioning that would not be available through classical space-time information. The quantum holographic theory describes how this phenomenon might take place. Further, it is accepted that the mind and associated brain with its 100 billion neurons function together as a massively parallel pattern matching (e.g. information) processor, capable of performing many tasks simultaneously. Most of this processing is done subconsciously or in the right hemisphere which is attributed to the intuitive part of the mind.

Conscious focused attention is a unique and singular task that takes place sequentially mostly in the left hemisphere in the cognitive part of the brain. The condition of attention deficit disorder (ADD) is precisely the problem of a percipient being unable to maintain a singular focus for a sufficient time to complete a desired task or observation. Thus the action of focusing attention by a percipient may be construed as a necessary condition for resonance (PCAR) to be established with the perceived object. Even for people with such a handicap, reducing stress, eliminating distractions, and quieting the mind via meditation may also improve one's ability to focus thereby improving the resonance condition.

Healers typically report such a focusing to create a resonance with the object of their healing activities. Once in resonance, they often report sensing in their mind some sort of picture which appears as a type of 3-D holographic image. They maintain that diseased or damaged tissues in the target often appear as fuzzy or appear somehow different from the normal tissue surrounding it. Sometimes they describe it as sensing energy blockages. They claim to be able to focus energy or somehow manipulate (e.g. intentionality) the diseased tissue which over time causes the image to change and take on the same characteristics of the healthy tissue surrounding it. Could this be the result of the act of intention of the healer resonating with the quantum emissions and subsequent absorptions by the diseased tissues?

Healers and other psychically sensitive individuals often enter into resonance with the object of their focused attention (or intention) by using an icon (e.g. a representation of the object of interest). Similarly people praying for others (not in a religious sense of supplication to a higher being) are suggestive of initiating a non-local resonance process with a target object. Healing prayer has existed in all cultures for millennia. If prayer did not produce some positive results, it is likely that religion would have abandoned it centuries ago. For most of its history healing prayer was attributed to supernatural agency rather than resonance with the target's QH. This is simply another example of phenomenology waiting while science catches up as in our colonial lightning example above.

In recent times Dossey (1993) and many others have attempted to document the efficacy of prayer, particularly healing prayer. Some claim the results establish the case for healing prayer. However the difficulties of controlling all the variables, the experimenter affect, etc. in such clinical studies leave many avenues for valid criticism. The fact that Radin's many studies demonstrated that attention alone produced non-local results in REGs (random event generators) and other machines in reducing randomness (e.g. increasing order) confirms that information has a nonlocal effect and may be correctly formulated as negative entropy. These results apply to healing prayer as well. In these cases, icons are often used to facilitate this resonant process. Icons can be an image, picture, representation or an article associated with the target object of the intention. What each of these modalities has in common is that they appear to provide a mechanism for the intender to "tune in" or resonate with the target. Touching an icon seems to satisfy the resonant (PCAR) requirement and probably allows the intender access to the information about the target not available from normal space-time information. Police agencies often use this modality with psychics who then focus their attention to gain information about a crime scene often with considerable success.

Healers and people praying may also utilize icons but in this case with focused intentionality to resonate with the person to be targeted by similar means. The use of icons to retrieve nonlocal information also suggests an explanation of water memory and homeopathy. Molecules of toxic substances from an original solution are removed by serial dilution. Could some of the water molecules resonate with the emitted photons from the original toxic substances and later resonate with the human immune system when absorbed by it?

If, as required in the theory of the Quantum Hologram, the icon has been in the presence of the individual or contains the signature of the person about whom information or healing is desired, the event history of the icon and that of the individual intersect. The phase relationships of the quantum emissions of the icon contains a record of the target object's journey in three dimensional space and time, as well as the quantum states through which it has passed on this journey. The sensitive individual, with a honed talent, often seems to be able to decode the information coded in these phase relationships of the photons emitted from the icon about the individual or object sought. It may also be the case with the bloodhound that additional non-local information has been gained about the subject, even though the classical explanation is that the animal is operating only with heightened olfactory sensing.

Although perception in the three dimensional world requires and utilizes resonance (PCAR), most humans do not routinely bring to conscious awareness non-local information when operating in ordinary three dimensional reality. We perceive objects as presented by space-time information, that is, shape, color, function (tree, chair, table, etc) but are not usually aware of the additional non-local information (location in space, threats, etc) unless there is strong emotional connection. Consider the case of an infant separated from its parents during time of war or unprecedented disaster. Years later, by a chance reunion, the now unfamiliar child and / or birth mother sense a strong connection while others sense nothing. Could this be because of the resonance between mother and child during pregnancy and through the birth process?

It usually takes training as provided by many esoteric traditions and / or certain naturally sensitive individuals to routinely perceive the non-local holographic information associated with a particular target object. There is considerable evidence to suggest that the brain / mind has these latter capabilities at birth. The development of language, suppression of these capabilities by cultural conditioning and subsequent lack of practice all contribute to the atrophy of natural ability of conscious, intuitive perceptions. Perhaps cultural conditioning is one of the reasons why so called reincarnation experiences are so common in children in eastern cultures while virtually unheard of in the west. The late Dr. Ian Stevenson (2001) of the department of Psychiatric Medicine at the University of Virginia traveled around the world and investigated children usually from the ages between 2 and 5 who claim to have lived previous lives.

"At the same time they have often displayed behaviors or phobia that were either unusual in their family or not explained by any current life events. In many cases of this type the child's statements have been shown to correspond accurately to facts in the life and death of a deceased person; in many of these cases the families concerned have had no contact before the case developed."

Our view is that although the reincarnation event is a real non-local event experienced by the child, the interpretation of the event is not correct. We believe that the person is in a high state of resonance with the quantum hologram of the deceased and is able to retrieve QH information about the deceased from that resonance condition. As the child ages, rational left brain processing begins to dominate and the child is no longer able to resonate with the QH of the deceased unless the child has been trained to maintain that state of altered consciousness. We would attribute a similar effect with someone who experiences an out-of-body experience (OBE). Again, this most likely represents a high state of resonance with the remote location and the experiencer is retrieving and processing the QH of the objects at the remote location being visited non-locally.

In cases like the ones just described, meditators, mystic adepts and natural psychics routinely demonstrate that non-local information is perceptible from physical objects and icons by focusing attention, quieting the left brain and allowing intuitive perceptions to enter conscious awareness. Those most practiced in meditation experience an altered sense of space-time, the dissolution of self, have access to universal knowledge and sometimes feel a unified sense of oneness with all of existence. Along with this sense of oneness comes a feeling of immense bliss and a great clarity of mind. We postulate that they have entered into a state of high resonance with the QH and have access to all the information that is implied by such unification. This seems to describe the epiphany that I (Edgar Mitchell) experienced on my return flight from the moon.

Particularly in western tradition, academic interest has been on left brain or rational processing rather than right brain intuitive functions. It is the left brain cognitive ability in humans that provides acceptable labeling of the intuitive, creative and artistic processes taking place in the right brain. Given the fact that with training and practice, all individuals can reestablish and deepen their cognitive access to intuitive, non-local information demonstrates that learning recall is taking place within the whole brain itself and involves enhanced coherence and coordination between the hemispheres and with the QH. This process is different and distinct from the left brain function of extending and extrapolating factual data and forming conclusions based on logical deduction to leap to an "intuitive" conclusion, while omitting the immediate steps leading to that conclusion.

When an object or person of interest is not in the immediate vicinity of the percipient so that space-time information obtained by normal senses is unavailable for receiving and interpreting nonlocal information, the method is somewhat different in obtaining resonance with the target. The case in point is the subject of Remote Viewing (RV) which is another latent ability we all have to some degree. RV allows us to describe and experience activities and events that are normally precluded from us with ordinary perception from our normal five senses.

Remote viewing has been researched extensively by Putoff (1996) and Putoff and Targ (1976) at Stanford Research Institute since the mid 1970's. Their work attracted the attention and funding from the U.S. Central Intelligence Agency and was conducted in secret for almost 20 years. Some of the work involved exploring the limits of what remote viewing could do and also in improving the quality and consistency of the result. Much of the remainder of the effort was in training operatives to collect intelligence information against foreign adversaries. The government funding of the effort ended after the collapse of the Soviet Union in the 1990's.

For the purposes of our discussion with RV, the questions we are interested in pertain to the "reference signal" used to decode the quantum holographic information in the absence of any classical space time signals and also how the condition of resonance (PCAR) is established by the percipient. Experimental protocols from RV normally provide clues to the location of the target object such as a description, a picture or location by latitude and longitude or an icon representing the target. These clues seem to be sufficient for the percipient to establish resonance with the target. Space-time information (as perceived by the normal five senses) about the target is not perceived by the percipient, nor does the object usually appear at its physical location in space time like a photograph or map in the mind. Rather the information is perceived and presented as internal information and the percipient must associate the perceptions with his / her internal data base of experience in order to recognize and describe the target's perceived attributes.

In the case of complex objects being remotely viewed, the perceived information is seldom so unambiguous as to be instantly recognizable as correct. Sketches, metaphors and analogies are usually employed to recognize and communicate the nonlocal information. A considerable amount of training, teamwork and experience are necessary to reliably and correctly extract complex nonlocal information from a distant location. The information appears to the percipient as sketchy, often dream-like and wispy, subtle impressions of the remote reality. Very skilled individuals may report the internal information as frequently vivid, clear and unambiguous. The remote viewing information received in this case is strictly non-local and, based on the hypothesis of QH, the received information is missing the normal space time component information from any of the five normal senses about the object necessary to completely identify and specify it via resonance.

It has been demonstrated that this intuitive mode of perception can be enhanced by training in most individuals. Perhaps additional training and greater acceptance of this capability will allow percipients to develop greater detail, accuracy and reliability in their skill. In principle, training will not only enhance the remote viewing skill and its accuracy, but should also cause the associated neural circuitry to become more robust as well.

In the absence of normal perceptual sensory signals such as light or sound to establish the resonance condition to provide a basis for decoding the target object's quantum hologram, an icon representing the object seems to be sufficient to allow the mind to focus on the target and to establish the resonant (PCAR) condition as we have described earlier. However a reference signal is also required to provide decoding of the encoded holographic phase dependant information. It has been suggested by Marcer (1998) by that any waves reverberating through the universe remain coherent with the waves at the source, and are thus sufficient to serve as the reference signal to decode the holographic information from any object's quantum hologram emanating from a remote location.

We conclude our discussion of potential QH applications with the experiments conducted by George De La Warr in the 1940's and 1950's. De La Warr was a British engineer who became interested in understanding the mechanisms associated with remote diagnosis and healing. His work was documented by Day (1966) in the 1960's. De La Warr began experiments with his wife, an accomplished psychic healer, to detect the radiation emitted in such processes. At first he thought this mechanism was related to some form of EM radiation but later realized that it was associated with resonance. He eventually built a diagnostic device which acted as a resonant cavity. Perhaps the strangest aspect of the discovery was that when the device was operated by his wife, she could focus her attention on a living target object and was able to produce a resonant condition between the target and the measuring device. She was also able to "project" this resonance condition and expose a blank photographic plate. She was eventually able to pick up resonances from plants, trees, humans and even diseased tissues.

Over time the De La Warrs built up a library of several hundred such photographic plates. Many years later Benford (2008) came across this library and had some of the photographs analyzed by modern 3-D CAD/CAM software (Bryce® 4). The analysis showed that the images were spatially encoded with a 3-D effect similar to those produced by fMRI machines but with much higher resolution. (Earlier we described the discovery made by Shempp that fMRI machines encode quantum information holographically). Recall that fMRI machines were not in existence until many years after these photographic plates were exposed by Mrs. De La Warr. These experiments along with recent discoveries associated with fMRI machines seem to provide compelling evidence that macro-scale quantum holography is a real phenomenon and is produced by conscious attention and intention by a percipient on objects of interest.

9. How Nature Learns

We end this section with our model of QH summarizing how nature (and all living entities) perceives, learns, adapts and evolves in its environment. This model is shown in figure 5. In this model, we show how establishing resonance (PCAR) between a percipient and a target object, the phase conjugate (mirror image) signaling paths connecting the two, can be labeled "perception" on the input side and either "attention" or "intention" on the output side. In the case where the object is a simple physical object (like an apple), our interest is on the non-local information perceived by the percipient about the apple. However from the point of view of the apple, information about the percipient is also available to the apple. The resonant condition between the two is a reciprocal relationship.

Nature's Learning Mechanism

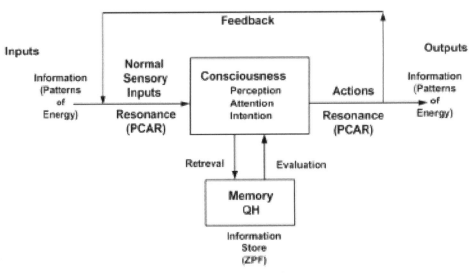

Figure 5. - How Nature Learns

The Quantum Holographic model predicts that the history of events of the target object (apple in this case) is carried in the apple's QH which implies that the "attention" or "intention" focused on the apple by the percipient causes that event to be recorded in the apple's QH. Clearly we cannot query the apple to inquire about its experience but none-the-less the interaction will create a phase shift in the apple's QH (interference pattern) which should be detectable. Although we are using anthropic labeling as we are discussing human perception with the apple, this phenomenon is rooted in natural (and primitive) nonlocal physical processes which are fundamental to the interaction between all objects whether living or not. The evolved complexities of perception, cognition, etc., associated with the brain, as yet have no obvious analogous label other than "non-locality and entanglement" to describe the interactive experience with the environment for simple objects like apples.

Once the resonance condition is established, the percipient can evaluate the results (via the feedback mechanism shown in Figure 5) and can then change its mind state with regard to the object being perceived. The perceived information can then be processed by brain functions so that cognition occurs with respect to the perceived information and thus allowing meaning to be assigned to it. Cognition and meaning require finding a relationship between the perceived information and the information residing in the percipient's memory and this information will be interpreted based on the percipient's beliefs and prior experience stored in its memory. The percipient can then form intent with respect to the object. In such cases the output labeled "action" changes from "attention" (passive state) to "intention" (pro-active state).

In self aware animals (e.g. those with a brain) cognition, meaning and intent with respect to an external object can often be described in simple terms, for example: enemy; fight or flight; food, eat; greet, etc. The nonlocal component of information, although present and creating effect, is operating below the level of conscious perception in humans and results in "instinctual" subconscious behaviors in animals. Classical modeling of this autonomous activity describes it in terms of classical information and energy flow in the central nervous system and the brain. However, as QH suggests, nonlocality is operating at all levels of activity, certainly there are resonances involving this non-local information operating throughout all the cells of an organism in parallel with classical space-time functions as described earlier in this paper.

The results for intentional effects of non-locality should be no more difficult to accept than the results for perception -- normal perception using the five senses. The resonant condition (PCAR) implies a symmetry whereby information flows in both directions between the object and the percipient such that each is both target object and percipient to the other. Only the complexity of the more ordered normal sensory mechanisms suggests a non-symmetrical relationship. In general, humans seem to have great difficulty accepting that thoughts, specifically intentionality, can cause action at a distance (remember Einstein's "spooky action at a distance"). Yet, it has been observed for centuries and only in recent decades has it been subjected to scientific scrutiny.

The case of resonance conditions via PCAR to create remote effects by transfer of non-local information between equally complex percipients like humans is not difficult to understand. Indeed, hundreds of successful experiments have established the case. In all these cases no energy transfer is required, only nonlocal information, as each percipient / target object has access to its own energy source. The case for intentionality creating remote effects in inanimate objects is more puzzling. Teleportation of quantum states has been successfully accomplished for particles as described by Darling (2005) and now has practical applications in quantum computing. Numerous studies by Radin (1997), and earlier by Dunne and Jahn (1988) show that macro-scale objects can also be changed or moved, but the energy transfer mechanism by which the classical states of a remote object are affected remains elusive but perhaps is related to utilizing energy directly from the zero point field.

10. Summary and Implications

Someone recently requested the authors describe quantum holography and its implications in two pages, a very difficult task indeed. It has taken us considerably more than that to get here. Nature is extremely complex and does not give up her secrets willingly. Humankind's efforts at understanding her rests on the shoulders of countless dedicated men and women who have come before and are yet to come. Clearly we have a long way to go before we understand it all. Perhaps what is truly most amazing about nature is that it appears to be knowable at all. Our investigations into the nature of consciousness leads us to believe that the best way to survive and sustain humankind as a civilization and to thrive as well is dependent upon the emergence of a new world view, one that understands our proper place in the larger scheme of nature. This includes a worldview that properly addresses, in verifiable scientific terms, our collective relationship to each other, to the biosphere, to the environment, and to the entire cosmos. Towards that end, the evidence that we have presented suggests that we live in a universe that operates according to the following principles. It is:

Self-organizing - All non living and living matter seems to be the result of the emergent complexity adapting and evolving in response to changes in the environment.

Intelligent - The universe utilizes information, processes it and assigns meaning to it. It seems to evaluate new experiences against stored information and "chooses" actions based on that evaluation based on feedback mechanisms.

Creative - All matter in the universe appears to be interconnected and communicates with itself to continually form more complex systems. These systems seem to regulate and organize themselves in ways that are flexible, adaptable and exhibit some form of purposeful behavior.

Trial and error - The habits of nature, its laws, and its operating principles, seem to adapt and evolve by trial and error. The more successful an adaptation is the more it is reinforced. The less successful it is, the more likely it would be to atrophy and eventually die out or fade away into disuse.

Interactive - All matter continually interacts with all other matter. There is no such thing as independent action. Everything is defined in relationship to everything else.

Learning - Experience is retained in nature's memory, the Quantum Hologram. Once information is created it is always available and never forgotten.

Participatory -The role of intention in conscious matter has demonstrable effect.

Evolving - Since its beginnings, nature has been developing into ever increasing levels of complexity in response to environmental changes or pressures resulting from natural processes.

Non-locally connected - All things in nature are interconnected in a very fundamental way beyond time and space. The exchange of information between any two objects occurs instantaneously no matter their space time separation and these interconnections cannot be shielded or attenuated.

Based on Quantum Principles - From the micro scale of subatomic particles to the largest objects in the cosmos and everything in between, all matter displays the quantum characteristics of entanglement, coherence, correlation and resonance.

This universe seems, in some sense, to be a living, evolving, adapting universe that utilizes information to organize itself and to create ever increasing levels of complexity. We are a part of it and cannot be separated from it and are interconnected with it all. Furthermore it appears to be a self referencing system (see Figure 6). As nature learns, habits form and those that lead to useful outcomes solidify and effectively become "hard coded". Even then these "habits of nature" (including us) adapt and evolve by trial and error as change occurs. It appears that nature has bootstrapped itself not only into existence but has evolved itself into the current state of complexity that we now observe all around us. Most astounding of all is that humankind has evolved to the point that we can ask questions and have begun to gain understanding fundamental to nature's very existence. Perhaps, then, we and all sentient beings really are one of nature's way of knowing about and experiencing itself. Not only that, in some sense, we seem to be able to influence its very evolution.

Our hypothesis of interconnectedness and oneness suggested by quantum attributes and processes have been espoused by ancient sages, avatars, mystics, spiritual leaders and shamans throughout all times and by all cultures. Just as modern man has evolved from our ape-like ancestors, so too must we evolve to the next level of sophistication and refinement, and by inference our civilization as well. Change, adaptation to that change and evolution seem to be nature's intrinsic mandate built in to the very fabric of reality. All creation must either perish or constantly evolve. Nature has demonstrated this principle throughout its entire history and has seen to it that there are no alternatives. The arrow of time flows in one direction only.

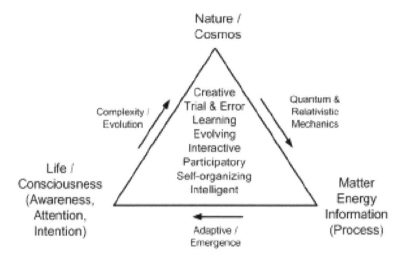

Figure 6 - Nature's Bootstrap Process

We have presented our hypothesis as a map of reality that appears to match observations and experimental evidence fairly well. It seems to account for many phenomena in nature that here-to-for had no explanations to account for them. However, as we have said throughout this manuscript, the map is not the territory. Instead it is nothing more than a model of that territory that makes predictions about how the territory will behave under certain circumstances. We believe that the cornerstones of our theory are built upon known and verified properties and processes of nature and perhaps some yet to be discovered. However, like all theories in science, all that we have proposed is testable. Those parts of it that are not validated will have to be modified, revised or discarded and replaced. Such is the nature of scientific inquiry. At the very least we hope that we will encourage discussion and research to further enhance humankind's understanding of nature.

It has been said that democracy requires an informed electorate to thrive and prosper. It would seem that that is excellent advice in most areas of human endeavor. Sound bites, personal biases, self serving interests have no place if we are to adapt and evolve in our understanding. We must remain open, be willing and desirous to be informed and, most of all, willingly engage in learning and discovering new knowledge about this world in which we live and our true place within it. The issues we face are too important to ignore either by willful neglect or lack of understanding. Our very survival and the survival of all life on earth depend upon it.

We leave you this ancient Sanskrit proverb:

God sleeps in the minerals,
Awakens in plants,
Walks in animals and,
Thinks in man.

References

Benford, M. (2000). Empirical Evidence Supporting Macro-Scale Quantum Holograph in Non-Local Effects, Journal of Theoretics, retrieved from archives at www.journaloftheoretics.com/Articles/2-5/Benford.htm.

Chalmers, D. (1996). The Conscious Mind, Oxford University Press, New York.

Church, D. (2007). The Genie in your Genes, Elite Books, Santa Rosa, CA.

Darling, D. (2005). Teleportation - The Impossible Leap, John Wiley & Sons. Hoboken, NJ.

Davies, P. (2008). The Goldilocks Enigma, Houghton Mifflin, Boston MA.

Day, L., De La Warr, G. (1966). Matter in the Making. Vincent Stuart LTD, London, UK.

Dossey, L. (1993). Healing Words- The Power of Prayer and the Practice of Medicine, Harper, San Francisco, CA.

Dunne,B., Jahn, R.G. (1988). Operator Related Anomalies in a Random Mechanical Cascade, JSE 2:pp 155-180.

Haisch, B. (2006). The God Theory, Red Wheel/Weiser LLC, San Francisco, CA.

Haisch, B., Reuda, A., Putoff, H. (1997). Physics of the Zero Point Field: Implications for Inertia, Gravity and Mass, Speculations in Science and Technology, Vol. 20, pp. 99-114.

Hameroff, S. (1994). Quantum Coherence in Microtubules: A Neural Basis for Emergent Consciousenss?, Journal of Consciousness Studies, Vol. 1, pp 91-118.

Hameroff, S. (1998). Quantum Computation in Brain Microtubules? The Penrose-Hameroff "Orch Or" Model of Consciousness. Philosophical Transactions: Mathematical, Physical and Engineering Sciences, Royal Society of London, Aug 25, 1998; 356(1743): 1869-1896.

Hameroff, S., Woolf, N. (2001), A Quantum Approach to Visual Consciousness, Trends in Cognitive Sciences, Vol. 5, Issue 11, pp. 472-478.

Harman W., Clark, J. (1994). New Metaphysical Foundations of Modern Science, Institute of Noetic Sciences, Sausalito, CA.

Ho, M. (1997). Quantum Coherence and Conscious Experience, Institute of Science in Society, Kybernetes 26, pp. 265-276.

Laszlo, E. (2004). Science and the Akashic Field, Inner Traditions, Rochester, VT.

Lipton, B. (2005). The Biology of Belief, Elite Books, Santa Rosa, CA, p 64.

Marcer, P. J. (1998). The Jigsaw, the Elephant and the Lighthouse, Proceedings of ANPA 20.

Marcer P., Schempp W. (1997). The Model of the Prokaryote Cell as an Anticipatory System Working by Quantum Holography, In: Dubois D. Proceedings of the First International Conference on Computing Anticipatory Systems, Liege, Belgium, August

11-15:307-313.

Marcer, P., Schempp, W. (1997). Model of the Neuron Working by Quantum Holography, Informatica Vol. 21, pp. 519-534.

Marcer, P.J. (1998). A Quantum Mechanical Model of the Evolution of Consciousness.

Mitchell, E. and Williams, D. (2008), The Way of the Explorer, New Page Books, Franklin Lakes, NJ.

Mitchell, E. (1995). A Dyadic Model of Consciousness, World Futures, Vol. 46. pp. 69-78.

Mitchell, E. (2001). Natures Mind: The Quantum Hologram, Institute of Noetic Sciences, Petalma, CA.

Mitchell, E., (2003). Quantum Holography: A Basis for the Interface Between Mind and Matter, Bioelectromagnetic Medicine, Marcel Dekker, New York.

Penrose, R. (1994). Shadows of Mind, Oxford University Press, Oxford.

Pribram, K. (1999). Brain and the Composition of Conscious Experience, Journal of Consciousness Studies, No. 5, pp. 19-42.

Pribram, K. (1999) Quantum Holography: Is it relevant to Brain Function?, Information Sciences Vol. 115, pp. 97-102.

Puthoff, H.E. (1996). CIA Initiated Remote Viewing Program at Stanford Research Institute, JSE 10:63-76.

Puthoff, H.E. and Targ, R. (1976). A Perceptual Channel for Information Transfer over Kilometer Distances: Historical Perspective and Recent Research, proceedings of the IEEE 64:329-354.

Radin, D. (1997). The Conscious Universe, Harper, San Francisco, CA.

Radin, D. (2006). Entangled Minds, Para-

view, NY.

Schempp, W. (1998). Magnetic Resonance Imaging: Mathematical Foundations and Applications, Wiley-Liss, New York.

Schempp W. (1999). Sub-Reimannian Geometry and Clinical Magnetic Resonance Tomography, Math Meth Appl Sci 22:867-922.

Schempp, W. and Mueller, K. (2007), Bandpass filter processing strategies in non-invasive sympectic spinor response imaging, Inf. Computation. Sci. 4, pp. 211-232.

Schempp, W. (2008), The Fourier holographic encoding strategy of symplectic spinor visualization, New Directions in Holography, pp. 479-522.

Schmeidler, G.R., Craig, J.G. (1972). Moods and ESP Scores in Group testing, Journal of ASPR, Vol. 66, no. 3, pp 280-287.

Schlitz, M., Wiserman, R. (1997). Experimenter Effects and the Remote Detection of Staring, Journal of Parapsychology, Vol. 61, September.

Sheldrake, R. (1981). A New Science of Life: The Hypothesis of Formative Causation, Tarcher, Los Angeles.

Sheldrake, R. (1997). Mind, Memory, and Archetype: Morphic Resonance and the Collective Unconscious, Psychological Perspectives.

Sheldrake, R. (1999). Dogs That know When Their Owners Are Coming Home, Random House, NY, NY.

Stevenson, I. (2001). Children Who Remember Previous Lives: A Question of Reincarnation, revised ed., Jefferson, NC, McFarland & Company.

Utts, J.M. (1991). Replication and Meta-Analysis in Parapsychology, Statistical Science, 6: 363-382.

Consciousness in the Universe: Neuroscience, Quantum Space-Time Geometry and Orch OR Theory

Roger Penrose, PhD, OM, FRS[1],
and Stuart Hameroff, MD[2]

[1]Emeritus Rouse Ball Professor, Mathematical Institute, Emeritus Fellow, Wadham College, University of Oxford, Oxford, UK
[2]Professor, Anesthesiology and Psychology, Director, Center for Consciousness Studies, The University of Arizona, Tucson, Arizona, USA

Abstract

The nature of consciousness, its occurrence in the brain, and its ultimate place in the universe are unknown. We proposed in the mid 1990's that consciousness depends on biologically 'orchestrated' quantum computations in collections of microtubules within brain neurons, that these quantum computations correlate with and regulate neuronal activity, and that the continuous Schrödinger evolution of each quantum computation terminates in accordance with the specific Diósi–Penrose (DP) scheme of 'objective reduction' of the quantum state (OR). This orchestrated OR activity (Orch OR) is taken to result in a moment of conscious awareness and/or choice. This particular (DP) form of OR is taken to be a quantum-gravity process related to the fundamentals of spacetime geometry, so Orch OR suggests a connection between brain biomolecular processes and fine-scale structure of the universe. Here we review and update Orch OR in light of criticisms and developments in quantum biology, neuroscience, physics and cosmology. We conclude that consciousness plays an intrinsic role in the universe.

KEY WORDS: Consciousness, microtubules, OR, Orch OR, quantum computation, quantum gravity

1. Introduction: Consciousness, Brain and Evolution

Consciousness implies awareness: subjective experience of internal and external phenomenal worlds. Consciousness is central also to understanding, meaning and volitional choice with the experience of free will. Our views of reality, of the universe, of ourselves depend on consciousness. Consciousness defines our existence.

Three general possibilities regarding the origin and place of consciousness in the universe have been commonly expressed.

(A) Consciousness is not an independent quality but arose as a natural evolutionary consequence of the biological adaptation of brains and nervous systems. The most popular scientific view is that consciousness emerged as a property of complex biological computation during the course of evolution. Opinions vary as to when, where and how consciousness appeared, e.g. only recently in humans, or earlier in lower organisms. Consciousness as evolutionary adaptation is commonly assumed to be epiphenomenal (i.e. a secondary effect without independent influence), though it is frequently argued to confer beneficial advantages to conscious species (Dennett, 1991; 1995; Wegner, 2002).

(B) Consciousness is a quality that has always been in the universe. Spiritual and religious approaches assume consciousness has been in the universe all along, e.g. as the 'ground of being', 'creator' or component of an omnipresent 'God'. Panpsychists attribute consciousness to all matter. Idealists contend consciousness is all that exists, the material world an illusion (Kant, 1781).

(C) Precursors of consciousness have always been in the universe; biology evolved a mechanism to convert conscious precursors to actual consciousness. This is the view implied by Whitehead (1929; 1933) and taken in the Penrose-Hameroff theory of 'orchestrated objective reduction' ('Orch OR'). Precursors of consciousness, presumably with proto-experiential qualities, are proposed to exist as the potential ingredients of actual consciousness, the physical basis of these proto-conscious elements not necessarily being part of our current theories of the laws of the universe (Penrose and Hameroff, 1995; Hameroff and Penrose, 1996a; 1996b).

2. Ideas for how consciousness arises from brain action

How does the brain produce consciousness? An enormous amount of detailed knowledge about brain function has accrued; however the mechanism by which the brain produces consciousness remains mysterious (Koch, 2004). The prevalent scientific view is that consciousness somehow emerges from complex computation among simple neurons which each receive and integrate synaptic inputs to a threshold for bit-like firing. The brain as a network of 10^{11} 'integrate-and-fire' neurons computing by bit-like firing and variable-strength chemical synapses is the standard model for computer simulations of brain function, e.g. in the field of artificial intelligence ('AI').

The brain-as-computer view can account for non-conscious cognitive functions including much of our mental processing and control of behavior. Such non-conscious cognitive processes are deemed 'zombie modes', 'auto-pilot', or 'easy problems'. The 'hard problem' (Chalmers, 1996) is the question of how cognitive processes are accompanied or driven by phenomenal conscious experience and subjective feelings, referred to by philosophers as 'qualia'. Other issues also suggest the brain-as-computer view may be incomplete, and that other approaches are required. The conventional brain-as-computer view fails to account for:

The 'hard problem' Distinctions between conscious and non-conscious processes are not addressed; consciousness is assumed to emerge at a critical level (neither specified nor testable) of computational complexity mediating otherwise non-conscious processes.

'Non-computable' thought and understanding, e.g. as shown by Gödel's theorem (Penrose, 1989; 1994).

'Binding and synchrony', the problem of how disparate neuronal activities are bound into unified conscious experience, and how neuronal synchrony, e.g. gamma synchrony EEG (30 to 90 Hz), the best measurable correlate of consciousness does not derive from neuronal firings.

Causal efficacy of consciousness and any semblance of free will. Because measurable brain activity corresponding to a stimulus often occurs after we've responded (seemingly consciously) to that stimulus, the brain-as-computer view depicts consciousness as epiphenomenal illusion (Dennett, 1991; 1995; Wegner, 2002).

Cognitive behaviors of single cell organisms. Protozoans like Paramecium can swim, find food and mates, learn, remember and have sex, all without synaptic computation (Sherrington, 1957).

In the 1980s Penrose and Hameroff (separately) began to address these issues, each against the grain of mainstream views.

3. Microtubules as Biomolecular Computers

Hameroff had been intrigued by seemingly intelligent, organized activities inside cells, accomplished by protein polymers called microtubules (Hameroff and Watt, 1982; Hameroff, 1987). Major components of the cell's structural cytoskeleton, microtubules also accounted for precise separation of chromosomes in cell division, complex behavior of Paramecium, and regulation of synapses within brain neurons (Figure 1). The intelligent function and periodic lattice structure of microtubules suggested they might function as some type of biomolecular computer.

Microtubules are self-assembling polymers of the peanut-shaped protein dimer tubulin, each tubulin dimer (110,000 atomic mass units) being composed of an alpha and beta monomer (Figure 2). Thirteen linear tubulin chains ('protofilaments') align side-to-side to form hollow microtubule cylinders (25 nanometers diameter) with two types of hexagonal lattices. The A-lattice has multiple winding patterns which intersect on protofilaments at specific intervals matching the Fibonacci series found widely in nature and possessing a helical symmetry (Section 9), suggestively sympathetic to large-scale quantum processes.

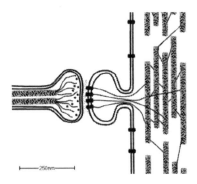

Figure 1. Schematic of portions of two neurons. A terminal axon (left) forms a synapse with a dendritic spine of a second neuron (right). Interiors of both neurons show cytoskeletal structures including microtubules, actin and microtubule-associated proteins (MAPs). Dendritic microtubules are arrayed in mixed polarity local networks, interconnected by MAPs. Synaptic inputs are conveyed to dendritic microtubules by ion flux, actin filaments, second messengers (e.g. CaMKII, see Hameroff et al, 2010) and MAPs.

Along with actin and other cytoskeletal structures, microtubules establish cell shape, direct growth and organize function of cells including brain neurons. Various types of microtubule-associated proteins ('MAPs') bind at specific lattice sites and bridge to other microtubules, defining cell architecture like girders and beams in a building. One such MAP is tau, whose displacement from microtubules results in neurofibrillary tangles and the cognitive dysfunction of Alzheimer's disease (Brunden et al, 2011). Motor proteins (dynein, kinesin) move rapidly along microtubules, transporting cargo molecules to specific locations.

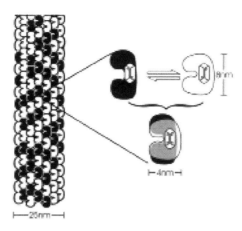

Figure 2. Left: Portion of single microtubule composed of tubulin dimer proteins (black and white) in A-lattice configuration. Right, top: According to pre-Orch OR microtubule automata theory (e.g. Hameroff and Watt, 1982; Rasmussen et al, 1990), each tubulin in a microtubule lattice switches between alternate (black and white) 'bit' states, coupled to electron cloud dipole London forces in internal hydrophobic pocket. Right, bottom: According to Orch OR, each tubulin can also exist as quantum superposition (quantum bit, or 'qubit') of both states, coupled to superposition of London force dipoles in hydrophobic pocket.

Microtubules also fuse side-by-side in doublets or triplets. Nine such doublets or triplets then align to form barrel-shaped mega-cylinders called cilia, flagella and centrioles, organelles responsible for locomotion, sensation and cell division. Either individually or in these larger arrays, microtubules are responsible for cellular and intra-cellular movements requiring intelligent spatiotemporal organization. Microtubules have a lattice structure comparable to computational systems. Could microtubules process information?

The notion that microtubules process information was suggested in general terms by Sherrington (1957) and Atema (1973). With physicist colleagues through the 1980s, Hameroff developed models of microtubules as information processing devices, specifically molecular ('cellular') automata, self-organizing computational devices (Figure 3). Cellular automata are computational systems in which fundamental units, or 'cells' in a grid or lattice can each exist in specific states, e.g. 1 or 0, at a given time (Wolfram, 2002). Each cell interacts with its neighbor cells at discrete, synchronized time steps, the state of each cell at any particular time step determined by its state and its neighbor cell states at the previous time step, and rules governing the interactions. In such ways, using simple neighbor interactions in simple lattice grids, cellular automata can perform complex computation and generate complex patterns.

Cells in cellular automata are meant to imply fundamental units. But biological cells are not necessarily simple, as illustrated by the clever Paramecium. Molecular automata are cellular automata in which the fundamental units, bits or cells are states of molecules, much smaller than biological cells. A dynamic, interactive molecular grid or lattice is required.

Microtubules are lattices of tubulin dimers which Hameroff and colleagues modeled as molecular automata. Discrete states of tubulin were suggested to act as bits, switching between states, and interacting (via dipole-dipole coupling) with neighbor tubulin bit states in 'molecular automata' computation (Hameroff and Watt, 1982; Rasmussen et al., 1990; Tuszynski et al., 1995). The mechanism for bit-like switching at the level of each tubulin was proposed to depend on the van der Waals–London force in non-polar, water-excluding regions ('hydrophobic pockets') within each tubulin.

Proteins are largely heterogeneous arrays of amino acid residues, including both water-soluble polar and water-insoluble non-polar groups, the latter including phenylalanine and tryptophan with electron resonance clouds (e.g. phenyl and indole rings). Such non-polar groups coalesce during protein folding to form homogeneous water-excluding 'hydrophobic' pockets within which instantaneous dipole couplings between nearby electron clouds operate. These are London forces which are extremely weak but numerous and able to act collectively in hydrophobic regions to influence and determine protein state (Voet and Voet, 1995).

London forces in hydrophobic pockets of various neuronal proteins are the mechanisms by which anesthetic gases selectively erase consciousness (Franks and Lieb, 1984). Anesthetics bind by their own London force attractions with electron clouds of the hydrophobic pocket, presumably impairing normally-occurring London forces governing protein switching required for consciousness (Hameroff, 2006).

In Figure 2, and as previously used in Orch OR, London forces are illustrated in cartoon fashion. A single hydrophobic pocket is depicted in tubulin, with portions of two electron resonance rings in the pocket. Single electrons in each ring repel each other, as their electron cloud net dipole flips (London force oscillation). London forces in hydrophobic pockets were used as the switching mechanism to distinguish discrete states for each tubulin in microtubule automata. In recent years tubulin hydrophobic regions and switching in the Orch OR proposal that we describe below have been clarified and updated (see Section 8).

To synchronize discrete time steps in microtubule automata, tubulins in microtubules were assumed to oscillate synchronously in a manner proposed by Fröhlich for biological coherence. Biophysicist Herbert Fröhlich (1968; 1970; 1975) had suggested that biomolecular dipoles constrained in a common geometry and voltage field would oscillate coherently, coupling, or condensing to a common vibrational mode. He proposed that biomolecular dipole lattices could convert ambient energy to coherent, synchronized dipole excitations, e.g. in the gigahertz (10^9 s^{-1}) frequency range. Fröhlich coherence or condensation can be either quantum coherence (e.g. Bose-Einstein condensation) or classical synchrony (Reimers et al., 2009).

In recent years coherent excitations have been found in living cells emanating from microtubules at 8 megahertz (Pokorny et al., 2001; 2004). Bandyopadhyay (2011) has found a series of coherence resonance peaks in single microtubules ranging from 12 kilohertz to 8 megahertz.

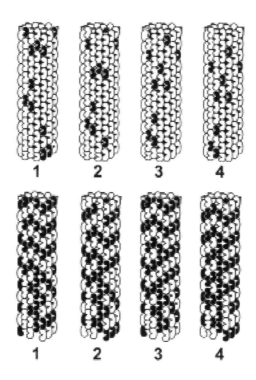

Figure 3. Microtubule automata (Rasmussen et al, 1990). Top: 4 time steps (e.g. at 8 megahertz, Pokorny et al, 2001) showing propagation of information states and patterns ('gliders' in cellular automata parlance). Bottom: At different dipole coupling parameter, bidirectional pattern movement and computation occur.

Rasmussen et al (1990) applied Fröhlich synchrony (in classical mode) as a clocking mechanism for computational time steps in simulated microtubule automata. Based on dipole couplings between neighboring tubulins in the microtubule lattice geometry, they found traveling gliders, complex patterns, computation and learning. Microtubule automata within brain neurons could potentially provide another level of information processing in the brain.

Approximately 10^8 tubulins in each neuron switching and oscillating in the range of 10^7 per second (e.g. Pokorny 8 MHz) gives an information capacity at the microtubule level of 10^{15} operations per second per neuron. This predicted capacity challenged and annoyed AI whose estimates for information processing at the level of neurons and synapses were virtually the same as this single-cell value, but for the entire brain (10^{11} neurons, 10^3 synapses per neuron, 10^2 transmissions per synapse per second = 10^{16} operations per second). Total brain capacity when taken at the microtubule level (in 10^{11} neurons) would potentially be 10^{26} operations per second, pushing the goalpost for AI brain equivalence farther into the future, and down into the quantum regime.

High capacity microtubule-based computing inside brain neurons could account for organization of synaptic regulation, learning and memory, and perhaps act as the substrate for consciousness. But increased brain information capacity per se didn't address most unanswered questions about consciousness (Section 2). Something was missing.

4. Objective Reduction (OR)

In 1989 Penrose published The Emperor's New Mind, which was followed in 1994 by Shadows of the Mind. Critical of AI, both books argued, by appealing to Gödel's theorem and other considerations, that certain aspects of human consciousness, such as understanding, must be beyond the scope of any computational system, i.e. 'non-computable'. Non-computability is a perfectly well-defined mathematical concept, but it had not previously been considered as a serious possibility for the result of physical actions. The non-computable ingredient required for human consciousness and understanding, Penrose suggested, would have to lie in an area where our current physical theories are fundamentally incomplete, though of important relevance to the scales that are pertinent to the operation of our brains. The only serious possibility was the incompleteness of quantum theory—an incompleteness that both Einstein and Schrödinger had recognized, despite quantum theory having frequently been argued to represent the pinnacle of 20th century scientific achievement. This incompleteness is the unresolved issue referred to as the 'measurement problem', which we consider in more detail below, in Section 5. One way to resolve it would be to provide an extension of the standard framework of quantum mechanics by introducing an objective form of quantum state reduction—termed 'OR' (objective reduction), an idea which we also describe more fully below, in Section 6.

In Penrose (1989), the tentatively suggested OR proposal would have its onset determined by a condition referred to there as 'the one-graviton' criterion. However, in Penrose (1995), a much better-founded criterion was used, now sometimes referred to as the Diósi–Penrose proposal (henceforth 'DP'; see Diósi 1987, 1989, Penrose 1993, 1996, 2000, 2009). This is an objective physical threshold, providing a plausible lifetime for quantum-superposed states. Other such OR proposals had also been put forward, from time to time (e.g. Kibble 1981, Pearle 1989, Pearle and Squires 1994, Ghirardi et al., 1986, 1990; see Ghirardi 2011, this volume) as solutions to the measurement problem, but had not originally been suggested as having anything to do with the consciousness issue. The Diósi-Penrose proposal is sometimes referred to as a 'quantum-gravity' scheme, but it is not part of the normal ideas used in quantum gravity, as will be explained below (Section 6). Moreover, the proposed connection between consciousness and quantum measurement is almost opposite, in the Orch OR scheme, to the kind of idea that had frequently been put forward in the early days of quantum mechanics (see, for example, Wigner 1961) which suggests that a 'quantum measurement' is something that occurs only as a result of the conscious intervention of an observer. This issue, also, will be discussed below (Section 5).

5. The Nature of Quantum Mechanics and its Fundamental Problem

The term 'quantum' refers to a discrete element of energy in a system, such as the energy E of a particle, or of some other subsystem, this energy being related to a fundamental frequency ν of its oscillation, according to Max Planck's famous formula (where h is Planck's constant):

$$E = h\,\nu.$$

This deep relation between discrete energy levels and frequencies of oscillation underlies the wave/particle duality inherent in quantum phenomena. Neither the word "particle" nor the word "wave" adequately conveys the true nature of a basic quantum entity, but both provide useful partial pictures.

The laws governing these submicroscopic quantum entities differ from those governing our everyday classical world. For example, quantum particles can exist in two or more states or locations simultaneously, where such a multiple coexisting superposition of alternatives (each alternative being weighted by a complex number) would be described mathematically by a quantum wavefunction. We don't see superpositions in the consciously perceived world; we see objects and particles as material, classical things in specific locations and states.

Another quantum property is 'non-local entanglement,' in which separated components of a system become unified, the entire collection of components being governed by one common quantum wavefunction. The parts remain somehow connected, even when spatially separated by significant distances (e.g. over 10 kilometres, Tittel et al., 1998). Quantum superpositions of bit states (quantum bits, or qubits) can be interconnected with one another through entanglement in quantum computers. However, quantum entanglements cannot, by themselves, be used to send a message from one part of an entangled system to another; yet entanglement can be used in conjunction with classical signaling to achieve strange effects—such as the strange phenomenon referred to as quantum teleportation—that classical signalling cannot achieve by itself (e.g. Bennett and Wiesner, 1992; Bennett et al., 1993; Bouwmeester et al., 1997; Macikic et al., 2002).

The issue of why we don't directly perceive quantum superpositions is a manifestation of the measurement problem referred to in Section 4. Put more precisely, the measurement problem is the conflict between the two fundamental procedures of quantum mechanics. One of these procedures, referred to as unitary evolution, denoted here by U, is the continuous deterministic evolution of the quantum state (i.e. of the wavefunction of the entire system) according to the fundamental Schrödinger equation, The other is the procedure that is adopted whenever a measurement of the system—or observation—is deemed to have taken place, where the quantum state is discontinuously and probabilistically replaced by another quantum state (referred to, technically, as an eigenstate of a mathematical operator that is taken to describe the measurement). This discontinuous jumping of the state is referred to as the reduction of the state (or the 'collapse of the wavefunction'), and will be denoted here by the letter R. The conflict that is termed the measurement problem (or perhaps more accurately as the measurement paradox) arises when we consider the measuring apparatus itself as a quantum entity, which is part of the entire quantum system consisting of the original system under observation together with this measuring apparatus. The apparatus is, after all, constructed out of the same type of quantum ingredients (electrons, photons, protons, neutrons etc.—or quarks and gluons etc.) as is the system under observation, so it ought to be subject also to the same quantum laws, these being described in terms of the continuous and deterministic U. How, then, can the discontinuous and probabilistic R come about as a result of the interaction (measurement) between two parts of the quantum system? This is the measurement problem (or paradox).

There are many ways that quantum physicists have attempted to come to terms with this conflict (see, for example, Bell 1966, Bohm 1951, Rae 1994, Polkinghorne 2002, Penrose, 2004). In the early 20th century, the Danish physicist Niels Bohr, together with Werner Heisenberg, proposed the pragmatic 'Copenhagen interpretation', according to which the wavefunction of a quantum system, evolving according to U, is not assigned any actual physical 'reality', but is taken as basically providing the needed 'book-keeping' so that eventually probability values can be assigned to the various possible outcomes of a quantum measurement. The measuring device itself is explicitly taken to behave classically and no account is taken of the fact that the device is ultimately built from quantum-level constituents. The probabilities are calculated, once the nature of the measuring device is known, from the state that the wavefunction has U-evolved to at the time of the measurement. The discontinuous "jump" that the wavefunction makes upon measurement, according to R, is attributed to the change in 'knowledge' that the result of the measurement has on the observer. Since the wavefunction is not assigned physical reality, but is considered to refer merely to the observer's knowledge of the quantum system, the jumping is considered simply to reflect the jump in the observer's knowledge state, rather than in the quantum system under consideration.

Many physicists remain unhappy with such a point of view, however, and regard it largely as a 'stop-gap', in order that progress can be made in applying the quantum formalism, without this progress being held up by a lack of a serious quantum ontology, which might provide a more complete picture of what is actually going on. One may ask, in particular, what it is about a measuring device that allows one to ignore the fact that it is itself made from quantum constituents and is permitted to be treated entirely classically. A good many proponents of the Copenhagen standpoint would take the view that while the physical measuring apparatus ought actually to be treated as a quantum system, and therefore part of an over-riding wavefunction evolving according to U , it would be the conscious observer, examining the readings on that device, who actually reduces the state, according to R , thereby assigning a physical reality to the particular observed alternative resulting from the measurement. Accordingly, before the intervention of the observer's consciousness, the various alternatives of the result of the measurement including the different states of the measuring apparatus would, in effect, still coexist in superposition, in accordance with what would be the usual evolution according to U . In this way, the Copenhagen viewpoint puts consciousness outside science, and does not seriously address the nature and physical role of superposition itself nor the question of how large quantum superpositions like Schrödinger's superposed live and dead cat (see below) might actually become one thing or another.

A more extreme variant of this approach is the 'multiple worlds hypothesis' of Everett (1957) in which each possibility in a superposition evolves to form its own universe, resulting in an infinite multitude of coexisting 'parallel' worlds. The stream of consciousness of the observer is supposed somehow to 'split', so that there is one in each of the worlds—at least in those worlds for which the observer remains alive and conscious. Each instance of the observer's consciousness experiences a separate independent world, and is not directly aware of any of the other worlds.

A more 'down-to-earth' viewpoint is that of environmental decoherence, in which interaction of a superposition with its environment 'erodes' quantum states, so that instead of a single wavefunction being used to describe the state, a more complicated entity is used, referred to as a density matrix. However decoherence does not provide a consistent ontology for the reality of the world, in relation to the density matrix (see, for example, Penrose 2004, Sections 29.3-6), and provides merely a pragmatic procedure. Moreover, it does not address the issue of how R might arise in isolated systems, nor the nature of isolation, in which an external 'environment' would not be involved, nor does it tell us which part of a system is to be regarded as the 'environment' part, and it provides no limit to the size of that part which can remain subject to quantum superposition.

Still other approaches include various types of objective reduction (OR) in which a specific objective threshold is proposed to cause quantum state reduction (e.g. Kibble 1981; Pearle 1989; Ghirardi et al., 1986; Percival, 1994; Ghirardi, 2011). The specific OR scheme that is used in Orch OR will be described in Section 6.

The quantum pioneer Erwin Schrödinger took pains to point out the difficulties that confront the U-evolution of a quantum system with his still-famous thought experiment called 'Schrödinger's cat'. Here, the fate of a cat in a box is determined by magnifying a quantum event (say the decay of a radioactive atom, within a specific time period that would provide a 50% probability of decay) to a macroscopic action which would kill the cat, so that according to Schrödinger's own U-evolution the cat would be in a quantum superposition of being both dead and alive at the same time. If this U-evolution is maintained until the box is opened and the cat observed, then it would have to be the conscious human observing the cat that results in the cat becoming either dead or alive (unless, of course, the cat's own consciousness could be considered to have already served this purpose). Schrödinger intended to illustrate the absurdity of the direct applicability of the rules of quantum mechanics (including his own U-evolution) when applied at the level of a cat. Like Einstein, he regarded quantum mechanics as an incomplete theory, and his 'cat' provided an excellent example for emphasizing this incompleteness. There is a need for something to be done about quantum mechanics, irrespective of the issue of its relevance to consciousness.

6. The Orch OR Scheme

Orch OR depends, indeed, upon a particular OR extension of current quantum mechanics, taking the bridge between quantum- and classical-level physics as a 'quantum-gravitational' phenomenon. This is in contrast with the various conventional viewpoints (see Section 5), whereby this bridge is claimed to result, somehow, from 'environmental decoherence', or from 'observation by a conscious observer', or from a 'choice between alternative worlds', or some other interpretation of how the classical world of one actual alternative may be taken to arise out of fundamentally quantum-superposed ingredients.

It must also be made clear that the Orch OR scheme involves a different interpretation of the term 'quantum gravity' from what is usual. Current ideas of quantum gravity (see, for example Smolin, 2002) normally refer, instead, to some sort of physical scheme that is to be formulated within the bounds of standard quantum field theory—although no particular such theory, among the multitude that has so far been put forward, has gained anything approaching universal acceptance, nor has any of them found a fully consistent, satisfactory formulation. 'OR' here refers to the alternative viewpoint that standard quantum (field) theory is not the final answer, and that the reduction R of the quantum state ('collapse of the wavefunction') that is adopted in standard quantum mechanics is an actual physical phenomenon which is not part of the conventional unitary formalism U of quantum theory (or quantum field theory) and does not arise as some kind of convenience or effective consequence of environmental decoherence, etc., as the conventional U formalism would seem to demand. Instead, OR is taken to be one of the consequences of melding together the principles of Einstein's general relativity with those of the conventional unitary quantum formalism U, and this demands a departure from the strict rules of U. According to this OR viewpoint, any quantum measurement—whereby the quantum-superposed alternatives produced in accordance with the U formalism becomes reduced to a single actual occurrence—is real objective physical phenomenon, and it is taken to result from the mass displacement between the alternatives being sufficient, in gravitational terms, for the superposition to become unstable.

In the DP (Diósi–Penrose) scheme for OR, the superposition reduces to one of the alternatives in a time scale τ that can be estimated (for a superposition of two states each of which can be taken to be stationary on its own) according to the formula

$$\tau \approx \hbar/E_G.$$

Here $\hbar$ (=h/2π) is Dirac's form of Planck's constant h and E_G is the gravitational self-energy of the difference between the two mass distributions of the superposition. (For a superposition for which each mass distribution is a rigid translation of the other, E_G is the energy it would cost to displace one component of the superposition in the gravitational field of the other, in moving it from coincidence to the quantum-displaced location; see Disói 1989, Penrose 1993, 2000, 2009).

According to Orch OR, the (objective) reduction is not the entirely random process of standard theory, but acts according to some non-computational new physics (see Penrose 1989, 1994). The idea is that consciousness is associated with this (gravitational) OR process, but occurs significantly only when the alternatives are part of some highly organized structure, so that such occurrences of OR occur in an extremely orchestrated form. Only then does a recognizably conscious event take place. On the other hand, we may consider that any individual occurrence of OR would be an element of proto-consciousness.

The OR process is considered to occur when quantum superpositions between slightly differing space-times take place, differing from one another by an integrated space-time measure which compares with the fundamental and extremely tiny Planck (4-volume) scale of space-time geometry. Since this is a 4-volume Planck measure, involving both time and space, we find that the time measure would be particularly tiny when the space-difference measure is relatively large (as with Schrödinger's cat), but for extremely tiny space-difference measures, the time measure might be fairly long, such as some significant fraction of a second. We shall be seeing this in more detail shortly, together with its particular relevance to microtubules. In any case, we recognize that the elements of proto-consciousness would be intimately tied in with the most primitive Planck-level ingredients of space-time geometry, these presumed 'ingredients' being taken to be at the absurdly tiny level of 10^{-35}m and 10^{-43}s, a distance and a time some 20 orders of magnitude smaller than those of normal particle-physics scales and their most rapid processes. These scales refer only to the normally extremely tiny differences in space-time geometry between different states in superposition, and OR is deemed to take place when such space-time differences reach the Planck level. Owing to the extreme weakness of gravitational forces as compared with those of the chemical and electric

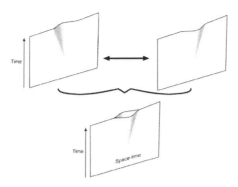

Figure 4. From Penrose, 1994 (P. 338). With four spatiotemporal dimensions condensed to a 2-dimensional spacetime sheet, mass location may be represented as a particular curvature of that sheet, according to general relativity. Top: Two different mass locations as alternative spacetime curvatures. Bottom: a bifurcating spacetime is depicted as the union ("glued together version") of the two alternative spacetime histories that are depicted at the top of the Figure. Hence a quantum superposition of simultaneous alternative locations may be seen as a separation in fundamental spacetime geometry.

forces of biology, the energy E_G is liable to be far smaller than any energy that arises directly from biological processes. However, E_G is not to be thought of as being in direct competition with any of the usual biological energies, as it plays a completely different role, supplying a needed energy uncertainty that then allows a choice to be made between the separated space-time geometries. It is the key ingredient of the computation of the reduction time τ. Nevertheless, the extreme weakness of gravity tells us there must be a considerable amount of material involved in the coherent mass displacement between superposed structures in order that τ can be small enough to be playing its necessary role in the relevant OR processes in the brain. These superposed structures should also process information and regulate neuronal physiology. According to Orch OR, microtubules are central to these structures, and some form of biological quantum computation in microtubules (most probably primarily in the more symmetrical A-lattice microtubules) would have to have evolved to provide a subtle yet direct connection to Planck-scale geometry, leading eventually to discrete moments of actual conscious experience.

The degree of separation between the space-time sheets is mathematically described in terms of a symplectic measure on the space of 4-dimensional metrics (cf. Penrose, 1993). The separation is, as already noted above, a space-time separation, not just a spatial one. Thus the time of separation contributes as well as the spatial displacement. Roughly speaking, it is the product of the temporal separation T with the spatial separation S that measures the overall degree of separation, and OR takes place when this overall separation reaches a critical amount. This critical amount would be of the order of unity, in absolute units, for which the Planck-Dirac constant $\hbar$, the gravitational constant G, and the velocity of light c, all take the value unity, cf. Penrose, 1994 - pp. 337-339. For small S, the lifetime $\tau \approx T$ of the superposed state will be large; on the other hand, if S is large, then τ will be small.

To estimate S, we compute (in the Newtonian limit of weak gravitational fields) the gravitational self-energy E_G of the difference between the mass distributions of the two superposed states. (That is, one mass distribution counts positively and the other, negatively; see Penrose, 1993; 1995.) The quantity S is then given by:

$$S \approx E_G$$

and $T \approx \tau$, whence

$$\tau \approx \hbar/E_G \text{ , i.e. } E_G \approx \hbar/\tau.$$

Thus, the DP expectation is that OR occurs with the resolving out of one particular space-time geometry from the previous superposition when, on the average, $\tau \approx \hbar/E_G$. Moreover, according to Orch OR, this is accompanied by an element of proto-consciousness.

Environmental decoherence need play no role in state reduction, according to this scheme. The proposal is that state reduction simply takes place spontaneously, according to this criterion. On the other hand, in many actual physical situations, there would be much material from the environment that would be entangled with the quantum-superposed state, and it could well be that the major mass displacement—and therefore the major contribution to E_G—would occur in the environment rather than in the system under consideration. Since the environment will be quantum-entangled with the system, the state-reduction in the environment will effect a simultaneous reduction in the system. This could shorten the time for the state reduction R to take place very considerably. It would also introduce an uncontrollable random element into the result of the reduction, so that any non-random (albeit non-computable, according to Orch OR) element influencing the particular choice of state that is actually resolved out from the superposition would be completely masked by this randomness. In these circumstances the OR-process would be indistinguishable from the R-process of conventional quantum mechanics. If the suggested non-computable effects of this OR proposal are to be laid bare, if E_G is to be able to evolve and be orchestrated for conscious moments, we indeed need significant isolation from the environment.

As yet, no experiment has been refined enough to determine whether this (DP) OR proposal is actually respected by Nature, but the experimental testing of the scheme is fairly close to the borderline of what can be achieved with present-day technology (see, for example, Marshall et al. 2003). One ought to begin to see the effects of this OR scheme if a small object, such as a 10-micron cube of crystalline material could be held in a superposition of two locations, differing by about the diameter of an atomic nucleus, for some seconds, or perhaps minutes.

A point of importance, in such proposed experiments, is that in order to calculate E_G it may not be enough to base the calculation on an average density of the material in the superposition, since the mass will be concentrated in the atomic nuclei, and for a displacement of the order of the diameter of a nucleus, this inhomogeneity in the density of the material can be crucial, and can provide a much larger value for E_G than would be obtained if the material is assumed to be homogeneous. The Schrödinger equation (more correctly, in the zero-temperature approximation, the Schrödinger–Newton equation, see Penrose 2000; Moroz et al. 1998) for the static unsuperposed material would have to be solved, at least approximately, in order to derive the expectation value of the mass distribution, where there would be some quantum spread in the locations of the particles constituting the nuclei.

For Orch OR to be operative in the brain, we would need coherent superpositions of sufficient amounts of material, undisturbed by environmental entanglement, where this reduces in accordance with the above OR scheme in a rough time scale of the general order of time for a conscious experience to take place. For an ordinary type of experience, this might be say about $\tau = 10^{-1}$s which concurs with neural correlates of consciousness, such as particular frequencies of electroencephalograhy (EEG).

Penrose (1989; 1994) suggested that processes of the general nature of quantum computations were occurring in the brain, terminated by OR. In quantum computers (Benioff 1982, Deutsch 1985, Feynman 1986), information is represented not just as bits of either 1 or 0, but also as quantum superposition of both 1 and 0 together (quantum bits or qubits) where, moreover, large-scale entanglements between qubits would also be involved. These qubits interact and compute following the Schrödinger equation, potentially enabling complex and highly efficient parallel processing. As envisioned in technological quantum computers, at some point a measurement is made causing quantum state reduction (with some randomness introduced). The qubits reduce, or collapse to classical bits and definite states as the output.

The proposal that some form of quantum computing could be acting in the brain, this proceeding by the Schrödinger equation without decoherence until some threshold for self-collapse due to a form of non-computable OR could be reached, was made in Penrose 1989. However, no plausible biological candidate for quantum computing in the brain had been available to him, as he was then unfamiliar with microtubules.

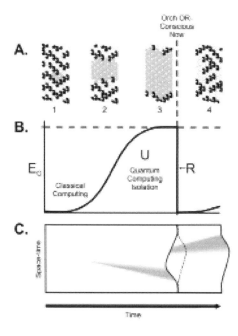

Figure 5. Three descriptions of an Orch OR conscious event by E_G $=\hbar/\tau$. A. Microtubule automata. Quantum (gray) tubulins evolve to meet threshold after Step 3, a moment of consciousness occurs and tubulin states are selected. For actual event (e.g. 25 msec), billions of tubulins are required; a small number is used here for illustration. B. Schematic showing U-like evolution until threshold. C. Space-time sheet with superposition separation reaches threshold and selects one reality/spacetime curvature.

7. Penrose-Hameroff Orchestrated Objective Reduction ('Orch OR')

Penrose and Hameroff teamed up in the early 1990s. Fortunately, by then, the DP form of OR mechanism was at hand to be applied to the microtubule-automata models for consciousness as developed by Hameroff. A number of questions were addressed.

How does $\tau \approx \hbar/E_G$ relate to consciousness? Orch OR considers consciousness as a sequence of discrete OR events in concert with neuronal-level activities. In $\tau \approx \hbar/E_G$, τ is taken to be the time for evolution of the pre-conscious quantum wavefunction between OR events, i.e. the time interval between conscious moments, during which quantum superpositions of microtubule states evolve according to the continuous Schrödinger equation before reaching (on the average) the $\tau \approx \hbar / E_G$ OR threshold in time τ, when quantum state reduction and a moment of conscious awareness occurs (Figure 5).

The best known temporal correlate for consciousness is gamma synchrony EEG, 30 to 90 Hz, often referred to as coherent 40 Hz. One possible viewpoint might be to take this oscillation to represent a succession of 40 or so conscious moments per second (τ=25 milliseconds). This would be reasonably consistent with neuroscience (gamma synchrony), with certain ideas expressed in philosophy (e.g. Whitehead 'occasions of experience'), and perhaps even with ancient Buddhist texts which portray consciousness as 'momentary collections of mental phenomena' or as 'distinct, unconnected and impermanent moments which perish as soon as they arise.' (Some Buddhist writings quantify the frequency of conscious moments. For example the Sarvaastivaadins, according to von Rospatt 1995, described 6,480,000 'moments' in 24 hours—an average of one 'moment' per 13.3 msec, ~75 Hz—and some Chinese Buddhism as one "thought" per 20 msec, i.e. 50 Hz.) These accounts, even including variations in frequency, could be considered to be consistent with Orch OR events in the gamma synchrony range. Accordingly, on this view, gamma synchrony, Buddhist 'moments of experience', Whitehead 'occasions of experience', and our proposed Orch OR events might be viewed as corresponding tolerably well with one another.

Putting τ=25msec in $E_G \approx \hbar / \tau$, we may ask what is E_G in terms of superpositioned microtubule tubulins? E_G may be derived from details about the superposition separation of mass distribution. Three types of mass separation were considered in Hameroff–Penrose 1996a for peanut-shaped tubulin proteins of 110,000 atomic mass units: separation at the level of (1) protein spheres, e.g. by 10 percent volume, (2) atomic nuclei (e.g. carbon, ~ 2.5 Fermi length), (3) nucleons (protons and neutrons). The most plausible calculated effect might be separation at the level of atomic nuclei, giving E_G as superposition of 2×10^{10} tubulins reaching OR threshold at 25 milliseconds.

Brain neurons each contain roughly 10^8 tubulins, so only a few hundred neurons would be required for a 25msec, gamma synchrony OR event if 100 percent of tubulins in those neurons were in superposition and avoided decoherence. It seems more likely that a fraction of tubulins per neuron are in superposition. Global macroscopic states such as superconductivity ensue from quantum coherence among only very small fractions of components. If 1 percent of tubulins within a given set of neurons were coherent for 25msec, then 20,000 such neurons would be required to elicit OR. In human brain, cognition and consciousness are, at any one time, thought to involve tens of thousands of neurons. Hebb's (1949) 'cell assemblies', Eccles's (1992) 'modules', and Crick and Koch's (1990) 'coherent sets of neurons' are each estimated to contain some 10,000 to 100,000 neurons which may be widely distributed throughout the brain (Scott, 1995).

Adopting $\tau \approx \hbar/E_G$, we find that, with this point of view with regard to Orch-OR, a spectrum of possible types of conscious event might be able to occur, including those at higher frequency and intensity. It may be noted that Tibetan monk meditators have been found to have 80 Hz gamma synchrony, and perhaps more intense experience (Lutz et al. 2004). Thus, according to the viewpoint proposed above, where we interpret this frequency to be associated with a succession of Orch-OR moments, then $E_G \approx \hbar/\tau$ would appear to require that there is twice as much brain involvement required for 80 Hz than for consciousness occurring at 40 Hz (or $\sqrt{2}$ times as much if the displacement is entirely coherent, since then the mass enters quadratically in E_G). Even higher (frequency), expanded awareness states of consciousness might be expected, with more neuronal brain involvement.

On the other hand, we might take an alternative viewpoint with regard to the probable frequency of Orch-OR actions, and to the resulting frequency of elements of conscious experience. There is the possibility that the discernable moments of consciousness are events that normally occur at a much slower pace than is suggested by the considerations above, and that they happen only at rough intervals of the order of, say, one half a second or so, i.e. ~500msec, rather than ~25msec. One might indeed think of conscious influences as perhaps being rather slow, in contrast with the great deal of vastly faster unconscious computing that might be some form of quantum computing, but without OR. At the present stage of uncertainty about such matters it is perhaps best not to be dogmatic about how the ideas of Orch OR are to be applied. In any case, the numerical assignments provided above must be considered to be extremely rough, and at the moment we are far from being in a position to be definitive about the precise way in which the Orch-OR is to operate. Alternative possibilities will need to be considered with an open mind.

How do microtubule quantum computation avoid decoherence? Technological quantum computers using e.g. ion traps as qubits are plagued by decoherence, disruption of delicate quantum states by thermal vibration, and require extremely cold temperatures and vacuum to operate. Decoherence must be avoided during the evolution toward time τ ($\approx \hbar/E_G$), so that the nonrandom (non-computable) aspects of OR can be playing their roles. How does quantum computing avoid decoherence in the 'warm, wet and noisy' brain?

It was suggested (Hameroff and Penrose, 1996a) that microtubule quantum states avoid decoherence by being pumped, laser-like, by Fröhlich resonance, and shielded by ordered water, C-termini Debye layers, actin gel and strong mitochondrial electric fields. Moreover quantum states in Orch OR are proposed to originate in hydrophobic pockets in tubulin interiors, isolated from polar interactions, and involve superposition of only atomic nuclei separation. Moreover, geometrical resonances in microtubules, e.g. following helical pathways of Fibonacci geometry are suggested to enable topological quantum computing and error correction, avoiding decoherence perhaps effectively indefinitely (Hameroff et al 2002) as in a superconductor.

The analogy with high-temperature superconductors may indeed be appropriate, in fact. As yet, there is no fully accepted theory of how such superconductors operate, avoiding loss of quantum coherence from the usual processes of environmental decoherence. Yet there are materials which support superconductivity at temperatures roughly halfway between room temperature and absolute zero (He et al., 2010). This is still a long way from body temperature, of course, but there is now some experimental evidence (Bandyopadhyay 2011) that is indicative of something resembling superconductivity (referred to as 'ballistic conductance'), that occurs in living A-lattice microtubules at body temperature. This will be discussed below.

Physicist Max Tegmark (2000) published a critique of Orch OR based on his calculated decoherence times for microtubules of 10^{-13} seconds at biological temperature, far too brief for physiological effects. However Tegmark didn't include Orch OR stipulations and in essence created, and then refuted his own quantum microtubule model. He assumed superpositions of solitons separated from themselves by a distance of 24 nanometers along the length of the microtubule. As previously described, superposition separation in Orch OR is at the Fermi length level of atomic nuclei, i.e. 7 orders of magnitude smaller than Tegmark's separation value, thus underestimating decoherence time by 7 orders of magnitude, i.e. from 10^{-13} secs to microseconds at 10^{-6} seconds. Hagan et al (2001) used Tegmark's same formula and recalculated microtubule decoherence times using Orch OR stipulations, finding 10^{-4} to 10^{-3} seconds, or longer due to topological quantum effects. It seemed likely biology had evolved optimal information processing systems which can utilize quantum computing, but there was no real evidence either way.

Beginning in 2003, published research began to demonstrate quantum coherence in warm biological systems. Ouyang and Awschalom (2003) showed that quantum spin transfer through phenyl rings (the same as those in protein hydrophobic pockets) is enhanced at increasingly warm temperatures. Other studies showed that quantum coherence occurred at ambient temperatures in proteins involved in photosynthesis, that plants routinely use quantum coherence to produce chemical energy and food (Engel et al, 2007). Further research has demonstrated warm quantum effects in bird brain navigation (Gauger et al, 2011), ion channels (Bernroider and Roy, 2005), sense of smell (Turin, 1996), DNA (Rieper et al., 2011), protein folding (Luo and Lu, 2011), biological water (Reiter et al., 2011) and microtubules.

Recently Anirban Bandyopadhyay and colleagues at the National Institute of Material Sciences in Tsukuba, Japan have used nanotechnology to study electronic conductance properties of single microtubules assembled from porcine brain tubulin. Their preliminary findings (Bandyopadhyay, 2011) include: (1) Microtubules have 8 resonance peaks for AC stimulation (kilohertz to 10 megahertz) which appear to correlate with various helical conductance pathways around the geometric microtubule lattice. (2) Excitation at these resonant frequencies causes microtubules to assemble extremely rapidly, possibly due to Fröhlich condensation. (3) In assembled microtubules AC excitation at resonant frequencies causes electronic conductance to become lossless, or 'ballistic', essentially quantum conductance, presumably along these helical quantum channels. Resonance in the range of kilohertz demonstrates microtubule decoherence times of at least 0.1 millisecond. (4) Eight distinct quantum interference patterns from a single microtubule, each correlating with one of the 8 resonance frequencies and pathways. (5) Ferroelectric hysteresis demonstrates memory capacity in microtubules. (6) Temperature-independent conductance also suggests quantum effects. If confirmed, such findings would demonstrate Orch OR to be biologically feasible.

How does microtubule quantum computation and Orch OR fit with recognized neurophysiology? Neurons are composed of multiple dendrites and a cell body/soma which receive and integrate synaptic inputs to a threshold for firing outputs along a single axon. Microtubule quantum computation in Orch OR is assumed to occur in dendrites and cell bodies/soma of brain neurons, i.e. in regions of integration of inputs in integrate-and-fire neurons. As opposed to axonal firings, dendritic/somatic integration correlates best with local field potentials, gamma synchrony EEG, and action of anesthetics erasing consciousness. Tononi (2004) has identified integration of information as the neuronal function most closely associated with consciousness. Dendritic microtubules are uniquely arranged in local mixed polarity networks, well-suited for integration of synaptic inputs.

Membrane synaptic inputs interact with post-synaptic microtubules by activation of microtubule-associated protein 2 ('MAP2', associated with learning), and calcium-calmodulin kinase II (CaMKII, Hameroff et al, 2010). Such inputs were suggested by Penrose and Hameroff (1996a) to 'tune', or 'orchestrate' OR-mediated quantum computations in microtubules by MAPs, hence 'orchestrated objective reduction', 'Orch OR'.

Proposed mechanisms for microtubule avoidance of decoherence were described above, but another question remains. How would microtubule quantum computations which are isolated from the environment, still interact with that environment for input and output? One possibility that Orch OR suggests is that perhaps phases of isolated quantum computing alternate with phases of classical environmental interaction, e.g. at gamma synchrony, roughly 40 times per second. (Computing pioneer Paul Benioff suggested such a scheme of alternating quantum and classical phases in a science fiction story about quantum computing robots.)

With regard to outputs resulting from processes taking place at the level of microtubules in Orch-OR quantum computations, dendritic/somatic microtubules receive and integrate synaptic inputs during classical phase. They then become isolated quantum computers and evolve to threshold for Orch OR at which they reduce their quantum states at an average time interval τ (given by by $\tau \approx \hbar/E_G$). The particular tubulin states chosen in the reduction can then trigger axonal firing, adjust firing threshold, regulate synapses and encode memory. Thus Orch OR can have causal efficacy in conscious actions and behavior, as well as providing conscious experience and memory.

Orch OR in evolution In the absence of Orch OR, non-conscious neuronal activities might proceed by classical neuronal and microtubule-based computation. In addition there could be quantum computations in microtubules that do not reach the Orch OR level, and thereby also remain unconscious.

This last possibility is strongly suggested by considerations of natural selection, since some relatively primitive microtubule infrastructure, still able to support quantum computation, would have to have preceded the more sophisticated kind that we now find in conscious animals. Natural selection proceeds in steps, after all, and one would not expect that the capability of the substantial level of coherence across the brain that would be needed for the non-computable OR of human conscious understanding to be reached, without something more primitive having preceded it. Microtubule quantum computing by U evolution which avoids decoherence would well be advantageous to biological processes without ever reaching threshold for OR.

Microtubules may have appeared in eukaryotic cells 1.3 billion years ago due to symbiosis among prokaryotes, mitochondria and spirochetes, the latter the apparent origin of microtubules which provided movement to previously immobile cells (e.g. Margulis and Sagan, 1995). Because Orch OR depends on $\tau \approx \hbar/E_G$, more primitive consciousness in simple, small organisms would involve smaller E_G, and longer times τ to avoid decoherence. As simple nervous systems and arrangements of microtubules grew larger and developed anti-decoherence mechanisms, inevitably a system would avoid decoherence long enough to reach threshold for Orch OR conscious moments. Central nervous systems around 300 neurons, such as those present at the early Cambrian evolutionary explosion 540 million years ago, could have τ near one minute, and thus be feasible in terms of avoiding decoherence (Hameroff, 1998d). Perhaps the onset of Orch OR and consciousness with relatively slow and simple conscious moments, precipitated the accelerated evolution.

Only at a much later evolutionary stage would the selective advantages of a capability for genuine understanding come about. This would require the non-computable capabilities of Orch OR that go beyond those of mere quantum computation, and depend upon larger scale infrastructure of efficiently functioning microtubules, capable of operating quantum-computational processes. Further evolution providing larger sets of microtubules (larger EG) able to be isolated from decoherence would enable, by $\tau \approx \hbar/E_G$, more frequent and more intense moments of conscious experience. It appears human brains could have evolved to having Orch OR conscious moments perhaps as frequently as every few milliseconds.

How could microtubule quantum states in one neuron extend to those in other neurons throughout the brain? Assuming microtubule quantum state phases are isolated in a specific neuron, how could that quantum state involve microtubules in other neurons throughout the brain without traversing membranes and synapses? Orch OR proposes that quantum states can extend by tunneling, leading to entanglement between adjacent neurons through gap junctions.

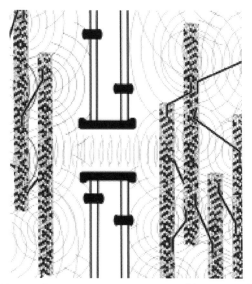

Figure 6. Portions of two neurons connected by a gap junction with microtubules (linked by microtubule-associated proteins, 'MAPs') computing via states (here represented as black or white) of tubulin protein subunits. Wavy lines suggest entanglement among quantum states (not shown) in microtubules.

Gap junctions are primitive electrical connections between cells, synchronizing electrical activities. Structurally, gap junctions are windows between cells which may be open or closed. When open, gap junctions synchronize adjacent cell membrane polarization states, but also allow passage of molecules between cytoplasmic compartments of the two cells. So both membranes and cytoplasmic interiors of gap-junction-connected neurons are continuous, essentially one complex 'hyper-neuron' or syncytium. (Ironically, before Ramon-y-Cajal showed that neurons were discrete cells, the prevalent model for brain structure was a continuous threaded-together syncytium as proposed by Camille Golgi.) Orch OR suggests that quantum states in microtubules in one neuron could extend by entanglement and tunneling through gap junctions to microtubules in adjacent neurons and glia (Figure 6), and from those cells to others, potentially in brain-wide syncytia.

Open gap junctions were thus predicted to play an essential role in the neural correlate of consciousness (Hameroff, 1998a). Beginning in 1998, evidence began to show that gamma synchrony, the best measureable correlate of consciousness, depended on gap junctions, particularly dendritic-dendritic gap junctions (Dermietzel, 1998; Draguhn et al, 1998; Galaretta and Hestrin, 1999). To account for the distinction between conscious activities and non-conscious 'auto-pilot' activities, and the fact that consciousness can occur in various brain regions, Hameroff (2009) developed the "Conscious pilot' model in which syncytial zones of dendritic gamma synchrony move around the brain, regulated by gap junction openings and closings, in turn regulated by microtubules. The model suggests consciousness literally moves around the brain in a mobile synchronized zone, within which isolated, entangled microtubules carry out quantum computations and Orch OR. Taken together, Orch OR and the conscious pilot distinguish conscious from non-conscious functional processes in the brain.

Libet's backward time referral In the 1970s neurophysiologist Benjamin Libet performed experiments on patients having brain surgery while awake, i.e. under local anesthesia (Libet et al., 1979). Able to stimulate and record from conscious human brain, and gather patients' subjective reports with precise timing, Libet determined that conscious perception of a stimulus required up to 500 msec of brain activity post-stimulus, but that conscious awareness occurred at 30 msec post-stimulus, i.e. that subjective experience was referred 'backward in time'.

Bearing such apparent anomalies in mind, Penrose put forward a tentative suggestion, in The Emperor's New Mind, that effects like Libet's backward time referral might be related to the fact that quantum entanglements are not mediated in a normal causal way, so that it might be possible for conscious experience not to follow the normal rules of sequential time progression, so long as this does not lead to contradictions with external causality. In Section 5, it was pointed out that the (experimentally confirmed) phenomenon of 'quantum teleportation' (Bennett et al., 1993; Bouwmeester et al., 1997; Macikic et al., 2002) cannot be explained in terms of ordinary classical information processing, but as a combination of such classical causal influences and the acausal effects of quantum entanglement. It indeed turns out that quantum entanglement effects—referred to as 'quantum information' or 'quanglement' (Penrose 2002, 2004)—appear to have to be thought of as being able to propagate in either direction in time (into the past or into the future). Such effects, however, cannot by themselves be used to communicate ordinary information into the past. Nevertheless, in conjunction with normal classical future-propagating (i.e. 'causal') signalling, these quantum-teleportation influences can achieve certain kinds of 'signalling' that cannot be achieved simply by classical future-directed means.

The issue is a subtle one, but if conscious experience is indeed rooted in the OR process, where we take OR to relate the classical to the quantum world, then apparent anomalies in the sequential aspects of consciousness are perhaps to be expected. The Orch OR scheme allows conscious experience to be temporally non-local to a degree, where this temporal non-locality would spread to the kind of time scale τ that would be involved in the relevant Orch OR process, which might indeed allow this temporal non-locality to spread to a time $\tau=500$ms. When the 'moment' of an internal conscious experience is timed externally, it may well be found that this external timing does not precisely accord with a time progression that would seem to apply to internal conscious experience, owing to this temporal non-locality intrinsic to Orch OR.

Measurable brain activity correlated with a stimulus often occurs several hundred msec after that stimulus, as Libet showed. Yet in activities ranging from rapid conversation to competitive athletics, we respond to a stimulus (seemingly consciously) before the above activity that would be correlated with that stimulus occurring in the brain. This is interpreted in conventional neuroscience and philosophy (e.g. Dennett, 1991; Wegner, 2002) to imply that in such cases we respond non-consciously, on auto-pilot, and subsequently have only an illusion of conscious response. The mainstream view is that consciousness is epiphenomenal illusion, occurring after-the-fact as a false impression of conscious control of behavior. We are merely 'helpless spectators' (Huxley, 1986).

However, the effective quantum backward time referral inherent in the temporal non-locality resulting from the quanglement aspects of Orch OR, as suggested above, enables conscious experience actually to be temporally non-local, thus providing a means to rescue consciousness from its unfortunate characterization as epiphenomenal illusion. Accordingy, Orch OR could well enable consciousness to have a causal efficacy, despite its apparently anomalous relation to a timing assigned to it in relation to an external clock, thereby allowing conscious action to provide a semblance of free will.

8. Orch OR Criticisms and Responses

Orch OR has been criticized repeatedly since its inception. Here we review and summarize major criticisms and responses.

Grush and Churchland, 1995. Philosophers Grush and Churchland (1995) took issue with the Gödel's theorem argument, as well as several biological factors. One objection involved the microtubule-disabling drug colchicine which treats diseases such as gout by immobilizing neutrophil cells which cause painful inflammation in joints. Neutrophil mobility requires cycles of microtubule assembly/disassembly, and colchicine prevents re-assembly, impairing neutrophil mobility and reducing inflammation. Grush and Churchland pointed out that patients given colchicine do not lose consciousness, concluding that microtubules cannot be essential for consciousness. Penrose and Hameroff (1995) responded point-by-point to every objection, e.g. explaining that colchicine does not cross the blood brain barrier, and so doesn't reach the brain. Colchicine infused directly into the brains of animals does cause severe cognitive impairment and apparent loss of consciousness (Bensimon and Chemat, 1991).

Tuszynski et al, (1998). Tuszynski et al (1998) questioned how extremely weak gravitational energy in Diósi-Penrose OR could influence tubulin protein states. In Hameroff and Penrose (1996a), the gravitational self-energy E_G for tubulin superposition was calculated for separation of tubulin from itself at the level of its atomic nuclei. Because the atomic (e.g. carbon) nucleus displacement is greater than its radius (the nuclei separate completely), the gravitational self-energy E_G is given by: $E_G=Gm^2/a_c$, where a_c is the carbon nucleus sphere radius equal to 2.5 Fermi distances, m is the mass of tubulin, and G is the gravitational constant. Brown and Tuszynski calculated E_G (using separation at the nanometer level of the entire tubulin protein), finding an appropriately small energy E of 10^{-27} electron volts (eV) per tubulin, infinitesimal compared with ambient energy kT of 10^{-4}eV. Correcting for the smaller superposition separation distance of 2.5 Fermi lengths in Orch OR gives a significantly larger, but still tiny 10^{-21}eV per tubulin. With 2×10^{10} tubulins per 25msec, the conscious Orch OR moment would be roughly 10^{-10}eV (10^{-29} joules), still insignificant compared to kT at 10^{-4}eV.

All this serves to illustrate the fact that the energy E_G does not actually play a role in physical processes as an energy, in competition with other energies that are driving the physical (chemical, electronic) processes of relevance. In a clear sense E_G is, instead, an energy uncertainty—and it is this uncertainty that allows quantum state reduction to take place without violation of energy conservation. The fact that E_G is far smaller than the other energies involved in the relevant physical processes is a necessary feature of the consistency of the OR scheme. It does not supply the energy to drive the physical processes involved, but it provides the energy uncertainty that allows the freedom for processes having virtually the same energy as each other to be alternative actions. In practice, all that E_G is needed for is to tell us how to calculate the lifetime τ of the superposition. E_G would enter into issues of energy balance only if gravitational interactions between the parts of the system were important in the processes involved. (The Earth's gravitational field plays no role in this either, because it cancels out in the calculation of E_G.) No other forces of nature directly contribute to E_G, which is just as well, because if they did, there would be a gross discrepancy with observational physics.

Tegmark, 2000. Physicist Max Tegmark (2000) confronted Orch OR on the basis of decoherence. This was discussed at length in Section 7.

Koch and Hepp, 2006. In a challenge to Orch OR, neuroscientists/physicists Koch and Hepp published a thought experiment in Nature, describing a person observing a superposition of a cat both dead and alive with one eye, the other eye distracted by a series of images (binocular rivalry). They asked 'Where in the observer's brain would reduction occur?', apparently assuming Orch OR followed the Copenhagen interpretation in which conscious observation causes quantum state reduction. This is precisely the opposite of Orch OR in which consciousness is the orchestrated quantum state reduction given by OR.

Orch OR can account for the related issue of bistable perceptions (e.g. the famous face/vase illusion, or Necker cube). Non-conscious superpositions of both possibilities (face and vase) during pre-conscious quantum superposition then reduce by OR at time τ to conscious perception of one or the other, face or vase. The reduction would occur among microtubules within neurons interconnected by gap junctions in various areas of visual and pre-frontal cortex and other brain regions.

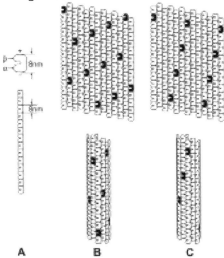

Figure 7. Simulating Fröhlich coherence in microtubules. A) Linear column of tubulins (protofilament) as simulated by Reimers et al (2010) which showed only weak Fröhlich condensation. B) and C) 2-dimensional tubulin sheets with toroidal boundary conditions

(approximating 3-dimensional microtubule) simulated by Samsonovich et al (1992) shows long range Fröhlich resonance, with long-range symmetry, and nodes matching experimentally-observed MAP attachment patterns.

Reimers et al (2009) described three types of Fröhlich condensation (weak, strong and coherent, the first classical and the latter two quantum). They validated 8 MHz coherence measured in microtubules by Pokorny (2001; 2004) as weak condensation. Based on simulation of a 1-dimensional linear chain of tubulin dimers representing a microtubule, they concluded only weak Fröhlich condensation occurs in microtubules. Claiming Orch OR requires strong or coherent Fröhlich condensation, they concluded Orch OR is invalid. However Samsonovich et al (1992) simulated a microtubule as a 2-dimensional lattice plane with toroidal boundary conditions and found Fröhlich resonance maxima at discrete locations in super-lattice patterns on the simulated microtubule surface which precisely matched experimentally observed functional attachment sites for microtubule-associated proteins (MAPs). Further, Bandyopadhyay (2011) has experimental evidence for strong Fröhlich coherence in microtubules at multiple resonant frequencies.

McKemmish et al (2010) challenged the Orch OR contention that tubulin switching is mediated by London forces, pointing out that mobile π electrons in a benzene ring (e.g. a phenyl ring without attachments) are completely delocalized, and hence cannot switch between states, nor exist in superposition of both states. Agreed. A single benzene cannot engage in switching. London forces occur between two or more electron cloud ring structures, or other non-polar groups. A single benzene ring cannot support London forces. It takes two (or more) to tango. Orch OR has always maintained two or more non-polar groups are necessary (Figure 8). McKemmish et al are clearly mistaken on this point.

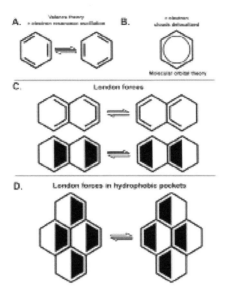

Figure 8. A) Phenyl ring/benzene of 6 carbons with three extra π electrons/double bonds which oscillate between two configurations according to valence theory. B) Phenyl ring/benzene according to molecular orbital theory in which π electrons/double bonds are delocalized, thus preventing oscillation between alternate states. No oscillation/switching can occur. C) Two adjacent phenyl rings/benzenes in which π electrons/double bonds are coupled, i.e. van der Waals London (dipole dispersion) forces. Two versions are shown: In top version, lines represent double bond locations; in bottom version, dipoles are filled in to show negative charge locations. D) Complex of 4 rings with London forces.

McKemmish et al further assert that tubulin switching in Orch OR requires significant conformational structural change (as indicated in Figure 2), and that the only mechanism for such conformational switching is due to GTP hydrolysis, i.e. conversion of guanosine triphophate (GTP) to guanosine diphosphate (GDP) with release of phosphate group energy, and tubulin conformational flexing. McKemmish et al correctly point out that driving synchronized microtubule oscillations by hydrolysis of GTP to GDP and conformational changes would be prohibitive in terms of energy requirements and heat produced. This is agreed. However, we clarify that tubulin switching in Orch OR need not actually involve significant conformational change (e. g. as is illustrated in Figure 2), that electron cloud dipole states (London forces) are sufficient for bit-like switching, superposition and qubit function. We acknowledge tubulin conformational switching as discussed in early Orch OR publications and illustrations do indicate significant conformational changes. They are admittedly, though unintentionally, misleading.

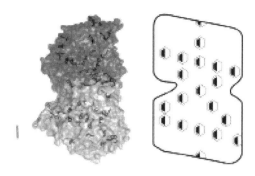

Figure 9. Left: Molecular simulation of tubulin with beta tubulin (dark gray) on top and alpha tubulin (light gray) on bottom. Non-polar amino acids phenylalanine and tryptophan with aromatic phenyl and indole rings are shown. (By Travis Craddock and Jack Tuszynski.) Right: Schematic tubulin with non-polar hydrophobic phenyl rings approximating actually phenyl and indole rings. Scale bar: 1 nanometer.

The only tubulin conformational factor in Orch OR is superposition separation involved in E_G, the gravitational self-energy of the tubulin qubit. As previously described, we calculated E_G for tubulin separated from itself at three possible levels: 1) the entire protein (e.g. partial separation, as suggested in Figure 2), 2) its atomic nuclei, and 3) its nucleons (protons and neutrons). The dominant effect is 2) separation at the level of atomic nuclei, e.g. 2.5 Fermi length for carbon nuclei (2.5 femtometers; 2.5×10^{-15} meters). This shift may be accounted for by London force dipoles with Mossbauer nuclear recoil and charge effects (Hameroff, 1998). Tubulin switching in Orch OR requires neither GTP hydrolysis nor significant conformational changes.

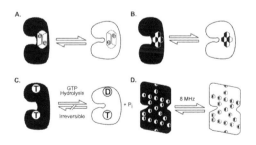

Figure 10. Four versions of the schematic Orch OR tubulin bit (superpositioned qubit states not shown). A) Early version showing conformational change coupled to/driven by single hydrophobic pocket with two aromatic rings. B) Updated version with single hydrophobic pocket composed of 4 aromatic rings. C) McKemmish et al (2009) mis-characterization of Orch OR tubulin bit as irreversible conformational change driven by GTP hydrolysis. D) Current version of Orch OR bit with no significant conformational change (change occurs at the level of atomic nuclei) and multiple hydrophobic pockets arranged in channels.

Schematic depiction of the tubulin bit, qubit and hydrophobic pockets in Orch OR has evolved over the years. An updated version is described in the next Section.

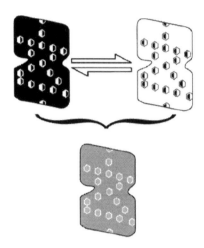

Figure 11. 2011 Orch OR tubulin qubit. Top: Alternate states of tubulin dimer (black and white) due to collective orientation of London force electron cloud dipoles in non-polar hydrophobic regions. There is no evident conformational change as suggested in previous versions; conformational change occurs at the level of atomic nuclei. Bottom: Depiction of tubulin (gray) superpositioned in both states.

9. Topological Quantum Computing in Orch OR

Quantum processes in Orch OR have consistently been ascribed to London forces in tubulin hydrophobic pockets, non-polar intra-protein regions, e.g. of π electron resonance rings of aromatic amino acids including tryptophan and phenylalanine. This assertion is based on (1) Fröhlich's suggestion that protein states are synchronized by electron cloud dipole oscillations in intra-protein non-polar regions, and (2) anesthetic gases selectively erasing consciousness by London forces in non-polar, hydrophobic regions in various neuronal proteins (e.g. tubulin, membrane proteins, etc.). London forces are weak, but numerous and able to act cooperatively to regulate protein states (Voet and Voet, 1995).

The structure of tubulin became known in 1998 (Nogales et al, 1998), allowing identification of non-polar amino acids and hydrophobic regions. Figure 9 shows locations of phenyl and indole π electron resonance rings of non-polar aromatic amino acids phenylalanine and tryptophan in tubulin. The ring locations are clustered along somewhat continuous pathways (within 2 nanometers) through tubulin. Thus, rather than hydrophobic pockets, tubulin may have within it quantum hydrophobic channels, or streams, linear arrays of electron resonance clouds suitable for cooperative, long-range quantum London forces. These quantum channels within each tubulin appear to align with those in adjacent tubulins in microtubule lattices, matching helical winding patterns (Figure 12). This in turn may support topological quantum computing in Orch OR.

Quantum bits, or qubits in quantum computers are generally envisioned as information bits in superposition of simultaneous alternative representations, e.g. both 1 and 0. Topological qubits are superpositions of alternative pathways, or channels which intersect repeatedly on a surface, forming 'braids'. Quasiparticles called anyons travel along such pathways, the intersections forming logic gates, with particular braids or pathways corresponding with particular information states, or bits. In superposition, anyons follow multiple braided pathways simultaneously, then reduce, or collapse to one particular pathway and functional output. Topological qubits are intrinsically resistant to decoherence.

An Orch OR qubit based on topological quantum computing specific to microtubule polymer geometry was suggested in Hameroff et al. (2002). Conductances along particular microtubule lattice geometry, e.g. Fibonacci helical pathways, were proposed to function as topological bits and qubits. Bandyopadhyay (2011) has preliminary evidence for ballistic conductance along different, discrete helical pathways in single microtubules

As an extension of Orch OR, we suggest topological qubits in microtubules based on quantum hydrophobic channels, e.g. continuous arrays of electron resonance rings within and among tubulins in microtubule lattices, e.g. following Fibonacci pathways. Cooperative London forces (electron cloud dipoles) in quantum hydrophobic channels may enable long-range coherence and topological quantum computing in microtubules necessary for optimal brain function and consciousness.

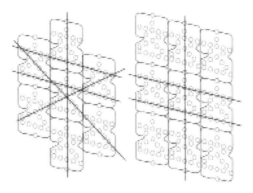

Figure 12. Left: Microtubule A-lattice configuration with lines connecting proposed hydrophobic channels of near-contiguous (<2 nanometer separation) electron resonance rings of phenylalanine and tryptophan. Right: Microtubule B-lattice with fewer such channels and lacking Fibonacci pathways. B-lattice microtubules have a vertical seam dislocation (not shown).

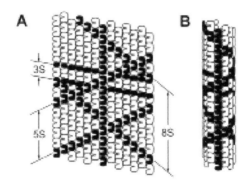

Figure 13. Extending microtubule A-lattice hydrophobic channels (Figure 12) results in helical winding patterns matching Fibonacci geometry. Bandyopadhyay (2011) has evidence for ballistic conductance and quantum inteference along such helical pathways which may be involved in topological quantum computing. Quantum electronic states of London forces in hydrophobic channels result in slight superposition separation of atomic nuclei, sufficient E_G for Orch OR. This image may be taken to represent superposition of four possible topological qubits which, after time T=tau, will undergo OR, and reduce to specific pathway(s) which then implement function.

10. Conclusion: Consciousness in the Universe

Our criterion for proto-consciousness is OR . It would be unreasonable to refer to OR as the criterion for actual consciousness, because, according to the DP scheme, OR processes would be taking place all the time, and would be providing the effective randomness that is characteristic of quantum measurement. Quantum superpositions will continually be reaching the DP threshold for OR in non-biological settings as well as in biological ones, and usually take place in the purely random environment of a quantum system under measurement. Instead, our criterion for consciousness is Orch OR, conditions for which are fairly stringent: superposition must be isolated from the decoherence effects of the random environment for long enough to reach the DS threshold. Small superpositions are easier to isolate, but require longer reduction times τ. Large superpositions will reach threshold quickly, but are intrinsically more difficult to isolate. Nonetheless, we believe that there is evidence that such superpositions could occur within sufficiently large collections of microtubules in the brain for τ to be some fraction of a second.

Very large mass displacements can also occur in the universe in quantummechanical situations, for example in the cores of neutron stars. By OR , such superpositions would reduce extremely quickly, and classically unreasonable superpositions would be rapidly eliminated. Nevertheless, sentient creatures might have evolved in parts of the universe that would be highly alien to us. One possibility might be on neutron star surfaces, an idea that was developed ingeniously and in great detail by Robert Forward in two science-fiction stories (Dragon's Egg in 1980, Starquake in 1989). Such creatures (referred to as 'cheelas' in the books, with metabolic processes and OR-like events occurring at rates of around a million times that of a human being) could arguably have intense experiences, but whether or not this would be possible in detail is, at the moment, a very speculative matter. Nevertheless, the Orch OR proposal offers a possible route to rational argument, as to whether life of a totally alien kind such as this might be possible, or even probable, somewhere in the universe.

Such speculations also raise the issue of the 'anthropic principle', according to which it is sometimes argued that the particular dimensionless constants of Nature that we happen to find in our universe are 'fortuitously' favorable to human existence. (A dimensionless physical constant is a pure number, like the ratio of the electric to the gravitational force between the electron and the proton in a hydrogen atom, which in this case is a number of the general order of 10^{40}.) The key point is not so much to do with human existence, but the existence of sentient beings of any kind. Is there anything coincidental about the dimensionless physical constants being of such a nature that conscious life is possible at all? For example, if the mass of the neutron had been slightly less than that of the proton, rather than slightly larger, then neutrons rather than protons would have been stable, and this would be to the detriment of the whole subject of chemistry. These issues are frequently argued about (see Barrow and Tipler 1986), but the Orch OR proposal provides a little more substance to these arguments, since a proposal for the possibility of sentient life is, in principle, provided.

The recently proposed cosmological scheme of conformal cyclic cosmology (CCC) (Penrose 2010) also has some relevance to these issues. CCC posits that what we presently regard as the entire history of our universe, from its Big-Bang origin (but without inflation) to its indefinitely expanding future, is but one aeon in an unending succession of similar such aeons, where the infinite future of each matches to the big bang of the next via an infinite change of scale. A question arises whether the dimensionless constants of the aeon prior to ours, in the CCC scheme, are the same as those in our own aeon, and this relates to the question of whether sentient life could exist in that aeon as well as in our own. These questions are in principle answerable by observation, and again they would have a bearing on the extent or validity of the Orch OR proposal. If Orch OR turns out to be correct, in it essentials, as a physical basis for consciousness, then it opens up the possibility that many questions may become answerable, such as whether life could have come about in an aeon prior to our own, that would have previously seemed to be far beyond the reaches of science.

Moreover, Orch OR places the phenomenon of consciousness at a very central place in the physical nature of our universe, whether or not this 'universe' includes aeons other than just our own. It is our belief that, quite apart from detailed aspects of the physical mechanisms that are involved in the production of consciousness in human brains, quantum mechanics is an incomplete theory. Some completion is needed, and the DP proposal for an OR scheme underlying quantum theory's R-process would be a definite possibility. If such a scheme as this is indeed respected by Nature, then there is a fundamental additional ingredient to our presently understood laws of Nature which plays an important role at the Planck-scale level of space-time structure. The Orch OR proposal takes advantage of this, suggesting that conscious experience itself plays such a role in the operation of the laws of the universe.

Acknowledgment We thank Dave Cantrell, University of Arizona Biomedical Communications for artwork.

References

Atema, J. (1973). Microtubule theory of sensory transduction. Journal of Theoretical Biology, 38, 181-90.

Bandyopadhyay A (2011) Direct experimental evidence for quantum states in microtubules and topological invariance. Abstracts: Toward a Science of Consciousness 2011, Sockholm, Sweden, HYPERLINK "http://www.consciousness.arizona.edu"www.consciousness.arizona.edu

Barrow, J.D. and Tipler, F.J. (1986) The Anthropic Cosmological Principle (OUP, Oxford).

Bell, J.S. (1966) Speakable and Unspeakable in Quantum Mechanics (Cambridge Univ. Press, Cambridge; reprint 1987).

Benioff, P. (1982). Quantum mechanical Hamiltonian models of Turing Machines. Journal of Statistical Physics, 29, 515-46.

Bennett C.H., and Wiesner, S.J. (1992). Communication via 1- and 2-particle operators on Einstein-Podolsky-Rosen states. Physical Reviews Letters, 69, 2881-84.

Bensimon G, Chemat R (1991) Microtubule disruption and cognitive defects: effect of colchicine on teaming behavior in rats. Pharmacol. Biochem. Behavior 38:141-145.

Bohm, D. (1951) Quantum Theory (Prentice–Hall, Englewood-Cliffs.) Ch. 22, sect. 15-19. Reprinted as: The Paradox of Einstein, Rosen and Podolsky, in Quantum Theory and Measurement, eds., J.A. Wheeler and W.H. Zurek (Princeton University Press, Princeton, 1983).

Bernroider, G. and Roy, S. (2005) Quantum entanglement of K ions, multiple channel states and the role of noise in the brain. SPIE 5841-29:205–14.

Bouwmeester, D., Pan, J.W., Mattle, K., Eibl, M., Weinfurter, H. and Zeilinger, A. (1997) Experimental quantum teleportation. Nature 390 (6660): 575-579.

Brunden K.R., Yao Y., Potuzak J.S., Ferrer N.I., Ballatore C., James M.J., Hogan A.M., Trojanowski J.Q., Smith A.B. 3rd and Lee V.M. (2011) The characterization of microtubule-stabilizing drugs as possibletherapeutic agents for Alzheimer's disease and related taupathies. Pharmacological Research, 63(4), 341-51.

Chalmers, D. J., (1996). The conscious mind - In search of a fundamental theory. Oxford University Press, New York.

Crick, F., and Koch, C., (1990). Towards a neurobiological theory of consciousness.

Seminars in the Neurosciences, 2, 263-75.

Dennett, D.C. (1991). Consciousness explained. Little Brown, Boston. MA.

Dennett, D.C. (1995) Darwin's dangerous idea: Evolution and the Meanings of Life, Simon and Schuster.

Dermietzel, R. (1998) Gap junction wiring: a 'new' principle in cell-to-cell communication in the nervous system? Brain Research Reviews. 26(2-3):176-83.

Deutsch, D. (1985) Quantum theory, the Church–Turing principle and the universal quantum computer, Proceedings of the Royal Society (London) A400, 97-117.

Diósi, L. (1987) A universal master equation for the gravitational violation of quantum mechanics, Physics Letters A 120 (8):377-381.

Diósi, L. (1989). Models for universal reduction of macroscopic quantum fluctuations Physical Review A, 40, 1165-74.

Draguhn A, Traub RD, Schmitz D, Jefferys (1998). Electrical coupling underlies high-frequency oscillations in the hippocampus in vitro. Nature, 394(6689), 189-92.

Eccles, J.C. (1992). Evolution of consciousness. Proceedings of the National Academy of Sciences, 89, 7320-24.

Engel GS, Calhoun TR, Read EL, Ahn T-K, Mancal T, Cheng Y-C, Blankenship RE, Fleming GR (2007) Evidence for wavelike energy transfer through quantum coherence in photosynthetic systems. Nature 446:782-786.

Everett, H. (1957). Relative state formulation of quantum mechanics. In Quantum Theory and Measurement, J.A. Wheeler and W.H. Zurek (eds.) Princeton University Press, 1983; originally in Reviews of Modern Physics, 29, 454-62.

Feynman, R.P. (1986). Quantum mechanical

computers. Foundations of Physics, 16(6), 507-31.

Forward, R. (1980) Dragon's Egg. Ballentine Books.

Forward, R. (1989) Starquake. Ballentine Books.

Fröhlich, H. (1968). Long-range coherence and energy storage in biological systems. International Journal of Quantum Chemistry, 2, 641-9.

Fröhlich, H. (1970). Long range coherence and the actions of enzymes. Nature, 228, 1093.

Fröhlich, H. (1975). The extraordinary dielectric properties of biological materials and the action of enzymes. Proceedings of the National Academy of Sciences, 72, 4211-15.

Galarreta, M. and Hestrin, S. (1999). A network of fast-spiking cells in the neocortex connected by electrical synapses. Nature, 402, 72-75.

Gauger E., Rieper E., Morton J.J.L., Benjamin S.C., Vedral V. (2011) Sustained quantum coherence and entanglement in the avian compass http://arxiv.org/abs/0906.3725.

Ghirardi, G.C., Rimini, A., and Weber, T. (1986). Unified dynamics for microscopic and macroscopic systems. Physical Review D, 34, 470.

Ghirardi, G.C., Grassi, R., and Rimini, A. (1990). Continuous-spontaneous reduction model involving gravity. Physical Review A, 42, 1057-64.

Grush R., Churchland P.S. (1995), 'Gaps in Penrose's toilings', J. Consciousness Studies, 2 (1):10-29.

Hagan S, Hameroff S, and Tuszynski J, (2001). Quantum Computation in Brain Microtubules? Decoherence and Biological Feasibility, Physical Review E, 65, 061901.

Hameroff, S.R., and Watt R.C. (1982). Information processing in microtubules. Journal of Theoretical Biology, 98, 549-61.

Hameroff, S.R.(1987) Ultimate computing: Biomolecular consciousness and nanotechnology. Elsevier North-Holland, Amsterdam.

Hameroff, S.R., and Penrose, R., (1996a). Orchestrated reduction of quantum coherence in brain microtubules: A model for consciousness. In: Toward a Science of Consciousness ; The First Tucson Discussions and Debates. Hameroff, S.R., Kaszniak, and Scott, A.C., eds., 507-540, MIT Press, Cambridge MA, 507-540. Also published in Mathematics and Computers in Simulation (1996) 40:453-480.

Hameroff, S.R., and Penrose, R. (1996b). Conscious events as orchestrated spacetime selections. Journal of Consciousness Studies, 3(1), 36-53.

Hameroff, S. (1998a). Quantum computation in brain microtubules? The Penrose-Hameroff "Orch OR" model of consciousness. Philosophical Transactions of the Royal Society (London) Series A, 356, 1869-1896.

Hameroff, S. (1998b). 'Funda-mentality': is the conscious mind subtly linked to a basic level of the universe? Trends in Cognitive Science, 2, 119-127.

Hameroff, S. (1998c). Anesthesia, consciousness and hydrophobic pockets – A unitary quantum hypothesis of anesthetic action. Toxicology Letters, 100, 101, 31-39.

Hameroff, S. (1998d). HYPERLINK "http://www.hameroff.com/penrose-hameroff/cambrian.html"Did consciousness cause the Cambrian evolutionary explosion? In: Toward a Science of Consciousness II: The Second Tucson Discussions and Debates. Eds. Hameroff, S.R., Kaszniak, A.W., and Scott, A.C., MIT Press, Cambridge, MA.

Hameroff, S., Nip, A., Porter, M., and Tuszynski, J. (2002). Conduction pathways in microtubules, biological quantum computation and microtubules. Biosystems, 64(13), 149-68.

Hameroff S.R., & Watt R.C. (1982) Information processing in microtubules. Journal of Theoretical Biology 98:549-61.

Hameroff, S.R. (2006) The entwined mysteries of anesthesia and consciousness. Anesthesiology 105:400-412.

Hameroff, S.R, Craddock TJ, Tuszynski JA (2010) Memory 'bytes' – Molecular match for CaMKII phosphorylation encoding of microtubule lattices. Journal of Integrative Neuroscience 9(3):253-267.

He, R-H., Hashimoto, M., Karapetyan. H., Koralek, J.D., Hinton, J.P., Testaud, J.P., Nathan, V., Yoshida, Y., Yao, H., Tanaka, K., Meevasana, W., Moore, R.G., Lu, D.H.,Mo, S-K., Ishikado, M., Eisaki, H., Hussain, Z., Devereaux, T.P., Kivelson, S.A., Orenstein, Kapitulnik, J.A., Shen, Z-X. (2011) From a Single-Band Metal to a High Temperature Superconductor via Two Thermal Phase Transitions. Science, 2011;331 (6024): 1579-1583.

Hebb, D.O. (1949). Organization of Behavior: A Neuropsychological Theory, John Wiley and Sons, New York.

Huxley TH (1893; 1986) Method and Results: Essays.

Kant I (1781) Critique of Pure Reason (Translated and edited by Paul Guyer and Allen W. Wood, Cambridge University Press, 1998).

Kibble, T.W.B. (1981). Is a semi-classical theory of gravity viable? In Quantum Gravity 2: a Second Oxford Symposium; eds. C.J. Isham, R. Penrose, and D.W. Sciama (Oxford University Press, Oxford), 63-80.

Koch, C., (2004) The Quest for Conscious-ness: A Neurobiological Approach, Englewood, CO., Roberts and Co.

Koch C, Hepp K (2006) Quantm mechanics in the brain. Nature 440(7084):611.

Libet, B., Wright, E.W. Jr., Feinstein, B., & Pearl, D.K. (1979) Subjective referral of the timing for a conscious sensory experience. Brain 102:193-224.

Luo L, Lu J (2011) Temperature dependence of protein folding deduced from quantum transition. http://arxiv.org/abs/1102.3748

Lutz A, Greischar AL, Rawlings NB, Ricard M, Davidson RJ (2004) Long-term meditators self-induce high-amplitude gamma synchrony during mental practice The Proceedings of the National Academy of Sciences USA 101(46)16369-16373.

Macikic I., de Riedmatten H., Tittel W., Zbinden H. and Gisin N. (2002) Long-distance teleportation of qubits at telecommunication wavelengths Nature 421, 509-513.

Margulis, L. and Sagan, D. 1995. What is life? Simon and Schuster, N.Y.

Marshall, W, Simon, C., Penrose, R., and Bouwmeester, D (2003). Towards quantum superpositions of a mirror. Physical Review Letters 91, 13-16; 130401.

McKemmish LK, Reimers JR, McKenzie RH, Mark AE, Hush NS (2009) Penrose-Hameroff orchestrated objective-reduction proposal for human consciousness is not biologically feasible. Physical Review E. 80(2 Pt 1):021912.

Moroz, I.M., Penrose, R., and Tod, K.P. (1998) Spherically-symmetric solutions of the Schrödinger–Newton equations:. Classical and Quantum Gravity, 15, 2733-42.

Nogales E, Wolf SG, Downing KH. (1998) HYPERLINK "http://dx.doi.org/10.1038/34465"Structure of the αβ-tubulin dimer by electron crystallography.

Nature. 391, 199-203.

Ouyang, M., & Awschalom, D.D. (2003) Coherent spin transfer between molecularly bridged quantum dots. Science 301:1074-78.

Pearle, P. (1989). Combining stochastic dynamical state-vector reduction with spontaneous localization. Physical Review A, 39, 2277-89.

Pearle, P. and Squires, E.J. (1994). Bound-state excitation, nucleon decay experiments and models of wave-function collapse. Physical Review Letters, 73(1), 1-5.

Penrose, R. (1989). The Emperor's New Mind: Concerning Computers, Minds, and the Laws of Physics, Oxford University Press, Oxford.

Penrose, R. (1993). Gravity and quantum mechanics. In General Relativity and Gravitation 13. Part 1: Plenary Lectures 1992. Proceedings of the Thirteenth International Conference on General Relativity and Gravitation held at Cordoba, Argentina, 28 June - 4 July 1992. Eds. R.J.Gleiser, C.N.Kozameh, and O.M.Moreschi (Inst. of Phys. Publ. Bristol and Philadelphia), 179-89.

Penrose, R. (1994). Shadows of the Mind; An Approach to the Missing Science of Consciousness. Oxford University Press, Oxford.

Penrose, R. (1996). On gravity's role in quantum state reduction. General Relativity and Gravitation, 28, 581-600.

Penrose, R. (2000). Wavefunction collapse as a real gravitational effect. In Mathematical Physics 2000, Eds. A.Fokas, T.W.B.Kibble, A.Grigouriou, and B.Zegarlinski. Imperial College Press, London, 266-282.

Penrose, R. (2002). John Bell, State Reduction, and Quanglement. In Quantum Unspeakables: From Bell to Quantum Information, Eds. Reinhold A. Bertlmann and Anton Zeilinger , Springer-Verlag, Berlin, 319-331.

Penrose, R. (2004). The Road to Reality: A Complete Guide to the Laws of the Universe. Jonathan Cape, London.

Penrose, R. (2009). Black holes, quantum theory and cosmology (Fourth International Workshop DICE 2008), Journal of Physics, Conference Series 174, 012001.

Penrose, R. (2010). Cycles of Time: An Extraordinary New View of the Universe. Bodley Head, London.

Penrose R. and Hameroff S.R. (1995) What gaps? Reply to Grush and Churchland. Journal of Consciousness Studies.2:98-112.

Percival, I.C. (1994) Primary state diffusion. Proceedings of the Royal Society (London) A, 447, 189-209.

Pokorný, J., Hasek, J., Jelínek, F., Saroch, J. & Palan, B. (2001) Electromagnetic activity of yeast cells in the M phase. Electro Magnetobiol 20, 371–396.

Pokorný, J. (2004) Excitation of vibration in microtubules in living cells. Bioelectrochem. 63: 321-326.

Polkinghorne, J. (2002) Quantum Theory, A Very Short Introduction. Oxford University Press, Oxford.

Rae, A.I.M. (1994) Quantum Mechanics. Institute of Physics Publishing; 4th edition 2002.

Rasmussen, S., Karampurwala, H., Vaidyanath, R., Jensen, K.S., and Hameroff, S. (1990) Computational connectionism within neurons: A model of cytoskeletal automata subserving neural networks. Physica D 42:428-49.

Reimers JR, McKemmish LK, McKenzie RH, Mark AE, Hush NS (2009) Weak, strong, and coherent regimes of Frohlich condensation and their applications to terahertz medicine and quantum consciousness Proceedings of the National Academy of Sciences USA

106(11):4219-24

Reiter GF, Kolesnikov AI, Paddison SJ, Platzman PM, Moravsky AP, Adams MA, Mayers J (2011) Evidence of a new quantum state of nano-confined water http://arxiv.org/abs/1101.4994

Rieper E, Anders J, Vedral V (2011) Quantum entanglement between the electron clouds of nucleic acids in DNA. http://arxiv.org/abs/1006.4053.

Samsonovich A, Scott A, Hameroff S (1992) Acousto-conformational transitions in cytoskeletal microtubules: Implications for intracellular information processing. Nanobiology 1:457-468.

Sherrington, C.S. (1957) Man on His Nature, Second Edition, Cambridge University Press.

Smolin, L. (2002). Three Roads to Quantum Gravity. Basic Books. New York.

Tegmark, M. (2000) The importance of quantum decoherence in brain processes. Physica Rev E 61:4194-4206.

Tittel, W, Brendel, J., Gisin, B., Herzog, T., Zbinden, H., and Gisin, N. (1998) Experimental demonstration of quantum correlations over more than 10 km, Physical Reiew A, 57:3229-32.

Tononi G (2004) An information integration theory of consciousness BMC Neuroscience 5:42.

Turin L (1996) A spectroscopic mechanism for primary olfactory reception Chem Senses 21(6) 773-91.

Tuszynski JA, Brown JA, Hawrylak P, Marcer P (1998) Dielectric polarization, electrical conduction, information processing and quantum computation in microtubules. Are they plausible? Phil Trans Royal Society A 356:1897-1926.

Tuszynski, J.A., Hameroff, S., Sataric, M.V., Trpisova, B., & Nip, M.L.A. (1995) Ferroelectric behavior in microtubule dipole lattices; implications for information processing, signaling and assembly/disassembly. Journal of Theoretical Biology 174:371–80.

Voet, D., Voet, J.G. 1995. Biochemistry, 2nd edition. Wiley, New York.

von Rospatt, A., (1995) The Buddhist Doctrine of Momentariness: A survey of the origins and early phase of this doctrine up to Vasubandhu (Stuttgart: Franz Steiner Verlag).

Wegner, D.M. (2002) The illusion of conscious will Cambridge MA, MIT Press.

Whitehead, A.N., (1929) Process and Reality. New York, Macmillan.

Whitehead, A.N. (1933) Adventure of Ideas, London, Macmillan.

Wigner E.P. (1961). Remarks on the mind-body question, in The Scientist Speculates, ed. I.J. Good (Heinemann, London). In Quantum Theory and Measurement, eds., J.A. Wheeler and W.H. Zurek, Princeton Univsity Press, Princeton, MA. (Reprinted in E. Wigner (1967), Symmetries and Reflections, Indiana University Press, Bloomington).

Wolfram, S. (2002) A New Kind of Science. Wolfram Media incorporated.

Quantum Physics and the Multiplicity of Mind: Split-Brains, Fragmented Minds, Dissociation, Quantum Consciousness

R. Joseph, Ph.D.

Emeritus, Brain Research Laboratory, Northern California

Abstract

Quantum physics and Einstein's theory of relativity make assumptions about the nature of the mind which is assumed to be a singularity. In the Copenhagen model of physics, the process of observing is believed to effect reality by the act of perception and knowing which creates abstractions and a collapse function thereby inducing discontinuity into the continuum of the quantum state. This gives rise to the uncertainty principle. Yet neither the mind or the brain is a singularity, but a multiplicity which include two dominant streams of consciousness and awareness associated with the left and right hemisphere, as demonstrated by patients whose brains have been split, and which are superimposed on yet other mental realms maintained by the brainstem, thalamus, limbic system, and the occipital, temporal, parietal, and frontal lobes. Like the quantum state, each of these minds may also become discontinuous from each other and each mental realm may perceive their own reality. Illustrative examples are detailed, including denial of blindness, blind sight, fragmentation of the body image, phantom limbs, the splitting of the mind following split-brain surgery, and dissociative states where the mind leaves the body and achieves a state of quantum consciousness and singularity such that the universe and mind become one.

1. Introduction

In 1905 Albert Einstein published his theories of relativity, which promoted the thesis that reality and its properties, such as time and motion had no objective "true values", but were "relative" to the observer's point of view (Einstein, 1905a,b,c). However, what if the observer is not a singularity and has more than one point of view and more than one stream of observing consciousness? And what if these streams of consciousness were also relative?

Quantum physics, as exemplified by the Copenhagen school (Bohr, 1934, 1958, 1963; Heisenberg, 1930, 1955, 1958), also makes assumptions about the nature of reality as related to an observer, the "knower" who is conceptualized as a singularity. Because the physical world is relative to being known by a "knower" (the observing consciousness), then the "knower" can influence the nature of the reality which is being observed. In consequence, what is known vs what is not known becomes relatively imprecise (Heisenberg, 1958).

For example, as expressed by the Heisenberg uncertainty principle (Heisenberg, 1955, 1958), the more precisely one physical property is known the more unknowable become other properties, whose measurements become correspondingly imprecise. The more precisely one property is known, the less precisely the other can be known and this is true at the molecular and atomic levels of reality. Therefore it is impossible to precisely determine, simultaneously, for example, both the position and velocity of an electron.

However, we must ask: if knowing A, makes B unknowable, and if knowing B makes A unknowable, wouldn't this imply that both A and B, are in fact unknowable? If both A and B are manifestations of the processing of "knowing," and if observing and measuring can change the properties of A or B, then perhaps both A and B are in fact properties of knowing, properties of the observing consciousness, and not properties of A or B.

In quantum physics, nature and reality are represented by the quantum state. The electromagnetic field of the quantum state is the fundamental entity, the continuum that constitutes the basic oneness and unity of all things.

The physical nature of this state can be "known" by assigning it mathematical properties (Bohr, 1958, 1963). Therefore, abstractions, i.e., numbers, become representational of a hypothetical physical state. Because these are abstractions, the physical state is also an abstraction and does not possess the material consistency, continuity, and hard, tangible, physical substance as is assumed by Classical (Newtonian) physics. Instead, reality, the physical world, is created by the process of observing, measuring, and knowing (Heisenberg, 1955).

Consider an elementary particle, once this positional value is assigned, knowledge of momentum, trajectory, speed, and so on, is lost and becomes "uncertain." The particle's momentum is left uncertain by an amount inversely proportional to the accuracy of the position measurement which is determined by values assigned by the observing consciousness. Therefore, the nature of reality, and the uncertainty principle is directly affected by the observer and the process of observing and knowing (Heisenberg, 1955, 1958).

The act of knowing creates a knot in the quantum state; described as a "collapse of the wave function;" a knot of energy that is a kind of blemish in the continuum of the quantum field. This quantum knot bunches up at the point of observation, at the assigned value of measurement.

The process of knowing, makes reality, and the quantum state, discontinuous. "The discontinuous change in the probability function takes place with the act of registration…in the mind of the observer" (Heisenberg, 1958).

Reality, therefore, is a manifestation of alterations in the patterns of activity within the electromagnetic field which are perceived as discontinuous. The perception of a structural unit of information is not just perceived, but is inserted into the quantum state which causes the reduction of the wave-packet and the collapse of the wave function.

Knowing and not knowing, are the result of interactions between the mind and concentrations of energy that emerge and disappear back into the electromagnetic quantum field.

However, if reality is created by the observing consciousness, and can be made discontinuous, does this leave open the possibility of a reality behind the reality? Might there be multiple realities? And if consciousness and the observer and the quantum state is not a singularity, could each of these multiple realities also be manifestations of a multiplicity of minds?

Heinserberg (1958) recognized this possibility of hidden realities, and therefore proposed that the reality that exists beyond or outside the quantum state could be better understood when considered in terms of "potential" reality and "actual" realities. Therefore, although the quantum state does not have the ontological character of an "actual" thing, it has a "potential" reality; an objective tendency to become actual at some point in the future, or to have become actual at some point in the past.

Therefore, it could be said that the subatomic particles which make up reality, or the quantum state, do not really exist, except as probabilities. These "subatomic" particles have probable existences and display tendencies to assume certain patterns of activity that we perceive as shape and form. Yet, they may also begin to display a different pattern of activity such that being can become nonbeing and thus something else altogether.

The conception of a deterministic reality is therefore subjugated to mathematical probabilities and potentiality which is relative to the mind of a knower which effects that reality as it unfolds, evolves, and is observed (Bohr 1958, 1963; Heisenberg 1955, 1958). That is, the mental act of perceiving a non-localized unit of structural information, injects that mental event into the quantum state of the universe, causing "the collapse of the wave function" and creating a bunching up, a tangle and discontinuous knot in the continuity of the quantum state.

Einstein ridiculed these ideas (Pais, 1979): "Do you really think the moon isn't there if you aren't looking at it?"

Heisenberg (1958), cautioned, however, that the observer is not the creator of reality: "The introduction of the observer must not be misunderstood to imply that some kind of subjective features are to be brought into the description of nature. The observer has, rather, only the function of registering decisions, i.e., processes in space and time, and it does not matter whether the observer is an apparatus or a human being; but the registration, i.e., the transition from the "possible" to the "actual," is absolutely necessary here and cannot be omitted from the interpretation of quantum theory."

Shape and form are a function of our perception of dynamic interactions within the continuum which is the quantum state. What we perceive as mass (shape, form, length, weight) are dynamic patterns of energy which we selectively attend to and then perceive as stable and static, creating discontinuity within the continuity of the quantum state. Therefore, what we are perceiving and knowing, are only fragments of the continuum.

However, we can only perceive what our senses can detect, and what we detect as form and shape is really a mass of frenzied subatomic electromagnetic activity that is amenable to detection by our senses and which may be known by a knowing mind. It is the perception of certain aspects of these oscillating patterns of continuous evolving activity, which give rise to the impressions of shape and form, and thus discontinuity, as experienced within the mind.

This energy that makes up the object of our perceptions, is therefore but an aspect of the electromagnetic continuum which has assumed a specific pattern during the process of being sensed and processed by those regions of the brain and mind best equipped to process this information.

Perceived reality, therefore, becomes a manifestation of mind.

However, if the mind is not a singularity, and if we possessed additional senses or an increased sensory channel capacity, we would perceive yet other patterns and other realities which would be known by those features of the mind best attuned to them. If the mind is not a singularity but a multiplicity, this means that both A and B, may be known simultaneously.

2. Duality vs Multiplicity

In the Copenhagen model, the observer is external to the quantum state the observer is observing, and they are not part of the collapse function but a witness of it (Bohr, 1958, 1963; Heisenberg 1958). However, if the Copenhagen model is correct, and as the cosmos contains observers, then the standard collapse formulation can not be used to describe the entire universe as the universe contains observers (von Neumann, 1932, 1937).

Further, reality becomes, at a minimum, a duality (observer and observed) with the potential to become a multiplicity.

As described by DeWitt and Graham (1973; Dewitt, 1971), "This reality, which is described jointly by the dynamical variables and the state vector, is not the reality we customarily think of, but is a reality composed of many worlds. By virtue of the temporal development of the dynamical variables the state vector decomposes naturally into orthogonal vectors, reflecting a continual splitting of the universe into a multitude of mutually unobservable but equally real worlds, in each of which every good measurement has yielded a definite result and in most of which the familiar statistical quantum laws hold."

The minimal duality is that aspect of reality which is observed, measured, and known, and that which is unknown.

However, this minimal duality is an illusion as indicated not only by the potential to become multiplicity, but by the nature of mind which is not a singularity (Joseph, 1982, 1986a; 1988a,b).

Even if we disregard the concept of "mind" and substitute the word "brain", the fact remains that the brain is not a singularity. The human brain is functionally specialized with specific functions and different mental states localized to specific areas, each of which is capable of maintaining independent and semi-independent aspects of conscious-awareness (Joseph 1986a,b, 1988a,b, 1992, 1999a). Different aspects of the same experience and identical aspects of that experience may be perceived and processed by different brain areas in different ways (Gallagher and Joseph, 1982; Joseph 1982; Joseph and Gallagher 1985; Joseph et al., 1984).

Therefore, although it has been said that orthodox quantum mechanics is completely concordant with the defining characteristics of Cartesian dualism, this is an illusion. Cartesian duality assumes singularity of mind, when in fact, the overarching organization of the mind- and the brain- is both dualistic and multiplistic.

If quantum physics is "mind-like" (actual/operational at the quantum level, but mentalistic on the ontological level) then quantum physics, or rather, the quantum state (reality, the universe) is not a duality, but a multiciplicity. Indeed, the entire concept of duality is imposed on reality by the dominant dualistic nature of the brain and mind which subordinates not just reality, but the multiplicity of minds maintained within the human brain (Joseph, 1982).

Like the Copenhagen school, Von Neumann's formulation of quantum mechanics (1932, 1937), fails to recognize or understand the multiple nature of mind and reality. Von Neumann postulated that the physical aspects of nature are represented by a density matrix. The matrix, therefore, could be conceptualized as a subset of potential realities, and that by averaging the values of these evolving matrices, the state of the universe and thus of reality, can be ascertained as a unified whole. However, in contrast to the Copenhagen interpretation, Von Neumann shifted the observer (his brain) into the quantum universe and thus made it subject to the rules of quantum physics.

Ostensibly and explicitly, Von Neumann's conceptions are based on a conception of mind as a singularity acting on the quantum state which contains the brain. Von Neumann's mental singularity, therefore, imposes itself on reality, such that each "event" that occurs within reality, is associated with one specific experience of the singularity-mind. Thus, Von Neumann assumes the brain and mind has only "one experience" which corresponds with "one event;" and this grossly erroneous misconception of the nature of the brain and mind, unfortunately, is erroneously accepted as fact by most cosmologists and physicists. Further, he argues that in the process of knowing, the quantum state of this singularity brain/mind also collapses, or rather, is reduced in a mathematically quantifiable manner, just as the quantum universe is collapsed and reduced by being known (Von Neumann, 1932, 1937).

However, the brain and mind are not a singularity, but a multiplicity (Joseph, 1982, 1988a,b, 1999a). Nevertheless, Von Neumann's conceptions can be applied to the multiplicity of mind/brain when each mental realm is considered individually as an interactional subset of the multiplicity.

3. The Multiplicity of Mind and Perception

According to Von Neumann (1932), the "experiential increments in a person's knowledge" and "reductions of the quantum mechanical state of that person's brain" corresponds to the elimination of all those perceptual functions that are not necessary or irrelevant to the knowing of the event and the increase in the knowledge associated with the experience.

If considered from the perspective of an isolated aspect of the mind and the dominating stream of consciousness, Von Neuman's conceptions are essentially correct. However, neither the brain nor the mind function in isolation but in interaction with other neural tissues and mental/perceptual/sensory realms (Joseph 1982, 1992, 1999a). Perceptual functions are not "eliminated" and removed from the brain. Instead, they are prevented from interfering with the attentional processes of one aspect of the multiplicity of mind which dominates during the knowing event (Joseph, 1986b, 1999a).

Consider, by way of example, you are sitting in your office reading this text. The pressure of the chair, the physical sensations of your shoes and clothes, the musculature of your body as it holds one then another position, the temperature of the room, various odors and fragrances, a multitude of sounds, visual sensations from outside your area of concentration and focus, and so on, are all being transmitted to the brainstem, midbrain, and olfactory limbic system. These signals are then relayed to various subnuclei within the thalamus.

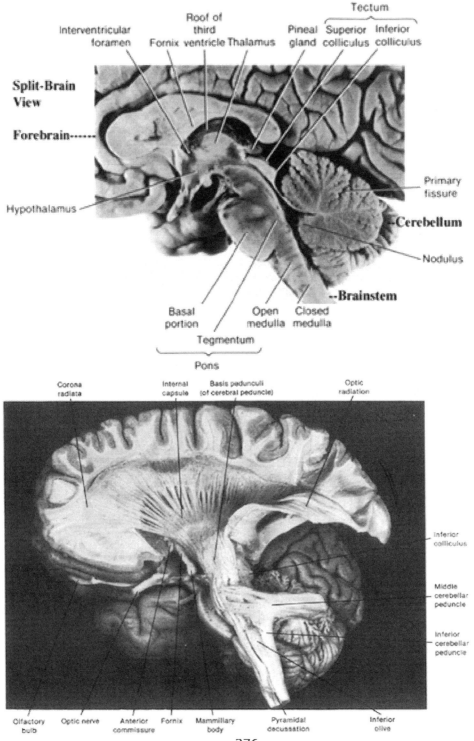

The neural tissues of the brainstem, midbrain, limbic system and thalamus are associated with the "old brain." However, those aspects of consciousness we most closely associated with humans are associated with the "new brain" the neocortex (Joseph, 1982, 1992). Therefore, although you may be "aware" of these sensations while they are maintained within the old brain, you are not "conscious" of them, unless a decision is made to become conscious or they increase sufficiently in intensity that they are transferred to the neocortex and forced into the focus of consciousness (Joseph, 1982, 1986b, 1992, 1999a).

The old brain is covered by a gray mantle of new cortex, neocortex. The sensations alluded to are transferred from the old brain to the thalamus which relays these signals to the neocortex. Human consciousness and the "higher" level of the multiplicity of mind, are associated with the "new brain."

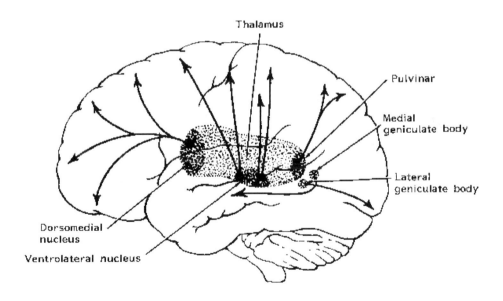

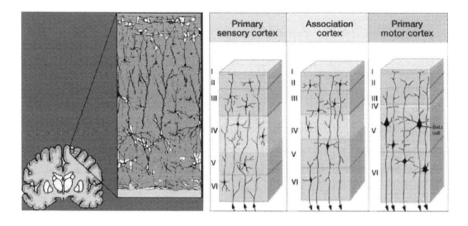

For example, visual input is transmitted from the eyes to the midbrain and thalamus and is transferred to the primary visual receiving area maintained in the neocortex of the occipital lobe (Casagrande & Joseph 1978, 1980; Joseph and Casagrande, 1978). Auditory input is transmitted from the inner ears to the brainstem, midbrain, and thalamus, and is transferred to the primary auditory receiving area within the neocortex of the temporal lobe. Tactual-physical stimuli are also transmitted from the thalamus to the primary somatosensory areas maintained in the neocortex of the parietal lobe. From the primary areas these signals are transferred to the adjoining "association" areas, and simple percepts become more complex by association (Joseph, 1996).

Monitoring all this perceptual and sensory activity within the thalamus and neocortex is the frontal lobes of the brain, also known as the senior executive of the brain and personality (Joseph 1986b, 1999a; Joseph et al., 1981). It is the frontal lobes which maintain the focus of attention and which can selectively inhibit any additional processing of signals received in the primary areas.

There are two frontal lobes, a right and left frontal lobe which communicate via a bridge of nerve fibers. Each frontal lobe, and subdivisions within each are concerned with different types of mental activity (Joseph, 1999a).

The left frontal lobe, among its many functions, makes possible the ability to speak. It is associated with the verbally expressive, speaking aspects of consciousness. However, there are different aspects of consciousness associated not only with the frontal lobe, but with each lobe of the brain and its subdivisions (Joseph, 1986b; 1996, 1999a).

4. Knowing Yet Not Knowing: Disconnected Consciousness

Consider the well known phenomenon of "word finding difficulty" also known as "tip of the tongue." You know the word you want (the "thingama-jig") but at the same time, you can't gain access to it. That is, one aspect of consciousness knows the missing word, but another aspect of consciousness associated with talking and speech can't gain access to the word. The mind is disconnected from itself. One aspect of mind knows, the other aspect of mind does not.

This same phenomenon, but much more severe and disabling, can occur if the nerve fiber pathway linking the language areas of the left hemisphere are damaged. For example, Broca's area in the frontal lobe expresses humans speech. Wernicke's area in the temporal lobe comprehends speech. The inferior parietal lobe associates and assimilates associations so that, for example, we can say the word "dog" and come up with the names of dozens of different breeds and then describe them (Joseph, 1982; Joseph and Gallagher 1985; Joseph et al., 1984). Therefore, if Broca's area is disconnected from the posterior language areas, one aspect of consciousness may know what it wants to say, but the speaking aspect of consciousness will be unable to gain access to it and will have nothing to say. This condition is called "conduction aphasia."

Or consider damage which disconnects the parietal lobe from Broca's area. If you place an object, e.g., a comb, out-of-sight, in the person's right hand, and ask them to name the object, the speaking aspect of consciousness may know something is in the hand, but will be unable to name it. However, although they can't name it, and can't guess if shown pictures, if the patient is asked to point to the correct object, they will correctly pick out the comb (Joseph, 1996).

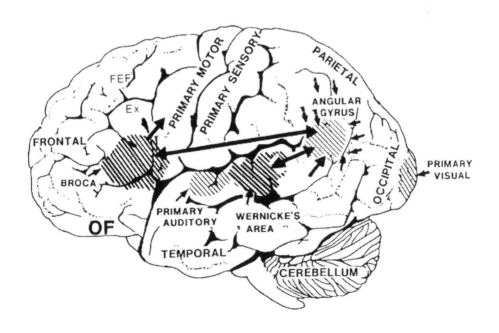

Therefore, part of the brain and mind may act purposefully (e.g. picking out the comb), whereas another aspect of the brain and mind is denied access to the information that the disconnected part of the mind is acting on.

Thus, the part of the brain and mind which is perceiving and knowing, is not the same as the part of the brain and mind which is speaking. This phenomenon occurs even in undamaged brains, when the multiplicity of minds which make up one of the dominant streams of consciousness, become disconnected and/or are unable to communicate.

5. The Visual Mind: Denial of Blindness

All visual sensations first travel from the eyes to the thalamus and midbrain. At this level, these visual impressions are outside of consciousness, though we may be aware of them. These visual sensations are then transferred to the primary visual receiving areas and to the adjacent association areas in the neocortex of the occipital lobe. Once these visual impressions reach the neocortex, consciousness of the visual word is achieved. Visual consciousness is made possible by the occipital lobe.

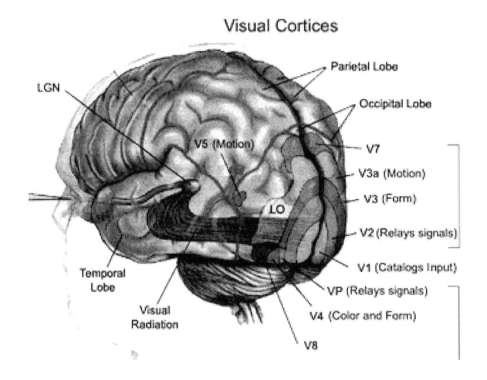

Visual Cortices

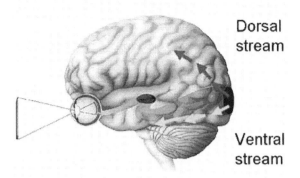

Destruction of the occipital lobe and its neocortical visual areas results in cortical blindness (Joseph, 1996). The consciousness mind is blinded and can not see or sense anything except vague sensations of lightness and darkness. However, because visual consciousness is normally maintained within the occipital lobe, with destruction of this tissue, the other mental systems will not know that they can't see. The remaining mental system do not know they are blind.

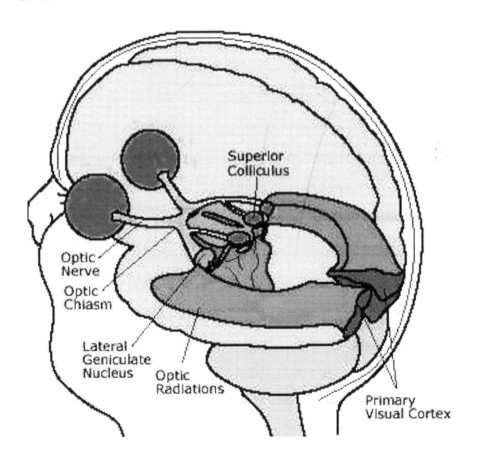

Wernicke's area in the left temporal lobe in association with the inferior parietal lobe comprehends and can generate complex language. Normally, visual input is transferred from the occipital to the inferior parietal lobe (IPL) which is adjacent to Wernicke's area and the visual areas of the occipital lobe. Once these signals arrive in the IPL a person can name what they see; the visual input is matched with auditory-verbal signals and the conscious mind can label and talk about what is viewed (Joseph, 1982, 1986b; Joseph et al., 1984). Talking and verbally describing what is seen is made possible when this stream of information is transferred to Broca's area in the left frontal lobe (Joseph, 1982, 1999a). It is Broca's area which speaks and talks.

Therefore, with complete destruction of the occipital lobe, visual consciousness is abolished whereas the other mental system remain intact but are unable to receive information about the visual world. In consequence, the verbal aspects of consciousness and the verbal-language mind does not know it can't see because the brain area responsible for informing these mental system about seeing, no longer exists. . In fact the language-dependent conscious mind will deny that it is blind; and this is called: Denial of blindness.

Normally, if it gets dark, or you close your eyes, the visual mind becomes conscious of this change in light perception and will alert the other mental realms. These other mental realms do not process visual signals and therefore they must be informed about what the visual mind is seeing. If the occipital lobe is destroyed, visual consciousness is destroyed, and the rest of the brain cannot be told that visual consciousness can't see. Therefore, the rest of the brain does not know it is blind, and when asked, will deny blindness and will make up reasons for why they bump into furniture or can't recognize objects held before their eyes (Joseph, 1986b, 1988a).

For example, when unable to name objects, they might confabulate an explanation: "I see better at home." Or, "I tripped because someone moved the furniture."

Even if you tell them they are blind, they will deny blindness; that is, the verbal aspects of consciousness will claim it can see, when it can't. The Language-dependent aspects of consciousness does not know that it is blind because information concerning blindness is not being received from the mental realms which support visual consciousness.

The same phenomenon occurs with small strokes destroying just part of the occipital lobe. Although a patient may lose a quarter or even half of their visual field, they may be unaware of it. This is because that aspect of visual consciousness no longer exists and can't inform the other mental realms of its condition.

6. "Blind Sight"

The brains of reptiles, amphibians, and fish do not have neocortex. Visual input is processed in the midbrain and thalamus and other old-brain areas as these creatures do not possess neocortex or lobes of the brain. In humans, this information is also received in the brainstem and thalamus and is then transferred to the newly evolved neocortex.

As is evident in non-mammalian species, these creatures can see, and they are aware of their environment. They possess an older-cortical (brainstem-thalamus) visual awareness which in humans is dominated by neocortical visual consciousness.

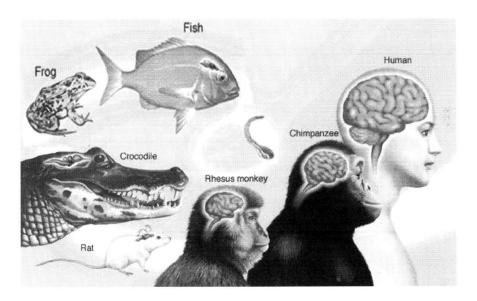

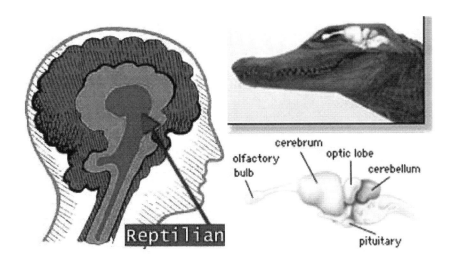

(Left) Human Brain. Reptile Brain (Right)

Therefore, even with complete destruction of the visual neocortex, and after the patient has had time to recover, some patients will demonstrate a non-conscious awareness of their visual environment. Although they are cortically blind and can't name objects and stumble over furniture and bump into walls, they may correctly indicate if an object is moving in front of their face, and they may turn their head or even reach out their arms to touch it-- just as a frog can see a fly buzzing by and lap it up with its tongue. Although the patient can't name or see what has moved in front of his face, he may report that he has a "feeling" that something has moved.

Frogs do not have neocortex and they do not have language, and can't describe what they see. However, humans and frogs have old cortex that process visual impressions and which can control and coordinate body movements. Therefore, although the neocortical realms of human consciousness are blind, the mental realms of the old brain can continue to see and can act on what it sees; and this is called: Blind sight (Joseph, 1996).

7. Body Consciousness: Denial of the Body, and Phantom Limbs

All tactile and physical-sensory impressions are relayed from the body to the brainstem and the thalamus, and are then transferred to the primary receiving and then the association area for somatosensory information located in the neocortex of the parietal lobe (Joseph, 1986b, 1996). The entire image of the body is represented in the parietal lobes (the right and left half of the body in the left and right parietal lobe respectively), albeit in correspondence with the sensory importance of each body part. Therefore, more neocortical space is devoted to the hands and fingers than to the elbow.

It is because the body image and body consciousness is maintained in the parietal area of the brain, that victims of traumatic amputation and who lose an arm or a leg, continue to feel as if their arm or their leg is still attached to the body. This is called: phantom limbs. They can see the leg is missing, but they feel as if it is still there; body-consciousness remains intact even though part of the body is missing (Joseph, 1986b, 1996). They may also continue to periodically experience the pain of the physical trauma which led to the amputation, and this is called "phantom limb pain."

Thus, via the mental system of the parietal lobe, consciousness of what is not there, may appear to consciousness as if it is still there. This is not a hallucination. The image of the body is preserved in the brain and so to is consciousness of the body; and this is yet another example of experienced reality being a manifestation of the brain and mind. In this regard, reality is literally mapped into the brain and is represented within the brain, such that even when aspects of this "reality" are destroyed and no longer exists external to the brain, it nevertheless continues to be perceived and experienced by the brain and the associated realms of body-consciousness.

Conversely, if the parietal lobe is destroyed, particularly the right parietal lobe (which maintains an image of the left half of the body), half of the body image may be erased from consciousness (Joseph, 1986b, 1988a). The remaining realms of mind will lose all consciousness of the left half of the body, which, in their minds, never existed.

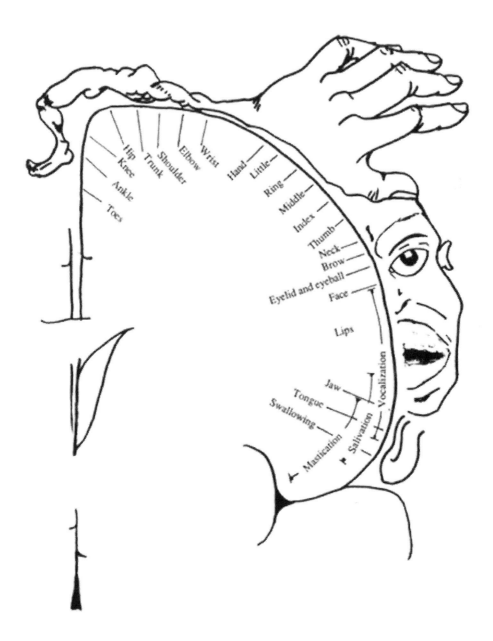

Doctor: "Give me your right hand!" (Patient offers right hand). "Now give me your left!" (The patient presents the right hand again. The right hand is held.) "Give me your left!" (The patient looks puzzled and does not move.) "Is there anything wrong with your left hand?"

Patient: "No, doctor."

Doctor: "Why don't you move it, then?"

Patient: "I don't know."

Doctor: "Is this your hand?" (The left hand is held before her eyes.)

Patient: "Not mine, doctor."

Doctor: "Whose hand is it, then?"

Patient: "I suppose it's yours, doctor."

Doctor: "No, it's not; I've already got two hands. look at it carefully." (The left hand is again held before her eyes.)

Patient: "It is not mine, doctor."

Doctor: "Yes it is, look at that ring; whose is it?" (Patient's finger with marriage ring is held before her eyes)

Patient: "That's my ring; you've got my ring, doctor. You're wearing my ring!"

Doctor: "Look at it—it is your hand."

Patient: "Oh, no doctor."

Doctor: "Where is your left hand then?"

Patient: "Somewhere here, I think." (Making groping movements near her left shoulder).

Because the body image has been destroyed, consciousness of that half of the body is also destroyed. The remaining mental systems and the language-dependent conscious mind will completely ignore and fail to recognize their left arm or leg because the mental system responsible for consciousness of the body image no longer exists. If the left arm or leg is shown to them, they will claim it belongs to someone else, such as the nurse or the doctor. They may dress or groom only the right half of their body, eat only off the right half of their plates, and even ignore painful stimuli applied to the left half of their bodies (Joseph, 1986b, 1988a).

However, if you show them their arm and leg (whose ownership they deny), they will admit these extremities exists, but will insist the leg or arm does not belong to them, even though the arm or the leg is wearing the same clothes covering the rest of their body. Instead, the language dependent aspects of consciousness will confabulate and make up explanations and thus create their own reality. One patient said the arm belonged to a little girl, whose arm had slipped into the patient's sleeve. Another declared (speaking of his left arm and leg), "That's an old man. He stays in bed all the time."

One such patient engaged in peculiar erotic behavior with his left arm and leg which he believed belonged to a woman. Some patients may develop a dislike for their left arms, try to throw them away, become agitated when they are referred to, entertain persecutory delusions regarding them, and even complain of strange people sleeping in their beds due to their experience of bumping into their left limbs during the night (Joseph, 1986b, 1988a). One patient complained that the person sharing her bed, tried to push her out of the bed and then insisted that if it happened again she would sue the hospital. Another complained about "a hospital that makes people sleep together." A female patient expressed not only anger but concern least her husband should find out; she was convinced it was a man in her bed.

The right and left parietal lobes maintain a map and image of the left and right half of the body, respectively. Therefore, when the right parietal lobe is destroyed, the language-dependent mental systems of the left half of the brain, having access only to the body image for the right half of the body, is unable to become conscious of the left half of their body, except as body parts that they then deduce must belong to someone else.

However, when the language dominant mental system of the left hemisphere denies ownerhip of the left extremity these mental system are in fact telling the truth. That is, the left arm and leg belongs to the right not the left hemisphere; the mental system that is capable of becoming conscious of the left half of their body no longer exist.

When the language axis (Joseph, 1982, 2000), i.e. the inferior parietal lobe, Broca's and Wernicke's areas, are functionally isolated from a particular source of information, the language dependent aspect of mind begins to make up a response based on the information available. To be informed about the left leg or left arm, it must be able to communicate with the cortical area (i.e. the parietal lobe) which is responsible for perceiving and analyzing information regarding the extremities. When no message is received and when the language axis is not informed that no messages are being transmitted, the language zones instead rely on some other source even when that source provides erroneous input (Joseph, 1982, 1986b; Joseph et al., 1984); substitute material is assimilated and expressed and corrections cannot be made (due to loss of input from the relevant knowledge source). The patient begins to confabulate. This is because the patient who speaks to you is not the 'patient' who is perceiving- they are in fact, separate; multiple minds exist in the same head.

8. Split-Brains and Split-Minds.

The multiplicity of mind is not limited to visual consciousness, body consciousness, or the language-dependent consciousness. Rather the multiplicity of mind include social consciousness, emotional consciousness, and numerous other mental realms linked with specific areas of the brain (Joseph, 1982, 1986a,b, 1988a,b, 1992, 1999a), such as the limbic system (emotion), frontal lobes (rational thought), the inferior temporal lobes (memory) and the two halves of the brain where multiple streams of mental activity become subordinated and dominated by two distinct realms of mind; consciousness and awareness (Joseph, 1982, 1986a,b, 1988a,b).

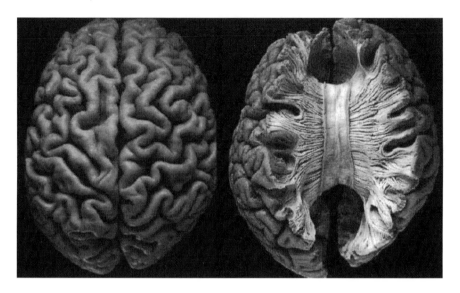

The brain is not a singularity. This is most apparent when viewing the right and left half of the brain which are divided by the interhemispheric fissure and almost completely split into two cerebral hemispheres. These two brain halves are connected by a rope of nerve fibers, the corpus callosum, which enables them to share and exchange some information, but not all information as these two mental realms maintain a conscious awareness of different realities.

For example, it is well established that the right cerebral hemisphere is dominant over the left in regard to the perception, expression and mediation of almost all aspects of social and emotional functioning and related aspects of social/emotional language and memory. Further, the right hemisphere is dominant for most aspects of visual-spatial perceptual functioning, the comprehension of body language, the recognition of faces including friend's loved ones, and one's own face in the mirror (Joseph, 1988a, 1996).

Recognition of one's own body and the maintenance of the personal body image is also the dominant realm of the right half of the brain (Joseph, 1986b, 1988a). The body image, for many, is tied to personal identity; and the same is true of the recognition of faces including one's own face.

The right is also dominant for perceiving and analyzing visual-spatial relationships, including the movement of the body in space (Joseph, 1982, 1988a). Therefore, one can throw or catch a ball with accuracy, dance across a stage, or leap across a babbling brook without breaking a leg.

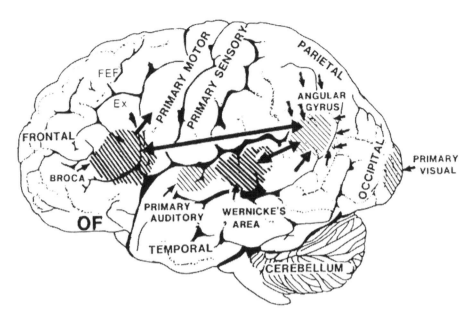

The perception of environmental sounds (water, wind, a meowing cat) and the social, emotional, musical, and melodic aspects of language, including the ability to sing, curse, or pray, are also the domain of the right hemisphere mental system (Joseph, 1982, 1988a). Hence, it is the right hemisphere which imparts the sounds of sarcasm, pride, humor, love, and so on, into the stream of speech, and which conversely can determine if others are speaking with sincerity, irony, or evil intentions.

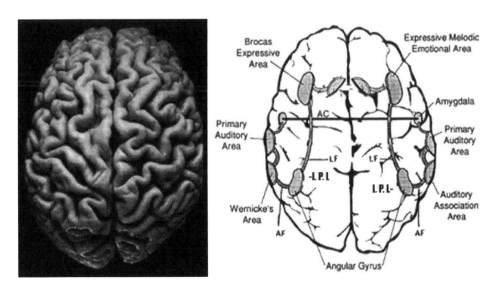

By contrast, expressive and receptive speech, linguistic knowledge and thought, mathematical and analytical reasoning, reading, writing, and arithmetic, as well as the temporal-sequential and rhythmical aspects of consciousness, are associated with the functional integrity of the left half of the brain in the majority of the population (Joseph, 1982, 1996). The language-dependent mind is linked to the left hemisphere.

Certainly, there is considerable overlap in functional representation. Moreover, these two mental system interact and assist the other, just as the left and right hands cooperate and assist the other in performing various tasks. For example, if you were standing at the bar in a nightclub, and someone were to tap you on the shoulder and say, "Do you want to step outside," it is the mental system of the left hemisphere which understands that a question about "outside" has been asked, but it is the mental system of the right which determines the underlying meaning, and if you are being threatened with a punch in the nose, or if a private conversation is being sought.

However, not all information can be transferred from the right to the left, and vice versa (Gallagher and Joseph, 1982; Joseph, 1982, 1988a; Joseph and Gallagher, 1985; Joseph et al., 1984). Because each mental system is unique, each "speaks a different language" and they cannot always communicate. Not all mental events can be accurately translated, understood, or even recognized by the other half of the brain. These two major mental systems, which could be likened to "consciousness" vs "awareness" exist in parallel, simultaneously, and both can act independently of the other, have different goals and desires, and come to completely different conclusions. Each mental system has its own reality.

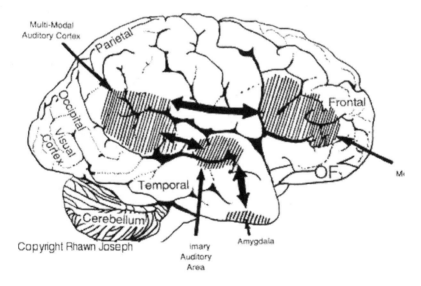

The existence of these two independent mental realms is best exemplified and demonstrated following "split-brain" surgery; i.e. the cutting of the corpus callosum fiber pathway which normally allows the two hemisphere's to communicate.

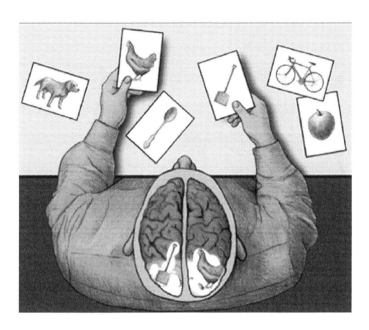

As described by Nobel Lauriate Roger Sperry (1966, p. 299), "Everything we have seen indicates that the surgery has left these people with two separate minds, that is, two separate spheres of consciousness. What is experienced in the right hemisphere seems to lie entirely outside the realm of awareness of the left hemisphere. This mental division has been demonstrated in regard to perception, cognition, volition, learning and memory."

The right half of the brain controls and perceives the left half of the body and visual space, whereas the right half of the body and visual space is the domain of the left hemisphere. Therefore, following split-brain surgery, if a comb, spoon, or some other hidden object is placed in the left hand (out of sight), the left hemisphere, and the language-dependent conscious mind, will not even know the left hand is holding something and will be unable to name it, describe it, or if given multiple choices point to the correct item with the right hand (Joseph 1988a,b; Sperry, 1966). However, the right hemisphere can raise the left hand and not only point to the correct object, but can pantomime its use.

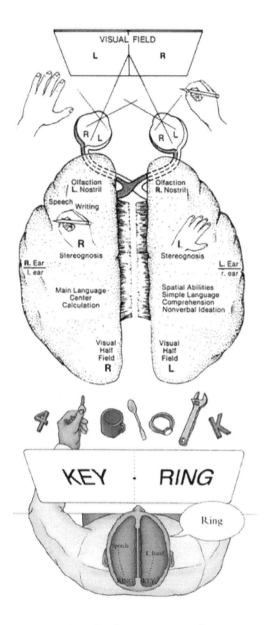

If the split-brain patient is asked to stare at the center of a white screen and words like "Key Ring" are quickly presented, such that the word "Key" falls in the left visual field (and thus, is transmitted to the right cerebrum) and the word "Rings" falls in the right field (and goes to the left hemisphere), the language dependent conscious mind will not see the word "Key." If asked, the language-dependent conscious mind will say "Ring" and will deny seeing the word "Key." However, if asked to point with the left hand, the mental system of the right hemisphere will correctly point to the word "Key."

Therefore, given events "A" and "B" one half of the brain may know A, but know nothing about B which is known only by the other half of the brain. In consequence, what is known vs what is not known becomes relatively imprecise depending on what aspects of reality are perceived and "known" by which mental system (Joseph 1986a; Joseph et al., 1984). There is no such thing as singularity of mind. Since the brain and mind is a multiplicity, "A" and "B" can be known simultaneously, even when one mind is knows nothing about the existence of A or B.

In that the brain of the normal as well as the "split-brain" patient maintains the neuroanatomy to support a multiplicity of mind, and the presence of two dominant psychic realms, it is therefore not surprising that "normal" humans often have difficulty "making up their minds," suffer internal conflicts over love/hate relationships, and are plagued with indecision even when staring into an open refrigerator and trying to decide what to eat. "Making up one's mind" can be an ordeal involving a multiplicity of minds.

However, this conflict becomes even more apparent following split-brain surgery and the cutting of the corpus callosum fiber pathway which links these two parallel streams of conscious-awareness.

Akelaitis (1945, p. 597) describes two patients with complete corpus callosotomies who experienced extreme difficulties making the two halves of their bodies cooperate. "In tasks requiring bimanual activity the left hand would frequently perform oppositely to what she desired to do with the right hand. For example, she would be putting on clothes with her right and pulling them off with her left, opening a door or drawer with her right hand and simultaneously pushing it shut with the left. These uncontrollable acts made her increasingly irritated and depressed."

Another patient experienced difficulty while shopping, the right hand would place something in the cart and the left hand would put it right back again and grab a different item.

A recently divorced male patient complained that on several occasions while walking about town he found himself forced to go some distance in another direction by his left leg. Later (although his left hemisphere was not conscious of it at the time) it was discovered that this diverted course, if continued, would have led him to his former wife's new home.

Geschwind (1981) reports a callosal patient who complained that his left hand on several occasions suddenly struck his wife--much to the embarrassment of his left (speaking) hemisphere. In another case, a patient's left hand attempted to choke the patient himself and had to be wrestled away.

Bogen (1979, p. 333) indicates that almost all of his "complete commissurotomy patients manifested some degree of intermanual conflict." One patient, Rocky, experienced situations in which his hands were uncooperative; the right would button up a shirt and the left would follow right behind and undo the buttons. For years, he complained of difficulty getting his left leg to go in the direction he (or rather his left hemisphere) desired. Another patient often referred to the left half of her body as "my little sister" when she was complaining of its peculiar and independent actions.

Another split-brain patient reported that once when she had overslept her left hand began slapping her face until she (i.e. her left hemisphere) woke up. This same patient, in fact, complained of several instances where her left hand had acted violently toward herself and other people (Joseph, 1988a).

Split brain patient, 2-C, complained of instances in which his left hand would perform socially inappropriate actions, such as striking his mother across the face (Joseph, 1988b). Apparently his left and right hemisphere also liked different TV programs. He complained of numerous instances where he (his left hemisphere) was enjoying a program, when, to his astonishment, the left half of his body pulled him to the TV, and changed the channel.

The right and left hemisphere also liked different foods and had different attitudes about exercise. Once, after 2-C had retrieved something from the refrigerator with his right hand, his left took the food, put it back on the shelf and retrieved a completely different item "Even though that's not what I wanted to eat!" On at least one occasion, his left leg refused to continue "going for a walk" and would only allow him to return home.

In the laboratory, 2-C's left hemisphere often became quite angry with his left hand, and he struck it and expressed hate for it. Several times, his left and right hands were observed to engage in actual physical struggles, beating upon each other. For example, on one task both hands were stimulated simultaneously (while out of view) with either the same or two different textured materials (e.g., sandpaper to the right, velvet to the left), and he was required to point (with the left and right hands simultaneously) to an array of fabrics that were hanging in view on the left and right of the testing apparatus. However, at no time was he informed that two different fabrics were being applied.

After stimulation he would pull his hands out from inside the apparatus and point with the left to the fabric felt by the left and with the right to the fabric felt by the right.

Surprisingly, although his left hand (right hemisphere) responded correctly, his left hemisphere vocalized: "Thats wrong!" Repeatedly he reached over with his right hand and tried to force his left extremity to point to the fabric experienced by the right (although the left hand responded correctly! His left hemisphere didn't know this, however). His left hand refused to be moved and physically resisted being forced to point at anything different. In one instance a physical struggle ensued, the right grappling with the left with the two halves of the body hitting and scratching at each other!

Moreover, while 2-C was performing this (and other tasks), his left hemisphere made statements such as: "I hate this hand" or "This is so frustrating" and would strike his left hand with his right or punch his left arm. In these instances there could be little doubt that his right hemisphere mental system was behaving with purposeful intent and understanding, whereas his left hemisphere mental system had absolutely no comprehension of why his left hand (right hemisphere) was behaving in this manner (Joseph, 1988b).

These conflicts are not limited to behavior, TV programs, choice of clothing, or food, but to actual feelings, including love and romance. For example, the right and left hemisphere of a male split-brain patient had completely different feelings about an ex-girlfriend. When he was asked if he wanted to see her again, he said "Yes." But at the same time, his left hand turned thumbs down!

Another split-brain patient suffered conflicts about his desire to smoke. Although is left hemisphere mental system enjoyed cigarettes, his left hand would not allow him to smoke, and would pluck lit cigarettes from his mouth or right hand and put them out. He had been trying to quit for years.

Because each head contains multiple minds, similar conflicts also plague those who have not undergone split-brain surgery. Each half of the brain and thus each mental system may have different attitudes, goals and interests. As noted above, 2-C experienced conflicts when attempting to eat, watch TV, or go for walks, his right and left hemisphere mental systems apparently enjoying different TV programs or types of food (Joseph 1988b). Conflicts of a similar nature plague us all. Split-brain patients are not the first to choke on self-hate or to harm or hate those they profess to love.

Each half of the brain is concerned with different types of information, and may react, interpret and process the same external experience differently and even reach different conclusions (Joseph 1988a,b; Sperry, 1966). Moreover, even when the goals are the same, the two halves of the brain may produce and attempt to act on different strategies.

Each mental system has its own reality. Singularity of mind, is an illusion.

9. Dissociation and Self-Consciousness

The multiplicity of mind is not limited to the neocortex but includes old cortical structures, such as the limbic system (Joseph 1992). Moreover, limbic nuclei such as the amygdala and hippocampus interact with neocortical tissues creating yet additional mental systems, such as those which rely on memory and which contribute to self-reflection, personal identity, and even self-consciousness (Joseph, 1992, 1998, 1999b, 2001).

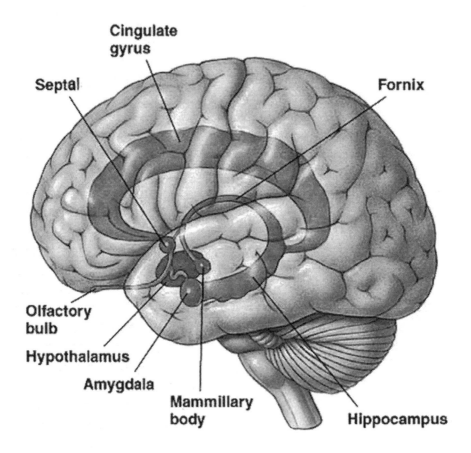

For example, both the amygdala and the hippocampus are implicated in the storage of long term memories, and both nuclei enable individuals to visualize and remember themselves engaged in various acts, as if viewing their behavior and actions from afar. Thus, you might see yourself and remember yourself engage in some activity, from a perspective outside yourself, as if you are an external witness; and this is a common feature of self-reflection and self-memory and is made possible by the hippocampus and overlying temporal lobe (Joseph, 1996, 2001).

The hippocampus in fact contains "place neurons" which cognitive map one's position and the location of various objects within the environment (Nadel, 1991; O'Keefe, 1976; Wilson & McNaughton, 1993). Further, if the subject moves about in that environment, entire populations of these place cells will fire. Moreover, some cells are responsive to the movements of other people in that environment and will fire as that person is observed to move around to different locations or corners of the room (Nadel, 1991; O'Keefe, 1976; Wilson and McNaughton, 1993).

Electrode stimulation, or other forms of heightened activity within the hippocampus and overlying temporal lobe can also cause a person to see themselves, in real time, as if their conscious mind is floating on the ceiling staring down at their body (Joseph, 1998, 1999b, 2001). During the course of electrode stimulation and seizure activity originating in the temporal lobe or hippocampus, patients may report that they have left their bodies and are hovering upon the ceiling staring down at themselves (Daly, 1958; Penfield, 1952; Penfield & Perot 1963; Williams, 1956). That is, their consciousness and sense of personal identity appears to split off from their body, such that they experience themselves as as a consciousness that is conscious of itself as a conscious that is detached from the body which is being observed.

One female patient claimed that she not only would float above her body, but would sometimes drift outside and even enter into the homes of her neighbors. Penfield and Perot (1963) describe several patients who during a temporal lobe seizure, or neurosurgical temporal lobe stimulation, claimed they split-off from their body and could see themselves down below. One woman stated: "it was though I were two persons, one watching, and the other having this happen to me." According to Penfield (1952), "it was as though the patient were attending a familiar play and was both the actor and audience."

Under conditions of extreme trauma, stress and fear, the amygdala, hippocampus and temporal lobe become exceedingly active (Joseph, 1998, 1999b). Under these conditions many will experience a "splitting of consciousness" and have the sensation they have left their body and are hovering beside or above themselves, or even that they floated away (Courtois, 2009; Grinker & Spiegel, 1945; Noyes & Kletti, 1977; van der Kolk 1987). That is, out-of-body dissociative experiences appear to be due to fear induced hippocampus (and amygdala) hyperactivation.

Likewise, during episodes of severe traumatic stress personal consciousness may be fragmented and patients may dissociate and experience themselves as splitting off and floating away from their body, passively observing all that is occurring (Courtois, 1995; Grinker & Spiegel, 1945; Joseph, 1999d; Noyes & Kletti, 1977; Southard, 1919; Summit, 1983; van der Kolk 1987).

Noyes and Kletti (1977) described several individuals who experienced terror, believed they were about to die, and then suffered an out-of body dissociative experience: "I had a clear image of myself... as though watching it on a television screen." "The next thing I knew I wasn't in the truck anymore; I was looking down from 50 to 100 feet in the air." "I had a sensation of floating. It was almost like stepping out of reality. I seemed to step out of this world."

One individual, after losing control of his Mustang convertible while during over 100 miles per hour on a rain soaked freeway, reported that "time seemed to slow down and then... part of my mind was a few feet outside the car zooming above it and then beside it and behind it and in front of it, looking at and analyzing the respective positions of my spinning Mustang and the cars surrounding me. Simultaneously I was inside trying to steer and control it in accordance with the multiple perspectives I was given by that part of my mind that was outside. It was like my mind split and one consciousness was inside the car, while the other was zooming all around outside and giving me visual feedback that enabled me to avoid hitting anyone or destroying my Mustang."

Numerous individuals from adults to children, from those born blind and deaf, have also reported experiencing a dissociative consciousness after profound injury causing near death (Eadie 1992; Rawling 1978; Ring 1980). Consider for example, the case of Army Specialist J. C. Bayne of the 196th Light Infantry Brigade. Bayne was "killed" in Chu Lai, Vietnam, in 1966, after being simultaneously machine gunned and struck by a mortar. According to Bayne, when he opened his eyes he was floating in the air, looking down on his burnt and bloody body: "I could see me... it was like looking at a manikin laying there... I was burnt up and there was blood all over the place... I could see the Vietcong. I could see the guy pull my boots off. I could see the rest of them picking up various things... I was like a spectator... It was about four or five in the afternoon when our own troops came. I could hear and see them approaching... I looked dead... they put me in a bag... transferred me to a truck and then to the morgue. And from that point, it was the embalming process. I was on that table and a guy was telling jokes about those USO girls... all I had on was bloody undershorts... he placed my leg out and made a slight incision and stopped... he checked my pulse and heartbeat again and I could see that too... It was about that point I just lost track of what was taking place.... [until much later] when the chaplain was in there saying everything was going to be all right.... I was no longer outside. I was part of it at this point" (reported in Wilson, 1987, pp 113-114; and Sabom, 1982, pp 81-82).

Therefore, be it secondary to the fear of dying, or depth electrode stimulation, these experiences all appear to be due to a mental system which enables a the conscious mind to detach completely from the body in order to make the body an object of consciousness (Joseph, 1998, 1999b, 2001).

10. Quantum Consciousness

It could be said that consciousness is consciousness of something other than consciousness. Consciousness and knowledge of an object, such as a chair, are also distinct. Consciousness is not the chair. The chair is not consciousness. The chair is an object of consciousness, and thus become discontinuous from the quantum state.

Consciousness is consciousness of something and is conscious of not being that object that is is conscious of. By knowing what it isn't, consciousness may know what it is not, which helps define what it is. This consciousness of not being the object can be considered the "collapse function" which results in discontinuity within the continuuum.

Further, it could be said that consciousness of consciousness, that is, self-consciousness, also imparts a duality, a separation, into the fabric of the quantum continuum. Therefore this consciousness that is the object of consciousness, becomes an abstraction, and may create a collapse function in the continuun.

However, in instances of dissociation, this consciousness is conscious of itself as a consciousness that is floating above its body; a body which contains the brain. The dissociative consciousness is not dissociated from itself as a consciousness, but only from its body. That is, there is an awareness of itself as a consciousness that is floating above the body, and this awareness is simultaneously one with that consciousness, as there is no separation, no abstractions, and no objectification. It is a singularity that is without form, without dimension, without shape.

Moreover, because this dissociated consciousness appears to be continuous with itself, there is no "collapse function" except in regard to the body which is viewed as an object of perception.

Therefore, in these instances we can not say that consciousness has split into a duality of observer and observed or knower and known, except in regard to the body. Dissociated consciousness is conscious of itself as consciousness; it is self-aware without separation and without reflecting. It is knowing and known, simultaneously.

In fact, many patients report that in the dissociated state they achieve or nearly achieved a state of pure knowing (Joseph, 1996, 2001).

A patient described by Williams (1956) claimed she was lifted up out of her body, and experienced a very pleasant sensation of elation and the feeling that she was "just about to find out knowledge no one else shares, something to do with the link between life and death." Another patient reported that upon leaving her body she not only saw herself down below, but was taken to a special place "of vast proportions, and I felt as if I was in another world" (Williams, 1956).

Other patients suffering from temporal lobe seizures or upon direct electrical activation have noted that things suddenly became "crystal clear" or that they had a feeling of clairvoyance, of having the ultimate truth revealed to them, of having achieved a sense of greater awareness and cosmic clarity such that sounds, smells and visual objects seemed to have a greater meaning and sensibility, and that they were achieving a cosmic awareness of the hidden knowledge of all things (Joseph, 1996, 2001).

Although consciousness and the object of consciousness, that which is known, are not traditionally thought of as being one and the same, in dissociative states, consciousness and knowing, may become one and the same.

The suggestion is of some type of cosmic unity, particularly as these patients also often report a progressive loss of the sense of individuality, as if they are merging into something greater than themselves, including a becoming one with all the knowledge of the universe; a singularity with god.

Commonly those who experience traumatic dissociative conscious states, not only float above the body, but report that they gradually felt they were losing all sense of individuality as they became embraced by a brilliant magnificent whiteness that extended out in all directions into eternity.

Therefore, rather than the dissociated consciousness acting outside the quantum state, it appears this mental state may represent an increasing submersion back into the continuity that is the quantum state, disappearing back into the continuum of singularity and oneness that is the quantum universe.

Dissociated consciousness may be but the last preamble before achieving the unity that is quantum consciousness, the unity of all things.

11. Conclusion: Quantum Consciousness and the Multiplicity of Mind

What is "Objective Reality" when the mind is a multiplicity which is capable of splitting up, observing itself, becoming blind to itself, and becoming blind to the features of the world which then cease to exist for the remaining mental realms?

Each mental system has its own "reality." Each observer is a multiplicity that engages in numerous simultaneous acts of observation. Therefore, non-local properties which do not have an objective existence independent of the "act of observation" by one mental system, may achieve existence when observed by another mental system. The "known" and the "unknown" can exist simultaneously and interchangeably and this may explain why we don't experience any macroscopic non-local quantum weirdness in our daily lives.

This means that quantum laws may apply to everything, from atoms to monkeys and woman and man and the multiplicity of mind. However, because of this multiplicity, this could lead to seemingly contradictory predictions and uncertainty when measuring macroscopically objective systems which are superimposed on microscopic quantum systems. Indeed, this same principle applies to the multiplicity of mind, where dominant parallel streams of conscious awareness may be superimposed on other mental systems, and which may be beset by uncertainty.

Because of the multiplicity of mind, as exemplified by dissociative states, the observer can also be observed, and thus, the observer is not really external to the quantum state as is required by the standard collapse formulation of quantum mechanics. This raises the possibility that the collapse formulation can be used to describe the universe as a whole which includes observers observing themselves being observed.

The multiplicity of mind also explains why an object being measured by one mental system therefore becomes bundled up into a state where it either determinately has or determinately does not have the property being measured. Measurements performed by one mental system are not being performed by others, such that the same object can have an initial state and a post-measurement state and a final state simultaneously as represented in multiple minds in parallel, or separate states as represented by each mental realm individually.

The collapse dynamics of observation supposedly guarantees that a system will either determinately have or determinately not have a particular property. However, because the observer is observing with multiple mental systems the object can both have and not have specific properties when it is being measure and not measured, simply because it is being measured and not measured, or rather, observed and not observed or its different features observed simultaneously by multiple mental systems. Therefore, it can be continuous and discontinuous in parallel, and different properties can be known and not known in parallel simultaneously.

And the same rules apply to the mental systems which exist in multiplicity within the head of a single observer. Mental systems can become continuous or discontinuous, and can be known and not known simultaneously, in parallel. Thus, the standard collapse formulation can be used to describe systems that contain observers, as the mind/observer can be simultaneously internal and external to the described system.

The mind is a multiplicity and there is no such thing as a "single observer state." Therefore, each element may be observed by multiple observer states which perceive multiple object systems thereby giving the illusion that the object has been transformed during the collapse function. What this also implies is that contrary to the standard or Copenhagen interpretations, states may have both definite position and definite momentum at the same time.

Each mental system perceives a different physical world giving rise to multiple worlds and multiple realities which may be subordinated by one or another more dominant stream of conscious awareness.

Moreover, as the multiplicity of mind can also detach and become discontinuous with the body, whereas dissociative consciousness is continuous with itself, this indicates that the mind is also capable of becoming one with the continuum, and can achieve singularity so that universe and mind become one.

References

Akelaitis, A. J. (1945). Studies on the corpus callosum. American Journal of Psychiatry, 101, 594-599.

Bogen, J. (1979). The other side of the brain. Bulletin of the Los Angeles Neurological Society. 34, 135-162.

Bohr, N. (1934/1987), Atomic Theory and the Description of Nature, reprinted as The Philosophical Writings of Niels Bohr, Vol. I, Woodbridge: Ox Bow Press.

Bohr, N. (1958/1987), Essays 1932-1957 on Atomic Physics and Human Knowledge, reprinted as The Philosophical Writings of Niels Bohr, Vol. II, Woodbridge: Ox Bow Press.

Bohr, N. (1963/1987), Essays 1958-1962 on Atomic Physics and Human Knowledge, reprinted as The Philosophical Writings of Niels Bohr, Vol. III, Woodbridge: Ox Bow Press.

Casagrande, V. A. & Joseph, R. (1978). Effects of monocular deprivation on geniculostriate connections in prosimian primates. Anatomical Record, 190, 359.

Casagrande, V. A. & Joseph, R. (1980). Morphological effects of monocular deprivation and recovery on the dorsal lateral geniculate nucleus in prosimian primates. Journal of Comparative Neurology, 194, 413-426.

Courtois, C. A. (2009). Treating Complex Traumatic Stress Disorders: An Evidence-Based Guide Daly, D. (1958). Ictal affect. American Journal of Psychiatry, 115, 97-108.

DeWitt, B. S., (1971). The Many-Universes Interpretation of Quantum Mechanics, in B. D.'Espagnat (ed.), Foundations of Quantum Mechanics, New York: Academic Press. pp. 167–218.

DeWitt, B. S. and Graham, N., editors (1973). The Many-Worlds Interpretation of Quantum Mechanics. Princeton University Press, Princeton, New-Jersey.

Eadie, B. J. (1993) Embraced by the light. New York, Bantam

Einstein, A. (1905a). Does the Inertia of a Body Depend upon its Energy Content? Annalen der Physik 18, 639-641.

Einstein, A. (1905b). Concerning an Heuristic Point of View Toward the Emission and Transformation of Light. Annalen der Physik 17, 132-148.

Einstein, A. (1905c). On the Electrodynamics of Moving Bodies. Annalen der Physik 17, 891-921.

Einstein, A. (1926). Letter to Max Born. The Born-Einstein Letters (translated by Irene Born) Walker and Company, New York.

Gallagher, R. E., & Joseph, R. (1982). Non-linguistic knowledge, hemispheric laterality, and the conservation of inequivalance. Journal of General Psychology, 107, 31-40.

Geschwind. N. (1981). The perverseness of the right hemisphere. Behavioral Brain Research, 4, 106-107.

Grinker, R. R., & Spiegel, J. P. (1945). Men Under Stress. McGraw-Hill.

Heisenberg. W. (1930), Physikalische Prinzipien der Quantentheorie (Leipzig: Hirzel). English translation The Physical Principles of Quantum Theory, University of Chicago Press.

Heisenberg, W. (1955). The Development of the Interpretation of the Quantum Theory, in W. Pauli (ed), Niels Bohr and the Development of Physics, 35, London: Pergamon pp. 12-29.

Heisenberg, W. (1958), Physics and Philosophy: The Revolution in Modern Science, London: Goerge Allen & Unwin.

Joseph, R. (1982). The Neuropsychology of Development. Hemispheric Laterality, Limbic Language, the Origin of Thought. Journal of Clinical Psychology, 44 4-33.

Joseph, R. (1986). Reversal of language and emotion in a corpus callosotomy patient. Journal of Neurology, Neurosurgery, & Psychiatry, 49, 628-634.

Joseph, R. (1986). Confabulation and delusional denial: Frontal lobe and lateralized influences. Journal of Clinical Psychology, 42, 845-860.

Joseph, R. (1988) The Right Cerebral Hemisphere: Emotion, Music, Visual-Spatial Skills, Body Image, Dreams, and Awareness. Journal of Clinical Psychology, 44, 630-673.

Joseph, R. (1988). Dual mental functioning in a split-brain patient. Journal of Clinical Psychology, 44, 770-779.

Joseph, R. (1992) The Limbic System: Emotion, Laterality, and Unconscious Mind. The Psychoanalytic Review, 79, 405-455.

Joseph, R. (1996). Neuropsychiatry, Neuropsychology, Clinical Neuroscience, 2nd Edition. Williams & Wilkins, Baltimore.

Joseph, R. (1998). Traumatic amnesia, repression, and hippocampal injury due to corticosteroid and enkephalin secretion. Child Psychiatry and Human Development. 29, 169-186.

Joseph, R. (1999a). Frontal lobe psychopathology: Mania, depression, aphasia, confabulation, catatonia, perseveration, obsessive compulsions, schizophrenia. Psychiatry, 62, 138-172.

Joseph, R. (1999b). The neurology of traumatic "dissociative" amnesia. Commentary and literature review. Child Abuse & Neglect. 23, 71-80.

Joseph, R. (2000). Limbic language/language axis theory of speech. Behavioral and Brain Sciences. 23, 439-441.

Joseph, R. (2001). The Limbic System and the Soul: Evolution and the Neuroanatomy of Religious Experience. Zygon, the Journal of Religion & Science, 36, 105-136.

Joseph, R., & Casagrande, V. A. (1978). Visual field defects and morphological changes resulting from monocular deprivation in primates. Proceedings of the Society for Neuroscience, 4, 1978, 2021.

Joseph, R. & Casagrande, V. A. (1980). Visual field defects and recovery following lid closure in a prosimian primate. Behavioral Brain Research, 1, 150-178.

Joseph, R., Forrest, N., Fiducia, N., Como, P., & Siegel, J. (1981). Electrophysiological and behavioral correlates of arousal. Physiological Psychology, 1981, 9, 90-95.

Joseph, R., Gallagher, R., E., Holloway, J., & Kahn, J. (1984). Two brains, one child: Interhemispheric transfer and confabulation in children aged 4, 7, 10. Cortex, 20, 317-331.

Joseph, R., & Gallagher, R. E. (1985). Interhemispheric transfer and the completion of reversible operations in non-conserving children. Journal of Clinical Psychology, 41, 796-800.

Nadel, L. (1991). The hippocampus and space revisited. Hippocampus, 1, 221-229.

Neumann, J. von, (1937/2001), "Quantum Mechanics of Infinite Systems. Institute for Advanced Study; John von Neumann Archive, Library of Congress, Washington, D.C.

Neumann, J. von, (1938), On Infinite Direct Products, Compositio Mathematica 6: 1-77.

Neumann, J. von, (1955), Mathematical Foundations of Quantum Mechanics, Princeton, NJ: Princeton University Press.

Noyes, R., & Kletti, R. (1977). Depersonalization in response to life threatening danger. Comprehensive Psychiatry, 18, 375-384.

O'Keefe, J. (1976). Place units in the hippocampus. Experimental Neurology, 51-78-100. Pais, A. (1979). Einstein and the quantum theory, Reviews of Modern Physics, 51, 863-914.

Penfield, W. (1952) Memory Mechanisms. Archives of Neurology and Psychiatry, 67, 178-191.

Penfield, W., & Perot, P. (1963) The brains record of auditory and visual experience. Brain, 86, 595-695.

Rawlins, M. (1978). Beyond Death's Door. Sheldon Press.

Ring, K. (1980). Life at Death: A Scientific Investigation of the Near-Death Experience. New York: Quill.

Sabom, M. (1982). Recollections of Death. New York: Harper & Row.

Southard, E. E. (1919). Shell-shock and other Neuropsychiatric Problems. Boston.

Sperry, R. (1966). Brain bisection and the neurology of consciousness. In F. O. Schmitt and F. G. Worden (eds). The Neurosciences. MIT press.

van der Kolk, B. A. (1985). Psychological Trauma. American Psychiatric Press.

Williams, D. (1956). The structure of emotions reflected in epileptic experiences. Brain, 79, 29-67.

Wilson, I. (1987). The After Death Experience. Morrow.

Wilson, M. A., & McNaughton, B. L. (1993). Dynamics of the hippocampus ensemble for space. Science, 261, 1055-1058.

Many Mansions: Special Relativity, Higher-Dimensional Space, Neuroscience, Consciousness and Time

John Smythies

Director, Integrative Neuroscience Program, Center for Brain and Cognition, University of California, San Diego

Abstract:

This paper first reviews what is known about the neural correlates of consciousness (NCCs), both at the nerve network and cellular levels, that lays stress the importance of small differences in the dynamic microanatomy of wiring patterns orchestrated by an epigenetic code. However, information about NCCs themselves does not throw light on the logically different problem of how NCCs are related to the phenomenal experiences they induce. To tackle that problem I suggest it is necessary to reformulate our basic concepts of space, time and matter, as well as replacing the psychoneural Identity Theory (IT), whose defects I outline. In particular neuroscience needs to be based on special relativity (SR) in place of the Newtonian cosmology that forms its present framework. This replaces the concept of neurons as 3D entities, that generate physicochemical events in a separate time, with the concept that neurons are 4D structures, whose world lines are extended in the 4D block universe of SR. This requires, as Broad noted, an ontologically independent conscious observer located in a space of its own (phenomenal space). The hypothesis of material dualism suggests that physical space-time (4D) and phenomenal space (3 spatial dimensions) plus 1 dimension of real time—t2, are cross-sections of a common higher dimensional space that are in relative motion in t2 along the time axis of the block universe. This movement generates the 'now' and the passage of the time that we experience. The contents of phenomenal space are our sensations, images and thoughts all causally related to (but not identical with) particular brain events. This hypothesis has implications for what has been called "the idea of another world".

Keywords: Neural correlates of consciousness, synchronized oscillations, epigenetic code, identity theory, special relativity, block universe, phenomenal consciousness, time, material dualism, Plato's cave, out-of-the-body experiences, near-death experiences, body-image, Hindu psychology, astral body

Introduction

Whereas our knowledge of the neural correlates of consciousness (NCCs) is steadily increasing under the impetus provided by advanced scanning and other neuroscientific techniques (Fingelkurts et al. 2013), the same cannot be said about what this correlation amounts to. A review of the current literature reveals a sorry state of entangled confusion in the very basic concepts with which this attempt is framed, relating in particular to our ideas about space, time, matter and phenomenal consciousness. The dominant hypothesis today is the Identity Theory (IT) which states that consciousness, however defined, must be identical with certain events in particular regions in the brain: but concrete details of how this is done have singularly failed to materialize. The purpose of this essay is to argue that, to order to clarify and solve this problem, it will be necessary to reformulate our basic concepts of space, time and matter. As a preliminary I will present a short account of what is currently known about NCCs.

Neural correlates of consciousness

This information can be presented at two scales—at the macroscopic level and the cellular level. In the former case the leading hypothesis is the Global Workspace theory (Bartolomei and Naccache 2011). This proposes that conscious processing results from coherent neuronal activity between widely distributed brain regions, with fronto-parietal associative cortices as key elements. The main activity involved is the synchronization of neuronal oscillations, in particular in two synchronized networks—the retrolandic (cognitive network) and the frontal (executive control network) (Leon-Carrion et al. 2012). These authors suggest that the executive control network could facilitate the synchronization and coherence of large populations of distant cortical neurons using high frequency oscillations on a precise temporal scale. They suggest that the synchrony between anterior and retrolandic regions is essential to awareness. Other aspects of the role of integrated networks in NCCs are presented by Achard et al. (2012), Demertzi et al. 2013, Orpwood et al. 2013, Lewis et al. (2012) and Smythies et al. (2014).

At the neuronal level some interesting information has been obtained.

Evidence from de- and re-afferentation and sensory pathway rerouting experiments show that the modality of a sensory neuron (i.e. whether it is an auditory or a visual neuron) is determined, not by where it is located, but by where it's afferent inflow comes from (Smythies and Edelstein 2013). For example, in blind patients skilled in Braille, axons from the hand region of the somatosensory cortex grow and take over adjacent, and now inactive, neurons in the visual cortex. If these ex-visual neurons are now activated by transcranial magnetic stimulation, the patient feels a touch on the finger. This change is orchestrated by the epigenetic code, whereby the afferent axon transfers instructional epigenetic material (transcription factor proteins and a variety of RNAs including microRNAs) to the post-synaptic neuron, which is thereby restructured (Smythies and Edelstein 2013). The differences between the different sensory cortices (visual, auditory and somatosensory) consist of subtle differences in the microanatomical wiring patterns (brought about in part by the epigenetic code) between these brain areas (Linden and Schriener 2003). Yet the results of their activation results in the enormously qualitatively different type of sensation experienced.

This raises another question. What is it about a neuron's activity that determines what kind of conscious sensation results—is it the pattern of action potentials? Or are sub-threshold dendritic potentials involved? Or it the total electrical field? There is some experimental evidence that throws some light upon this question. If we stimulate the retina with a flashing (stroboscopic) light at a frequency of between 6-18 Herz with both eyes open, the subject will see a series of simple, regular geometrical flickering patterns with such forms as parallel lines, grids, checkerboards, spirals, concentric circles and mazes (Smythies 1959a,b; 1960). However if we stimulate only one retina, the results is quite different. In this case the same geometrical patterns (called the bright phase) appear but these are soon replaced with another quite different series of pattern (called the dark phase). These are non-flickering oily swirls like oil on water or boiling lava, usually in two colors with green and red predominant. These two types of pattern then alternate in retinal rivalry. There is evidence that the dark phase patterns arise in the cortical neurons belonging to the closed eye (Brown and Gebhart 1948). The stimulation may come from the adjacent active neurons belonging to the open eye via direct current carried by the dense interneuronal network provided by the interlinked dendrites of GABAergic interneurons (Fukada et al. 2006). Thus the digital code carried by the open-eye cortical neurons appears to result in the perception of digital flickering geometrical patterns— whereas the analog code carried by the GABAergic network appears to result in the perception of analog oily swirls. However, none of this evidence is directly relevant to the question of what is the relation between these brain events and the events that take place on the stage of consciousness. To answer this we will have to take a look at our fundamental ideas about space, time and matter—starting with space and time.

Special Relativity

One foundational problem here is that, whereas Special Relatively (SR) is accepted in physics, the disciplines of biology and psychology are mired in Newtonian cosmology. Biology still deals with a Newtonian cosmos in which 3D spatially extended organisms move, evolve and behave in a separate time. In contrast, in the Minkowskian block universe of SR, an organism is a stationary 4D material object extended in a 4D space- time. The Earth, for instance is not a globular 3D object rotating in a spiral pathway around another 3D globular object—the sun: rather it is a stationary 4D hyperhelix that is wound around the stationary 4D sun. In Newtonian cosmology matter exists only at the 'now' of time, whereas in SR cosmology matter exists from the beginning to the end of time. Furthermore in SR cosmology the 'now' and the 'passage' of time are not supplied by the physical universe but are subjective 'illusions'. Newtonian cosmology and SR cosmology involve quite different accounts of Darwinian evolution. In the former organisms are born, grow and die over time. In the SR cosmology the evolution of organisms expresses the fact that the stationary world lines of the atoms that constitute them possess a more complicated structure if we examine them 'later' as compared with 'earlier' locations in the block universe. Darwinian evolution is a dynamic process in Newtonian cosmology, but it is a matter of 4D structure in SR cosmology. The appearance of dynamic changes in the physical world experienced by conscious observers is an illusion generated by the movement of the observing consciousness along the time-like dimension of the 4D block universe from the place labeled 'past' towards the place labeled 'future'. Current biology and neuroscience have not accommodated this fact and it is time to do so.

As I am not a physicist it will be fitting to list a series of statements presenting this case from a number of leading physicists and cosmologists Louis de Broglie was one of the founders of quantum theory. He put it thus: "Each observer, as his time passes, discovers, so to speak, new slices of space-time which appear to him as successive aspects of the materialworld, though in reality the ensemble of events constituting space-time exist prior to his knowledge of them... the aggregate of past, present and future phenomena are in some sense given a priori." (De Broglie, 1959)."

Russell Stannard, Emeritus Professor of Physics, at the Open University makes the static sculpture of the SR universe plain:"Physics itself recognizes no special moment called 'now' — the moment that acts as the focus of 'becoming' and divides the 'past' from the 'future'. In four-dimensional space-time nothing changes, there is no flow of time, everything simply is...It is only in consciousness that we come across the particular time known as 'now'... It is only in the context of mental time that it makes sense to say that all of physical space-time is. One might even go so far as to say that it is unfortunate that such dissimilar entities as physical time and mental time should carry the same name!" (Stannard, 1987).

Penrose himself (1994) says that in the universe described by special relativity "...particles do not even move, being represented by "static" curves drawn in space-time". Thus what we perceive as moving 3D objectare really successive cross sections of immobile 4D objects past which our field of observation is sweeping."

The list continues:

—Quine (1982): "A drastic departure from English is required in the matter of time. The view to adopt is the Minkowskian one, which sees time as a fourth dimension on a par with the three dimensions of
space."

—Lloyd (1978): "For the Quinean, what differences we see between past, present and future pertain to our limited mode of access to reality."

—Heller (1984): "...a physical object is not an enduring
hunk of matter but an enduring spatio-temporal hunk of matter."

—Eddington (1920): "Events do not happen: they are just there, and
we come across them ... [as] the observer on his voyage of exploration."

—Weyl (1922): "The objective world simply is, it does not happen. Only to the gaze of my consciousness crawling upward along the life-line [world line] of my body does a section of this world come to life as a fleeting image.'"

—Werth (1978) makes the important point that this new formulation applies to somatic sensation as well as to vision: "Our apparent body ['body image' is the neurological name for this] at each instant is simply a 'slice' of our four-dimensional body. That is the experiencing subject sequentially 'intersects' his four-dimensional

body and 'projects' the sequence of three-dimensional intersections upon the 'screen' of his consciousness: his body appears to him as being ever changing though in physical reality it is a static and immutable four-dimensional object."

—Lastly Broad (1953):

"...if we assume one additional spatial dimension beside the three we can observe, and if we suppose that our field of observation at any one moment is confined to the content of a {3,4}-fold which moves un formly at right angles to itself along a straight line in the {3,4}-fold, then there is no need to assume any other motion in the universe. This one uniform rectilinear motion of the observer's field of observation, together with the purely geometrical properties of the stationary material threads in the four-fold, will account for all the various observed motions (various in both magnitude and direction) of the material particles which are the appearances of these threads in the successive fields of observation."

Broad also points out that his assumption requires two 'times'. Time 1 has become fused with space into space-time. But a real time — t2 — is still required in which the 'observer's field of observation' moves through space-time.

However, these statements raise a problem. De Broglie speaks of 'each observer', Lloyd of 'our limited mode of access to reality', Eddington of 'the observer on his voyage of exploration', Broad of 'the observer's field of observation'. In these instances the terms 'observer' and 'our' cannot refer, as is usual, to the physical body of the scientist, for this is composed of the world lines of the atoms that make up the physical body and that belongs to the immobile block universe. So what is the "observer", "field of observation", and "gaze of my consciousness" that travels from the past into the future marking the fleeting 'now' of time as it does so? Before we can tackle this question we will need to look at another source of confusion underlying this whole subject. This is the almost universal confusion between physical space and phenomenal space that has its roots in the attempt to believe in two mutually incompatible theories of perception—namely Naïve Realism (NR) and the Representative Theory (RT).

Scientific theories emerge from a background of "common sense" ideas about the world. Early cosmological theories reflected the "obvious" fact that the earth is flat and that the heavens arch above it as a great crystal dome. It took centuries of observation and challenging of dogmas to realize that this model is mistaken. Likewise, most people today, including many philosophers, believe that NR gives an accurate account of how we perceive the world. That is that the colored objects that fill our visual field really are physical objects, or at least the surfaces of physical objects. In contrast the current scientific theory of (visual) perception holds that these colored objects, that we experience, are the products of a long and complex mechanical process which involves light rays landing on the retina and setting off neuronal reactions that spread to the visual cortex where the percepts that we experience are manufactured. Thus our visual system works like television and not like the simple telescope proposed by NR. The contents of our visual fields that we experience are constructs of the visual nervous system and are not direct views of external objects. However, unfortunately most scientists who may adhere to RT in their laboratories, slip back unwittingly into NR as soon as they get home. A similar state of affairs holds in the other spatially organized senses such as somatic sensation. Neurologists have known for more than a century that the body we experience is not the physical body itself but is an image of the body (the "body image") constructed by representative mechanisms of perception. As the neurologist Paul Schilder (1942, 1950) said "...the empirical method leads immediately to a deep insight that even our own body is beyond our immediate reach, that even our own body justifies Prospero's words "We are such stuff as dreams are made on and our little life is rounded by a sleep."

If we reject NR, and accept RT fully, then we can recognize how the problem of the relationship between phenomenal space and physical space arises. Physical space is that in which physical objects are located and extended. Phenomenal space is that in which our spatially organized sensations are located and extended. Under NR these two spaces can be topologically and geometrically the same. Phenomenal objects and events and physical objects and events can be located in the same location in space where they appear to be to the naïve observer. Whereas, under RT one of either of two other systems is necessary. The first is that phenomenal objects and physical objects can be in the same space but must be in different parts of it. Objects and events in phenomenal space can be located in the physical brain that is located in the physical world (as in the Identity Theory IT)—but they cannot be located in the external physical world where they appear to the naïve observer to be. The second possibility is that phenomenal space and physical space are different spaces as expressed in the cosmological theory known as material dualism, which will be the subject of the next section.

Material dualism

Material dualism is based on the premise that phenomenal space is a real space, with which we have direct experience, and which possesses topological and geometrical properties in which the events we experience are located (French 1987). Wright (1983) proposes that there is a primary 'phenomenal field' that actually exists in which sensations and after-images are located. Fitzgerald (1978) says "None [visual sensations] are located out in physical space: all are in a visual phenomenal space with causal relations with the observer's brain in that the brain's doings produce the sense-data in this space, and indeed the space itself." The neurologist Jason Brown (1991) gets it right I think: "Space itself is an object: volumetric, egocentric, and part of the mind of the observer...Mind is positioned in a space of its own making... We wonder about the limits of the universe but never ask what is beyond the space of a dream."

Phenomenal space may be defined in the following manner. If you obtain a spatially extended visual after-image (e.g. by looking at a square green illuminated surface and then closing your eyes) you can observe that the boundary of that after-image forms a closed Jordan curve that uniquely divides phenomenal space into one inside and one outside. This is an undeniable ontological and topological property of the after-image located in your own phenomenal space (visual field). The image is constructed by causal relations with specific NCCs in your visual cortex.

The fact that the after-image cannot be identical with these NCCs, and so that IT is false, can be shown by the following argument. Leibniz's Law of the Identity of Indiscernibles states that, for any entity A to be identical with an entity B, they must have all properties in common. For example the entities Monte Cervino and the Matterhorn have all their properties in common. 'Monte Cervinio' and 'Matterhorn' are just different names for the same entity. Whereas the after-image described above is square, red and its boundary forms a Jordan curve—whereas their causal NCCs have the shape of a distributed net, the color grey (according to Poirot) and their boundary does not form a Jordan curve. The after-image can be read by the conscious observer to have the same information as the NCCs (i.e. that there is a square red entitity out there) but only if that observer already knows that green lights produce red after-images. A similar situation holds for a TV set. The events portrayed have one format inside the set and quite a different format on the TV screen. The events inside the set are not identical with the events on the screen.

It might be argued that this argument fails to recognize the difference between an objective color (physical reflectance and adsorption spectra) and subjective color. In reply I would argue that the word 'color' here is being used to two different senses. The nature of a phenomenal color is simply experienced as a raw fact not amenable to further analysis, whereas the nature of an 'objective' color is discovered by scientific measurements. The 'inner nature' of an objective color—like the 'inner nature' of matter— is not something that we can discover.

With these considerations in mind, it is possible to ask what are the topological and geometrical relations between physical space (ignoring time for the moment) and phenomenal space. There are four, and only four, possible answers.

—PheS is topologically inside all of phyS within the range of vision (as expressed in NR).

—PheS is topologically inside only that portion of phyS that is inside the brain (as expressed in RT and IT).

—PheS and phyS are two different cross-sections of a common higher dimensional space (as suggested by C.D. Broad (1923), Bernard Carr (2008) and myself (Smythies 1994).

—PheS and phyS are wholly different spaces and bear no spatial relations with each other: only causal relations link their contents (physical and phenomenal events respectively (as suggested by Price 1953).

Since we know that NR is false, and the IT fails the Leibniz test, our choice is limited to the other two hypotheses. Of these the fourth can be treated as a minor variant of the third, so I will next discuss the Broad-Carr-Smythies hypothesis in some detail.

Dualistic concepts of mind reach far back into human history, but, in most, the autonomous mind was thought of in terms of non-material spirits in the manner later crystalized by Descartes. However, ideas that the mind might incorporate material elements were developed by the Hindu philosophers of the classical era. They suggested that the mind was material like the body, but of a form of matter so diaphanous as to be undetectable by ordinary instruments.

Joseph Priestly (1777) was the first in the West to take up this topic:

" But how anything could have extension, and yet be immaterial, without coinciding with our idea of mere empty space, I know not. I am therefore bound to conclude, that the sentient principle in man, containing ideas which certainly have parts [is] not the simple, indivisible, and immaterial substance that some have imagined it to be; but something that has real extension and therefore may have the other properties of matter."

The Cambridge philosopher C.D. Broad took the next, and very significant, step in 1923 when he wrote:

"For reasons already stated, it is impossible that sensa should literally occupy places in scientific space, though it may not, of course, be impossible to construct a space-like whole of more than three dimensions, in which sensa of all kinds, and scientific objects literally have places. If so, I suppose, that scientific space would be one kind of section of such a quasi-space, and e.g. a visual field would be another kind of section of the same quasi-space (pp. 392-393)."

Further details of this new theory were supplied by Smythies (1956) who provided links with both neurology and introspectionist psychology. The concept that phenomenal space and physical space are ontologically different spaces has also been expressed briefly by others: Ayer (1940) "...John Stuart Mill and Berkeley fail to distinguish properly between physical space and sensible space." — Russell (1948) "...the space in which the physical table is located must be different from the space we know by experience"—and Moore (1971) ""...it seems to me just possible that the two sensations in question [those belonging to two coins] though not circular in my private space may yet be circular in physical space". Unfortunately this work was almost ignored in the 1950s and 1960s owing to the rise of linguistic philosophy. Bernard Carr (2008) was the first physicist to enter this field when he published his theory that phenomenal space and physical space are both cross-sections of a higher-dimensional space. He writes: "My proposal is that mental and physical space can be integrated into a communal space which is higher dimensional, in the sense that it has more than the three dimensions perceived by our physical sensors. This involves what I call a "Universal Structure." (see Smythies 1994 pp. 149-150 for details).

This hypothesis can be illustrated by the following introspective experiments. Sit down in a comfortable chair in a dark room, close your eyes and observe what you experience. First direct your attention to the dark visual field in front of you. Ask yourself what this darkness consists of. Is it just nothing? However, that is not right as evidenced by the difference between retinal blindness and cortical blindness. In the former patients experience a black field whereas in the latter they experience nothing at all.

When you open your eyes your visual field becomes filled with colored mobile shapes i.e. your visual sensations. When you close your eyes again these vanish to be replaced by the black uniform field. So what lies behind this field? IT would say that other neurons lie behind it. This hypothesis entails that the black field itself consists of activity in NCCs and what lies behind them must be activity in pre-NCCs.

A similar situation holds in the case of somatic sensations. Sitting in your chair examine your bodily sensations. These will consist of a variety of feelings of touch, pressure, stretch, itch, proprioception, tingling and others that make up your body image. IT holds that these are composed of NCCs and what lies immediately outside them is activity in pre-NCCs—because your body image that you experience is identical, according to IT, not with your actual physical body but with Penfield's homunculus located in your somatosensory cortex. In contrast, the theory of material dualism holds that all the contents of your phenomenal consciousness, including your phenomenal visual field and your body-image, lie outside the brain altogether and are located in a space of their own.

We can illustrate this by considering how IT and this theory deal with the image of Plato's cave (Smythies 1994). In this model, prisoners have always been strapped to posts and cannot move their heads. Behind them a great fire burns. Statues of objects are carried behind them so that their shadows fall on the wall of the cave in front of the prisoners. Would not the prisoners, Plato asks, then consider that these shadows represent reality? In IT Plato's cave is the brain and the shadows represent NCCs in the visual cortex. In material dualism the cave is an extra part of the human organism (the 'consciousness module') located outside the brain in a (higher-dimensional) space of its own that has an inner screen on which the shadows (our actual visual sensations) are projected. For a modern version of Plato's cave we can use television. A mad scientist takes an infant and straps a TV set over its eyes with an external camera so that the developing child will see on its TV screen whatever the camera is pointing at. Would not this child grow up believing that the TV images, that are all she ever sees, were the objects televised themselves that she can feel by touch (Wright 1983).

To account for the 'now' and the passage of time in this new theory we must add a detail. As Broad (1953) noted in the earlier quotation, the theory needs two times. Time in the sense of past, present and future becomes the fourth dimension of space, as in SR. The 'now' and the passage of time requires a second real time t2 in which the time-traveling 'field of observation' described above travels from the past into the future. Geometrically this can be expressed in the following way. Any n-dimensional structure (say a cube) can be cut by two (n-1) D structures (in this case planes). The resulting planes can either be parallel or they can intersect. The 4D cross-section A of Carr's 5D Universal Structure that contains phenomenal space-time and the cross-section B that is physical space-time are different cross-sections of the Universal Structure. If these cross- sections are not parallel but intersect then they (and their contents) can be in relative motion to each other along the time axis of B in t2. This entails that the 'now' of time is wherever A (that carries phenomenal consciousness) has reached in its travel along B. The existence of this second time might find confirmation in some Near Death Experience reports which mention that during the experience the notions of time or of duration may disappear leading to notions of "no time" or "eternal present" along with the feeling of a 'second sort of time" (Jourdan 2011).

The proposed causal interactions between events in NCCs and events in phenomenal consciousness can be represented by higher-dimensional vectors. Causal interactions between events wholly inside A, or wholly inside B, can be represented by vectors (straight lines) that are geometrically wholly within A or wholly within B. Interactions between events in A and events in B can be represented by vectors that originate in one of these and terminate in the other, crossing the dimensional interface between these two spaces as they do so. A dimensional interface is any surface that an n- dimensional space presents to an n+1 dimensional space of which it is a cross section—for example the surface of a plane that is a cross-section of a cube.

Material dualism also has implications for "the idea of another world" (Price 1953). If phenomenal events are ontologically separate from physical events and exist in a space (or space-time) of their own, they could continue to exist in some form after the wreck of the brain. This hypothesis is congruent with the proposal that the physical world exists as a means of communication between Selves that lie outside it in a phenomenal world of their own. This supports the notion that the events reported by observers during out-of-the-body experiences (OBEs) and near-death experiences (NDEs) suggest what these post-mortem experiences may be like (Jourdan 2010). However, the theory suggests one basic change. Since it holds that the Self and its phenomenal consciousness were never geometrically in the physical body, the term out-of-the-body needs changing. During our present life the Self is located in the body-image, not the body, under any valid theory. To return to Plato's cave: the picture drawn by Plato refers to events during our present life. After the death of the brain the observers may be freed from their chains and can leave the cave (or sensorium) and are able to explore the beautiful countryside around it. Hindu psychology has long held that, in addition to our physical body, we also have an astral body that could survive the death of the physical body. Material dualism supports this idea but with an important difference. The Hindu theory is based on the idea that we experience the physical body: and the astral body only hovers in the wings as it were. However, the truth may be is that which we always experience—i.e. the body image— metamorphoses under different circumstances into the astral body during OBEs, NDEs and after death itself.

Conclusion

The theory of material dualism represents a paradigmic change in our basic concepts of space, time and matter.

—The real world, according to Newton, consists of 3D physical objects that exist in a separate time. Matter only exists at the 'now' of time.

—According to Special Relativity the real world consists a 4D block of matter in which t1 time and physical space are fused into space-time. Matter exists throughout space-time. The 'now' of time and the passage of time are held to be 'subjective illusions'.

—In material dualism the real world consists of a 5D spatiotemporal system (involving t1) of which the Einsteinian physical world and the phenomenal world are located in two different cross-sections. These both exist in real time t2. Thus the world contains two different kinds of matter i.e. physical matter (atoms and fields: brains and planets) and phenomenal matter (sensations, images and thoughts). The two interact via causal relations between events in the NCCs in the brain and events in phenomenal consciousness.

REFERENCES

Achard S, Delon-Martin C, Vértes PE, Renard F, Schenck M, Schneider F, Heinrich C, Kremer S, Bullmore ET. (2012) Hubs of brain functional networks are radically reorganized in comatose patients. Proc Natl Acad Sci U S A. 2012 Dec 11;109(50):20608-13. doi: 10.1073/pnas.1208933109. Epub 2012 Nov 26.

Ayer, A.J. (1940) comments I P. Laslett (ed.) The Physical Basis of mind.. Blackwell., Oxford, UK.

Bartolomei F1, Naccache L. (2011) The global workspace (GW) theory of consciousness and epilepsy. Behav Neurol. 2011;24(1):67-74. doi: 10.3233/BEN-2011-0313.

Broad, C.D. (1923), Scientific Thought (London: Routledge & Kegan Paul).

Broad, C.D. (1953) Religion, Philosophy and Psychical Research .(London: Routledge & Kegan Paul).

Brown and Gebhardt JW. (1948) Visual field articulation in the absence of spatial stimulus gradients. J. Exp. Psychol. 38, 188-200.

Brown, J. W. The Life of the Mind. London, Erlbaum, 1988.

Carr, B. (2008) Worlds apart? Proceedings of the Society for Psychical Research, 59, 1- 96.

de Broglie, L. (1959), 'A general survey of the scientific work of Albert Einstein', in Albert EinsteinPhilosopher-Scientist, ed. P.A. Schlipp (New York: Harper & Row), pp. 107–28.

Demertzi A, Soddu A, Laureys S. (2013) Consciousness supporting networks. Curr Opin Neurobiol. 2013 Apr;23(2):239-44. doi: 10.1016/j. conb.2012.12.003. Epub 2012 Dec 27. Review.

Eddington, A.S. (1920), Space, Time and Gravitation (Cambridge: Cambridge University Press).

Fingelkurts, A.A., Fingelkurts, A.A., Bagnato, S., Boccagni, C., and Galardi, G. (2013) Dissociation of vegetative and minimally conscious patients based on brain operational architectonics: factor of etiology. Clinical Electroencephalography and Neuroscience, 2013 May 10. [Epub ahead of print].

Fitzgerald, P. (1978) Review of C.W.K. Mundle Perception, Facts and Theories, in Philosophy of Science, 45, 165-169.

French R.E. (1987) The Geometry of Vision and the Mind Body Problem. New York: Lang.

Fukada H, Kosaka T, Singer W, Gakuske RA. (2006) Gap junctions among dendrites of cortical GABAergic neurons establish a dense and widespread intercolumnar network. J.Neurosci. 26, 8589-8604. doi: 10.1523/JNEUROSCI.4076-05.2006.

Heller, M. (1984), 'Temporal parts of four dimensional objects', Philosophical Studies, 46, pp. 323–34.

Jourdan J-P. (2010) Deadline. Paris: Les Tres Orangers.

Jourdan J-P. (2011) Near Death Experiences and the 5th dimensional spatio-temporal perspective. J. Cosmol. 14, 4743-4762. http://journalofcosmology.com/Consciousness152.html

Leibniz G. W. (1981) New Essays on Human Understanding. (P. Remnant and J. Bennett Tr.). Cambridge University Press. 1981.

Leon-Carrion J, Leon-Dominguez U, Pollonini L, Wu MH, Frye RE, Dominguez- Morales MR, Zouridakis G. (2012) Synchronization between the anterior and posterior cortex determines consciousness level in patients with traumatic brain injury (TBI). Brain Res. 2012 Oct 2;1476:22-30. doi: 10.1016/j.brainres.2012.03.055. Epub 2012 Mar 29.

Lewis LD1, Weiner VS, Mukamel EA, Donoghue JA, Eskandar EN, Madsen JR, Anderson WS, Hochberg LR, Cash SS, Brown EN, Purdon PL. (2012) Rapid fragmentation of neuronal networks at the onset of propofol-induced unconsciousness. Proc Natl Acad Sci U S A. 2012 Dec 4;109(49):E3377-86. doi: 10.1073/pnas.1210907109. Epub 2012 Nov 5.

Lloyd, G. (1978), 'Time and existence', Philosophy, 53, pp. 215–28.

Moore, G.E. (1971) Philosophical Studies. Harcourt and Brace, New York, US.

Orpwood R. (2013) Qualia could arise from information processing in local cortical networks. Front Psychol. 2013 Mar 14;4:121. doi: 10.3389/fpsyg.2013.00121. eCollection 2013.

Penrose, R. (1994), Shadows of the Mind: A Search for the Missing Science of Consciousness (Oxford: Oxford University Press).

Price, H.H. (1953) Survival and the idea of another world. Proc.Soc. Psychical Res. 50, 1-25.

Priestly, J. (1777) Disquisitions relating to Matter and Spirit. Johnson, London, UK.

Russell, B. (1948) Human Knowledge. Its Scope and Limits. Allen and Unwin, London, UK (pp. 45 & 582-593).

Quine, W.V. (1982), Methods of Logic (4th edn.) (Cambridge, MA: Harvard University Press).

Schilder, P. Mind. Perception and Thought in their Constructive Aspects. New York. Columbia University Press. 1942.

Schilder, P. The Image and Appearance of the Human Body. New York. International Universities Press, 1950.

Smythies J. (1959a) The stroboscopic patterns. Part I. The dark phase. Brit.J.Psychol. 50, 106-116.

Smythies J. (1939b) The stroboscopic patterns. Part II. The phenomenology of the bright phase and after-images. Brit.J.Psychol. 50, 305-324. DOI: 1e.1111/j.2044- 8295.1959.tb00710.x

Smythies J. (1960) The stroboscopic patterns: part III. Further experiments and discussion, Brit.J.Psychol, 247-255. DOI: 10.1111/j.2044-8295.1960.tb00747.x

Smythies, J. The Walls of Plato's Cave. Aldershot, Averbury Press, 1994.

Smythies J, Edelstein L. (2013) Transsynaptic modality codes in the brain: possible involvement of synchronized spike timing, microRNAs, exosomes and epigenetic processes. Frontiers in Intregrative Neuroscience. 2012;6:126. doi: 10.3389/fnint.2012.00126. Epub 2013 Jan 4.

Stannard, R. (1987), 'Making sense of God's time', The Times, August 22nd.

Werth, L.F. (1978), 'Normalizing the paranormal', American Philosophical Quarterly, 15, pp. 47–56.

Weyl, H. (1922), Space-Time-Matter (London: Constable).

Wright (1983) Inspecting images. Philosophy. 58. 57-72.

Made in the USA
Middletown, DE
25 February 2017